The
Seventies

Other titles in the Hutchinson Pocket series:

HUTCHINSON POCKET

The
Seventies

Helicon

Copyright © Helicon Publishing Ltd 1994

All rights reserved

Helicon Publishing Ltd
42 Hythe Bridge Street
Oxford OX1 2EP

Printed and bound in Great Britain by
Unwin Brothers Ltd, Old Woking, Surrey

ISBN 1–85986–021–4

British Cataloguing in Publication Data

A catalogue record for this book is available
from the British Library

Introduction

While the pop culture of the 1950s and '60s continued into the new decade, it was changing fast, perhaps symbolized most poignantly in 1970 by the break-up of the Beatles and, seven years later, by the death of 'the King', Elvis Presley. In an atmosphere of rising unemployment, the apparently insoluble Vietnam War, and the re-emergence of the Troubles in Northern Ireland, 'Flower power' faded to give way to shaven heads and punk rock.

The beginning of the decade was also marked by the death of the first president of France's fifth republic, Charles de Gaulle, so that without his emphatic *Non!*, in 1973, Britain finally became part of a greater Europe and joined the Common Market. But of all political events, there was one which gave a new cliché to the English language '–gate', as in Watergate! In 1972, five men were hired by the Committee to Re-elect the President (CREEP) to burgle the building in Washington DC where the Democratic Party had their election campaign headquarters. They were caught and, over the next two years, it became clear that the White House was directly involved in funding unethical political activities, including the break-in. Republican Richard Nixon was eventually forced to resign to avoid impeachment, the only American president ever to have left office in this way.

In 1975, Margaret Thatcher became the first woman to lead a political party in Britain when the former prime minister Edward Heath was forced to resign. She was, however, leading the Conservatives in opposition while the Labour administration officiated over the long-expected collapse of British industry epitomized by the bankruptcy of British Leyland. The seventies were not all gloom for Britain, however, for in 1970, Queen Elizabeth II celebrated the silver jubilee of her accession to the throne of

Great Britain and Northern Ireland; across the country the population turned out for street parties and more in twelve months of royalist patriotism.

The year 1978 brought industrial disputes, the 'winter of discontent', and a declared state of emergency to Britain while the Democrat president of the United States, the peanut farmer Jimmy Carter, presided over the Camp David talks between Egypt and Israel in an effort to bring an end to the bitter Arab-Israeli conflict. In Britain, the decade closed with a return to power of Thatcher's monetarist Conservatives on a law-and-order and free-market ticket. The Northern Ireland crisis refused to be diverted by a change of government, though, and the public was outraged by the IRA's murder of Lord Mountbatten and others. Meanwhile, the United States opened full diplomatic relations with China and severed its connection with Taiwan.

Browse through the book and the significant facet of each event stands out in bold type. Go to the back of the book and, as well as population, sporting, and other statistics, you will find the titles, artists, and dates of every hit single and album that topped the charts in Britain. With a short introduction to each year, *The Seventies* is a compact but comprehensive round-up of an intriguing decade.

Editorial Director
Michael Upshall

Contributors
Ingrid von Essen
Dr S P Martland
Neil Curtis

Managing Editor
Sheila Dallas

Project Editor
Neil Curtis

Produced by
Neil Curtis Publishing Services

Page layout
Richard Garratt Design

Index by
Neil Curtis

Production
Tony Ballsdon

The Seventies

1970

For Britain, 1970 was a time of political change. In the June general election (the first in which 18- to 21-year-olds could vote), Edward Heath's Conservative Party was unexpectedly returned to power. Heath, espousing free-market solutions to Britain's economic problems, appointed Margaret Thatcher as minister of education and science. This was not a good year for education for, across the United States, university campuses erupted in protest against the Vietnam War. And, at Kent State University, in Ohio, four student demonstrators were shot dead by the US National Guard. In an atmosphere of mutual recrimination, the Beatles, that symbol of the 1960s youth culture, broke up to pursue their individual careers. While, in Northern Ireland, the British army became increasingly enmeshed in an interethnic conflict that – to the rest of the country – seemed as unreal as it was surreal.

The attempted secession of **Biafra** from Nigeria ends with Biafra's surrender. The civil war and attendant famine have cost about 1 million lives.

Libya, under its new prime minister Moamer al-Khaddhafi, promises to cease aiding Frolinat anti-government rebels in **Chad**. France resumes arms sales to Libya.

Israeli forces attack **Egypt** near Cairo.

History teaches us that men and nations behave wisely once they have exhausted all other alternatives.
Israeli foreign minister **Abba Eban**, speech in London

 The **age of majority** in the UK is reduced to 18 from 21.

The **Boeing 747 jumbo jet** enters service, carrying up to 500 passengers.

The **Chicago Eight** are sentenced: US left-wing activists convicted of causing a riot at the Democratic convention 1968 include Abbie Hoffman and Tom Hayden; a mistrial has been declared in the case of Bobby Seale; two defence lawyers are given sentences for contempt of court. Eight police had also been charged but they are all acquitted.

Students' and workers' **demonstrations begin in Trinidad and Tobago** and continue until a state of emergency is imposed. Racism and repressive labour laws are the main sources of discontent.

Governor **George Wallace** of Alabama, USA, continues to resist racial integration in public schools and urges other Southern governors to do the same.

A conference at Ruskin College, Oxford, sparks the **women's liberation movement** in the UK.

English philosopher, mathematician, and pacifist **Bertrand Russell** dies at 97; he had been a leader of the Campaign for Nuclear Disarmament and the Committee of 100.

US abstract painter **Mark Rothko** commits suicide at 66.

Premiere in London of *Sleuth* by English dramatist Anthony Shaffer.

Simon and Garfunkel's LP *Bridge over Troubled Water* spends the first of 130 weeks in the UK charts. The duo break up later this year.

John Lennon releases **'Instant Karma'**, produced by Phil Spector.

The Nuclear **Nonproliferation Treaty** comes into force, according to which countries that do not already possess nuclear weapons ought not to obtain them. Nations that have not signed the treaty include China, France, India, Israel, Pakistan, and South Africa.

Prince Norodom Sihanouk of Cambodia is overthrown by the US-backed defence minister Lon Nol.

Passenger services begin on the newly completed **Trans-Australian Railway** from Sydney to Perth, a journey of 4,000 km/ 2,460 mi.

The musical *Applause* opens in New York, starring Lauren Bacall.

US singer and songwriter **James Taylor** makes his first album *Sweet Baby James*.

The *New English Bible* is published.

South Vietnamese and US forces enter **Cambodia** in large numbers.

We are all the President's men.
US national-security assistant **Henry Kissinger** on the US invasion of Cambodia

---

Earth Day is celebrated for the first time with environmentalist demonstrations in the USA.

Stephen Sondheim's musical *Company* opens in New York.

At Kent State University, Ohio, four **student demonstrators are killed** by the US National Guard; and two students are shot dead at Jackson State University, Mississippi. More than 400 US universities and colleges close in student protests against the Vietnam War.

Earthquake in Peru kills 70,000 people, injures 50,000, and destroys 186,000 buildings.

UK car and aerospace manufacturer Rolls-Royce receives £20 million from the government because of the high cost of developing a new jet engine for the **Lockheed Tristar**.

General election in the UK: Edward Heath becomes prime minister with a Conservative majority of 43. Margaret Thatcher becomes minister of education and science.

This would, at a stroke, reduce the rise in prices, increase productivity and reduce unemployment.
UK **Conservative Party** press release two days before the general election

In **Northern Ireland** a further 3500 troops are deployed. Rioting ensues.

Tonga, in SW Pacific Ocean, achieves independence from Britain within the Commonwealth, as a monarchy.

Unemployment in the USA reaches 5%.

The four-wheel-drive **Range-Rover** car is launched in the UK.

English dramatist David Storey's play *Home* stars John Gielgud and Ralph Richardson at the Royal Court Theatre, London.

US rock group the Grateful Dead release their least psychedelic album, *Workingman's Dead*.

The Methodist Church begins to **ordain women**.

The Marylebone Cricket Club (MCC) withdraws an invitation to the South African cricket team to tour England, because of objections to **apartheid**.

Britain's new chancellor of the Exchequer, **Ian Macleod**, dies at 56.

Portuguese premier, **Antonio Salazar**, dies; born 1932.

In **Belfast**, 2,000 British soldiers search 3,000 homes for arms. A curfew is imposed but does not end the violent unrest.

✳ **Peace agreement** signed between Egypt, Jordan, and Israel.

US Abstract Expressionist artist **Barnett Newman** dies at 65.

The *Oh Calcutta!* sex revue by theatre critic Kenneth Tynan and others opens at the Round House in London; it was first seen in New York 1969.

Britain's first free festival, **Phun City**, is held in Sussex, S England; the MC5 radical rock band from Detroit, Michigan, top the bill.

British troops in Belfast begin to use **rubber bullets**.

UK fashion magazines *Harper's Bazaar* and *Queen* merge into *Harper's and Queen*.

At 24, English dramatist **Christopher Hampton** puts on his first work *The Philanthropist* at the Royal Court Theatre, London. It stars English actor Alec McCowen.

English dramatist Alan Ayckbourn's comedy *How the Other Half Loves* has its premiere in London.

The third and last **Isle of Wight rock festival** ends acrimoniously in battles over the fences, and provides one of the last chances to see Jimi Hendrix.

Rock journalism is people who can't write interviewing people who can't talk for people who can't read.
US rock musician and composer **Frank Zappa**

English pop singer and pianist **Elton John** plays a series of concerts in Los Angeles that propel him to stardom.

Egypt's president **Gamal Abdel Nasser** dies at 52. Vice president **Anwar Sadat** is elected to succeed him.

King Hussein of Jordan survives an assassination attempt, an uprising, and a Syrian invasion in support of the Palestine Liberation Organization, which is expelled from Jordan and moves its headquarters to Beirut, Lebanon.

An **Arab hijack attempt** of an Israeli El Al flight to London fails and the surviving hijacker, Leila Khaled, is arrested, but is exchanged for hostages when three hijacked planes in Jordan are blown up by Palestinian guerrillas.

Brush fires in S California threaten parts of Los Angeles.

The Mary Tyler Moore Show begins on US television and will run until 1977.

US rock guitarist **Jimi Hendrix** dies at 27.

Goddamn it! He beat me to it.
US blues singer **Janis Joplin** on the death of rock
guitarist Jimi Hendrix

The first **New York Marathon** attracts 126 runners.

Fiji, in SW Pacific Ocean, achieves independence from Britain, within the Commonwealth. The first prime minister is Ratu Sir Kamisese Mara.

In Detroit, Michigan, 100 police officers besiege the **Black Panther headquarters** and arrest 23 people.

Divorce becomes legal in Italy.

✱ British Conservative politician **Kenneth Baker** enters Parliament via a by-election in the St Marylebone constituency, London.

Trash (released Oct) is the commercially most successful of US Pop artist Andy Warhol's films.

US blues singer **Janis Joplin** dies at 27. Her album *Pearl* will be released 1971.

In South Korea, 790 couples marry in a mass ceremony of the **Unification Church (Moonies)**.

Salvador Allende becomes president of Chile, the world's first democratically elected Marxist head of state. He embarks on a programme of social reform and nationalization.

Military **coup in Syria** puts Hafez al-Assad in power.

East Pakistan (Bangladesh) is flooded after a **cyclone**; 500,000 people are killed.

✱ Death of former French president **Charles de Gaulle** at 79.

Miss World contest in London is disrupted by feminist demonstrators.

Japanese novelist **Yukio Mishima** commits ritual suicide at 45 in protest against what he saw as the corruption of the nation and the loss of the samurai warrior tradition.

The body of US jazz saxophonist **Albert Ayler** is found floating in the East River, New York. He was 34.

Strikes and riots in Polish cities follow sudden food-price rises. They are violently suppressed by troops and police. Communist Party leader Wladyslaw Gomulka is forced to resign and is succeeded by Edward Gierek. In Feb 1971 Gomulka will be purged from the Party's Central Committee.

The Soviet *Venera 7* space probe makes a soft landing on Venus and sends back information for 23 minutes before succumbing to the planet's high temperature and pressure.

The **Beatles** split up.

The album *John Lennon Plastic Ono Band*, co-produced by Phil Spector, is released; it contains 'Working Class Hero' and 'Mother'.

Military **coup in Bolivia** puts General Juan Torres Gonzalez in power.

Congo becomes a Marxist people's republic.

Manuel Noriega becomes Panama's intelligence chief. He is an informant for the US Central Intelligence Agency and will become the country's effective ruler in the early 1980s.

The **Gambia** declares itself a republic; prime minister Dawda K Jawara becomes president.

Guyana becomes a republic within the Commonwealth, with Forbes Burnham as prime minister.

Colonel Mobutu Sese Seko is elected president of the Congo (Zaire), where he has assumed dictatorial power since 1965.

Czechoslovak politician **Alexander Dubček**, architect of the Prague Spring of now suppressed reforms, is expelled from the Communist Party.

In Canada, there is a separatist uprising by the **Québec Liberation Front**, members of which kidnap and kill minister Pierre Laporte.

The **Amal Shi'ite Muslim militia** is formed in Lebanon.

The capital of British Honduras (Belize) is moved from Belize

City to **Belmopan**, which, lying inland, is less vulnerable to hurricanes.

The US Army dumps 12,500 **nerve-gas canisters** in the sea off the Bahamas.

US left-wing activist **Angela Davis**, accused of supplying guns used in the murder of a judge, goes into hiding.

American Indian demonstrators temporarily seize the **Alcatraz** fortress in San Francisco Bay, California.

Angry Brigade left-wing urban guerrillas become active in the UK.

Equal Pay Act is introduced in the UK (not to take effect until 1975).

British Labour politician **Barbara Castle** resigns from the cabinet when her White Paper *In Place of Strife* on trade-union reform is abandoned.

The Bank of England introduces regular publication of a figure called **M1**, meaning notes and coins in circulation plus bank deposits that can be withdrawn without warning.

The **Gay Liberation Front** is formed in the UK (dissolved three years later).

A student **sit-in at Keele University**, England, demands representation on the senate (governing body).

British industry loses more days to **strikes and stoppages** than in any year since 1926.

Soviet satellite *Luna 17* is launched; its space probe *Lunokhod* takes photographs and makes soil analyses of the Moon's surface.

China and Japan both send **space probes** to the Moon.

Three US astronauts on their way to the Moon in *Apollo 13* have to turn round when the oxygen level drops in the spacecraft. They survive by entering the lunar module.

The **P & O shipping line** discontinues passenger service between the UK and India, which began 1840.

Norwegian ethnologist **Thor Heyerdahl** completes a crossing of the Atlantic in a papyrus reed boat.

The **Mexico City Metro** (underground) opens, carrying 1 million passengers a day.

The **charge-coupled device** is invented in the USA to photograph very faint images (for example, in astronomy).

Floppy disks for computers are introduced.

Cuba's sugar harvest is a record 8.5 million tonnes, but this is achieved at the cost of disrupting the rest of the economy by diverting investment, transport, and hundreds of thousands of workers.

The artificial sweetener **cyclamate** is banned in the UK and the USA, having been found to cause cancer in rats.

US chemist Linus Pauling begins advocating massive doses of **vitamin C**, and debate begins about whether humans benefit from megadoses of various vitamins.

Five different **amino acids** are found in a meteorite by US biochemist Cyril Ponnamperuma – born in Ceylon (Sri Lanka). These amino acids are constituents of protein molecules, but appear here not to have originated in living tissue. The discovery sheds light on how life arose on Earth.

Two US biochemists discover **recombinant DNA** (deoxyribonucleic acid), which increases genetic variation in living organisms.

Reverse transcriptase is discovered by two US scientists separately. It is an enzyme that enables retroviruses to multiply.

Commercial whalers slaughter 8,000 **minke whales** this year.

The first **videodisk** system is announced by Decca in Britain and AEG-Telefunken in Germany, but it will not be perfected until the 1980s.

BBC radio broadcasting is reorganized into Radio One, Two, Three, and Four.

Cigarette advertising is banned from US television (the UK introduced a ban 1965).

US TV series ***The Partridge Family*** makes a teen idol of actor and singer David Cassidy; the series will run until 1974.

The *Sun* tabloid newspaper in the UK introduces a daily **'page-3 girl'**, a seminaked pin-up, to promote sales.

Japanese architect **Kishō Kurokawa** designs several influential high-tech pavilions for Expo 70 in Osaka, Japan. His Takara Beautilion is an ingenuous construction of prefabricated units in a three-dimensional grid, typical of the Japanese Metabolist school of architecture.

The installation ***Living Room*** by British artist Carol Joseph contains apparently fungus-encrusted furniture.

Seek is a computer-controlled work of art in which a family of gerbils inhabit a changing environment of cubes, created by a group of architects at the Massachusetts Institute of Technology, USA.

English novelist **E M Forster** dies; born 1879. His works include *A Passage to India* 1924.

Alexander Solzhenitsyn is awarded the Nobel Prize for Literature

Patriarchal Attitudes by British writer Eva Figes is a work of feminist literary and social criticism.

US sociologist Alvin Toffler publishes *Future Shock*, about the psychological effects of the speed of technological development.

Sexual Politics by US writer Kate Millett is a landmark in feminist thinking.

An anaemic parody of the battle put up by a succession of magnificent socialist women in the last century.
British Labour politician **Barbara Castle** on *Sexual Politics* by US feminist Kate Millett

---

Australian academic Germaine Greer's polemical book *The Female Eunuch* attracts much comment on publication.

Women have very little idea of how much men hate them.
Australian academic **Germaine Greer**, *The Female Eunuch*

The first novel of English thriller writer Frederick Forsyth, *The Day of the Jackal,* is published.

English writer C P Snow's *Last Things* ends his *Strangers and Brothers* novel sequence.

English poet Ted Hughes publishes the poem sequence *Crow*.

Canadian novelist Robertson Davies publishes *Fifth Business*, the first novel of his Deptford trilogy.

US writer Richard Bach's New Age fable *Jonathan Livingston Seagull* becomes a best seller.

The teenage novel *Pennington's Seventeenth Summer* by British writer K M Peyton is the first of a sequence.

US filmmaker Robert Altman has his first commercial success with the antiwar comedy *M.A.S.H.*.

French director Claude Chabrol makes the film *Le Boucher/The Butcher*.

US actor Jack Nicholson stars in Bob Rafelson's *Five Easy Pieces*.

French film director François Truffaut casts himself as the scientist in *L'Enfant sauvage/The Wild Child*.

French filmmaker Eric Rohmer releases *Le Genou de Claire/Claire's Knee*.

US actor Dustin Hoffman stars in Arthur Penn's film *Little Big Man* about American Indians.

US B-movie director Russ Meyer makes *Beyond the Valley of the Dolls*, beloved by late-night audiences for years to come.

Donald Cammell and Nicolas Roeg direct the gangster film *Performance*, starring James Fox and Mick Jagger.

Italian director Bernardo Bertolucci makes the films *La strategia del ragno/The Spider's Stratagem* and *Il conformista/The Conformist*.

French director Jacques Demy bases the film *Peau d'âne* on a fairy tale.

English theatre director Peter Brook's production of *A Midsummer Night's Dream* for the Royal Shakespeare Company will be spoken of for years to come.

Peter Brook founds the **International Centre for Theatre Resources** in Paris, aiming to develop drama that works across language boundaries.

The **Young Vic** is founded as an offshoot of Britain's National Theatre.

English dramatist **David Mercer** has two plays premiered in London: *After Haggerty* by the Royal Shakespeare Company and *Flint* starring Michael Hordern.

British dramatist David Hare sets his play *Slag* in a girls' school.

US actor and director Sam Wanamaker conceives of building a theatre on the site of the **Globe** in Southwark, S London, where Shakespeare's plays were performed.

English actor Laurence Olivier plays Shylock in Shakespeare's *The Merchant of Venice* at the Old Vic Theatre, London, directed by Jonathan Miller.

English dramatist Robert Bolt's play *Vivat! Vivat Regina!*, about Elizabeth I and Mary Queen of Scots, has its premiere at the Chichester Festival Theatre, Sussex.

English actress Maggie Smith plays the title role in Henrik Ibsen's *Hedda Gabler* at the Old Vic Theatre, London.

The **Royal Shakespeare Company** becomes the first British theatre company to tour Japan, where Shakespeare's *The Winter's Tale* and *The Merry Wives of Windsor* are welcomed.

The English team of Andrew Lloyd Webber and Tim Rice write the musical *Jesus Christ Superstar*.

English composer Michael Tippett writes the opera *The Knot Garden*.

US soprano **Beverly Sills** makes her first appearance at the

Covent Garden Opera House in the title role of *Lucia di Lammermoor* by Italian composer Gaetano Donizetti.

English composer Richard Rodney Bennett writes the opera *Victory*.

British composer Alexander Goehr writes *Shadowplay* and *Sonata about Jerusalem*.

British composer Nicholas Maw's opera *The Rising of the Moon* has its premiere at the Glyndebourne festival.

US jazz trumpeter Miles Davis releases the classic album *Bitches Brew*.

The album *Layla and Other Assorted Love Songs* by Derek and the Dominos is a milestone for English blues guitarist Eric Clapton.

Scottish singer and songwriter Rod Stewart releases his second album, *Gasoline Alley*.

Canadian singer and songwriter Joni Mitchell releases *Ladies of the Canyon*.

The **Roman Catholic liturgy** is now performed in the local language rather than in Latin.

The **Roman Catholic Calendar of Saints** is revised by the pope, eliminating traditional saints such as St Christopher and leaving only 58 regarded as of worldwide importance.

The fashion industry introduces the **midi skirt**, reaching to midcalf, but long and mini-length skirts are at least as popular.

New **land-speed record** of 1,001.5 kph/622.3 mph set by Gary Gabelich (USA) in a rocket-powered car, *Blue Flame*.

Soviet weightlifter **Vasiliy Alexeev** becomes world champion for the first time; he will break 80 world records by 1977.

Australian cricketer **Dennis Lillee** plays in his first test match.

Australian tennis player **Margaret Court** wins the women's singles at Wimbledon and at Forest Hills.

Brazil, led by Pelé, defeats Italy to win the **soccer World Cup** for the third time and are awarded the Cup for all time.

Goalkeeper **Peter Shilton** is first capped for England's football squad.

Golfer, **Tony Jacklin** becomes the first British golfer to win the US Open Championship for half a century.

1971

With more working days lost through stoppages than at any time since the 1926 General Strike, 1971 was a year in which strikes and industrial disputes dominated the British political debate. Edward Heath introduced legislation designed to curb the power of trades unions. Also in 1971, Britain successfully concluded its negotiations to join the Common Market. In Northern Ireland, following a significant increase in interethnic violence, internment without trial is introduced. In Britain, it was decided to raise the school-leaving age from 15 to 16 years (takes effect 1972), and controversial minister of education Margaret Thatcher ended free school milk and curbed access to school meals. While the economy continued to deteriorate, unemployment reached the sensitive one million mark for the first time since 1945. In the United States, all aspects of life continued to be dominated by the seemingly insoluble Vietnam War. In the world of fashion, flares and cheese cloth made their appearance.

Idi Amin seizes power in a military coup in Uganda; prime minister Milton Obote goes into exile in Tanzania. Amin has more than 300,000 opponents killed.

> *Power is the ultimate aphrodisiac.*
> US national-security assistant **Henry Kissinger**

The UK's first **postal workers' strike** begins and lasts 47 days.

Divorce law is reformed in the UK so that 'irretrievable breakdown' is sufficient ground.

A human growth hormone, **somatropin**, is synthesized at the University of California.

The **Aswan High Dam** in Egypt begins generating electricity.

US vocal group the **Osmonds** have the first of many international hits, 'One Bad Apple'. They are a Mormon family of seven.

French fashion designer **Coco Chanel** dies at 87. She popularized the cardigan suit, the 'little black dress', suntans, and costume jewellery, and developed a range of perfumes, including Chanel No. 5.

Egyptian president Anwar Sadat offers Israel a full **peace treaty** on the basis of the pre-1967 borders, with no concessions for the Palestinians, but Israel, backed by the USA, rejects the offer.

Earthquake in Los Angeles, California, kills more than 50 people.

Laos is briefly invaded by South Vietnamese and US forces.

Women get the vote in Switzerland after a referendum but are denied it in Liechtenstein.

Decimal currency is introduced in the UK, replacing the ancient system of pounds, shillings, and pence.

British car and aircraft-engine manufacturer **Rolls-Royce** is nationalized to save it from financial collapse.

Australian media magnate Rupert Murdoch acquires control of **London Weekend Television**.

Civil war breaks out in **East Pakistan**. The war creates 2 million refugees.

James Chichester-Clark resigns as prime minister of Northern Ireland and is replaced by Brian Faulkner.

Lt **William Calley**, responsible for the US Army massacre of My Lai villagers in South Vietnam 1969, is sentenced to life imprisonment.

I will be extremely proud if My Lai shows the world what war is.
US Lt **William Calley** on being convicted of massacring Vietnamese civilians

---

South African civil-rights activist **Winnie Mandela** is sentenced to a year's imprisonment for defying a banning order which prohibits her from receiving visitors.

The most potent weapon in the hands of the oppressor is the mind of the oppressed.
South African civil-rights leader **Steve Biko**

English poet and novelist **Stevie Smith** dies at 67. Her works include *Novel on Yellow Paper* 1936 and several volumes of eccentrically direct verse.

English glam-rock group T Rex, led by singer Marc Bolan, have their first UK number one, **'Hot Love'**.

Slade, the most popular UK group of the decade, have number one hits with **'Coz I Luve You'** and **'Take Me Back 'Ome'**.

US singer and songwriter Carole King's *Tapestry* (released March USA, May UK) will become one of the decade's best-selling albums and stay 292 weeks in the US chart.

Haiti's dictator **Papa Doc** (François Duvalier) dies; born 1907. He is succeeded by his 19-year-old son Jean Claude (Baby Doc).

✳ **Provisional Irish Republican Army** is formed as an offshoot of the IRA.

In Cuba, an **Anti-Loafing Law** comes into force, making habitual absenteeism a crime. In the preceding months, hundreds of thousands of people hastily return to work.

Russian-born composer **Igor Stravinsky** dies at 88. His avant-garde music for the ballet *The Rite of Spring* caused great controversy in 1913.

US composer Stephen Sondheim's musical *Follies* opens in New York to run for 521 performances.

English rock group the Rolling Stones release the album *Sticky Fingers* on their own label. The Andy Warhol-designed sleeve incorporates a metal zipper.

East German communist leader **Walter Ulbricht** resigns and is succeeded by **Erich Honecker**.

In the UK the *Daily Mail* changes to tabloid format; the tabloid *Daily Sketch* closes down.

US passenger train services are merged into **Amtrak**.

The musical *Godspell* by Stephen Schwartz opens in New York for a run of 2,605 performances.

English composer Benjamin Britten's opera *Owen Wingrave* opens in London.

Publication of the *Pentagon Papers* begins in the USA. This top-secret document on the history of US involvement in the Vietnam War was leaked to the *New York Times* by an employee of the Defense Department. President Nixon attempts to stop publication, but the Supreme Court eventually rules in favour of press freedom.

Free milk for primary-school children is discontinued in the UK by education secretary Margaret Thatcher. This earns her the epithet 'milk-snatcher' from opponents of the measure.

The first orbital space station, the Soviet *Salyut 1*, launched in April, is occupied for 23 days by a crew of three, who die during their return to Earth when the *Soyuz* ferry craft depressurizes.

The **Glastonbury Fayre** free midsummer festival in England is addressed by Guru Maharaj Ji.

Voting age in the USA is reduced from 21 to 18.

Crash helmets will become compulsory for motorcyclists, the UK government announces.

Premiere of *Butley* by British dramatist Simon Gray.

US jazz trumpeter **Louis Armstrong** dies at 71. His skill at improvisation established the pre-eminence of the jazz soloist.

US rock singer **Jim Morrison** dies in Paris at 27. He was a founder member of the Doors and wrote the group's lyrics.

US soul and gospel singer Al Green has his first big hit with **'Tired of Being Alone'**.

In the Middle East, Qatar and the Trucial States (which become the **United Arab Emirates**) withdraw from the Federation of

Arab Emirates, leaving only Bahrain. All achieve independence from Britain (Aug and Sept). Sheik Sultan al-Nahayan, emir of Abu Dhabi, is elected president of the UAE.

The USA decouples the value of the **dollar** from the price of gold.

A new **Industrial Relations Act** in the UK comes into force; it contributes to the deterioration of relations between government and trades unions.

Internment, or detention without trial, is introduced in Northern Ireland for terrorist suspects, and 300 IRA supporters are interned. Some 7,000 people in Belfast are made homeless by sectarian arson.

The **Angry Brigade** British urban guerrillas are arrested.

Three editors of the underground magazine *Oz* are convicted of obscenity in the UK and given jail sentences, later overturned on appeal.

Former Beatle George Harrison organizes the fund-raising **Concert for Bangladesh** at Madison Square Garden, New York.

I was having to record Paul's songs and put up with him telling me how to play my own guitar.
George Harrison on life in the Beatles

Chinese politician **Lin Biao** is killed in a plane crash after an abortive coup attempt.

90 Soviet diplomats are expelled from the UK as **spies**.

Rebellion against **racism** in Attica Prison, New York State, is put down (39 prisoners killed).

The detective serial *Columbo*, starring US actor Peter Falk, begins on US television.

The *Old Grey Whistle Test* rock-music programme begins on British television.

John Lennon's album *Imagine* is released (Sept USA, Oct UK).

China is admitted to the United Nations (UN) and Taiwan is expelled.

The **Republic of the Congo** becomes Zaire and the **River Congo** is also renamed the Zaïre.

US pop singer **Michael Jackson** makes his first solo record, at the age of 12, 'Got to Be There' (released Oct USA, Jan 1972 UK).

US spacecraft *Mariner 9* becomes the first human-made object to go into orbit around another planet – Mars. It will map the entire Martian surface and send back photographs of the planet's moons.

Led Zeppelin IV, known as the runes album, will spend 151 weeks in the US chart (released Nov).

In the **East Pakistan** conflict, India intervenes on the side of Bangladesh, and it becomes independent under Sheik Mujibur Rahman. In Pakistan, power is transferred to Zulfiqar Ali Bhutto. There are nearly 2 million refugees from Bangladesh in India.

Austrian **Kurt Waldheim** becomes secretary general of the UN, replacing Burmese diplomat U Thant. Waldheim's wartime record with the German army will eventually make him internationally shunned.

At the end of the year, the USA has its first **trade deficit** since 1888.

Dom Mintoff becomes prime minister of Malta and begins ne-
gotiating for removal of British naval bases there.

Sierra Leone becomes a republic, with prime minister Siaka
Stevens as president.

War breaks out between North and South **Yemen** (until 1972).
The conflict is caused by clashes between the left-wing government of South Yemen and mercenaries operating from North
Yemen; hundreds of thousands of people have fled from South
to North Yemen since the accession of the Marxist National Front
in South Yemen 1970.

US troops in **South Vietnam** are reduced to 200,000; Australian
and New Zealand troops are withdrawn.

Coup in Syria brings Hafed al-Assad to power. He leads the
moderate wing of the Ba'ath Party.

Hastings Banda makes himself president for life in Malawi.

The **African National Council** is founded in Rhodesia (Zimbabwe) by Bishop Abel Muzorewa; it is the first genuine opposition party allowed to operate there since 1964.

General **George Grivas** returns to Cyprus to start a guerrilla
war against the government of Archbishop Makarios III.

Anguilla returns to being a British dependency. Its association
with St Christopher-Nevis has not worked out.

Strikes and student unrest prompt a military **coup in Turkey**:
Suleyman Demirel is forced to resign.

Death in office of **William Tubman**; born 1895. He was the first
president of Liberia (from 1944).

Environmental pressure groups **Greenpeace** and **Friends of the
Earth** are founded. Greenpeace's first direct action is to enter a

US nuclear test site in the Aleutian Islands in the N Pacific. As a result, only one of the proposed series of tests is carried out and the island concerned later becomes a bird sanctuary.

The **Bretton Woods agreement** on international exchange-rate stability is abandoned.

Ulster Defence Association formed in Northern Ireland in opposition to the IRA.

A **prices and incomes policy** is introduced in the UK.

A new **Immigration Act** creates further restrictions on UK immigration.

Quarter sessions and **assizes** in England and Wales are replaced by crown courts.

The first **women's-liberation** march is held in London.

The bankruptcy of British architectural entrepreneur **John Poulson** sets off investigations into widespread corruption in local government.

Control of the nuclear reactors at **Windscale**, Cumbria, NW England, is transferred from the UK Atomic Energy Authority to British Nuclear Fuels Ltd, and the plant is renamed Sellafield. It is the world's greatest discharger of radioactive waste.

The **theory of superconductivity** is proposed: electrical resistance in some metals vanishes at very low temperatures.

The first **microprocessor**, the Intel 4004, is announced by the US Intel Corporation. A microprocessor is a computer's central processing unit contained on a single integrated circuit. It heralds the introduction of the microcomputer.

In the US space programme, the *Apollo* missions *14* and *15* (July–August) bring back the first samples of **Moon rock**.

Viroids, disease-causing organisms even smaller than viruses, are isolated outside the living body.

Smoking and Health Now, a second report on the subject by Britain's Royal College of Physicians (RCP), speaks of a 'holocaust' of deaths from smoking. Action on Smoking and Health (ASH) is established as a pressure group in the UK by the RCP to mobilize and co-ordinate voluntary action against smoking; it engages in lobbying and education, and is financed by a government grant. Health warnings become compulsory on cigarette packets in the UK.

> *Cigarette smoking is now as important a cause of death as were the great epidemic diseases such as typhoid, cholera, and tuberculosis.*
> The **Royal College of Physicians**, *Smoking and Health Now*

The insecticide **DDT** is banned in the USA because it builds up in the food chain and causes cancer.

A new strain of **rice**, IR-20, is developed at the International Rice Research Institute in the Philippines. It gives a high yield and is resistant to bacterial blight and rice tungro virus, but requires heavy fertilization.

The UK television drama documentary *Edna, the Inebriate Woman* by Jeremy Sandford tackles another social problem but does not repeat the success of his *Cathy, Come Home*.

Japanese architects begin working on a hypothetical **floating city**.

The **Florey Building**, Oxford, undergraduate housing by British architect James Stirling, is completed (begun 1966).

The **John F Kennedy Center** in Washington DC, by US architect Edward Durrell Stone, is completed (begun 1964) at a cost of $70 million; it has been cited as an example of high camp.

US psychologist B F Skinner publishes *Beyond Freedom and Dignity*.

US historian Dee Brown publishes *Bury My Heart at Wounded Knee* about the American Indians.

US writer Bernard Malamud publishes the novel *The Tenants*.

US writer John Updike publishes the novel *Rabbit Redux*.

English children's writer William Mayne publishes the novel *A Game of Dark*.

English writer Jane Gardam publishes the teenage novel *A Long Way from Verona*.

English writer Leon Garfield publishes *The Strange Affair of Adelaide Harris*, a comic novel for children.

US writer Robert O'Brien publishes the children's animal fantasy *Mrs Frisby and the Rats of NIMH*.

Yugoslav film director Dusan Makavejev makes *WR: Mysteries of the Organism*.

US actress Jane Fonda gives one of her best performances in Alan Pakula's film *Klute*.

The film of Anthony Burgess's novel *A Clockwork Orange* is released, starring Malcolm McDowell, but will be withdrawn after allegations that it encourages violence.

US film director Peter Bogdanovich makes *The Last Picture Show*.

US film director Robert Altman makes *McCabe and Mrs Miller*, starring Warren Beatty and Julie Christie.

Italian director Luchino Visconti films *Death in Venice* from German writer Thomas Mann's story.

Joseph Losey's film *The Go-Between* is based on L P Hartley's novel, from a screenplay by Harold Pinter.

Swiss film director Alain Tanner attracts notice with *La Salamandre*.

French director Louis Malle makes the film *Le Souffle au coeur/ Murmur of the Heart*.

English filmmaker Nicolas Roeg directs *Walkabout* in Australia.

US film thriller *Shaft* by photographer Gordon Parks has music by Isaac Hayes.

US comedian Woody Allen makes his first film as director, *Bananas*.

English actor Michael Caine stars in the film *Get Carter*.

The **Hull Truck theatre company** is founded in England.

The play *Old Times*, by English dramatist Harold Pinter, opens.

English dramatist Edward Bond's *Lear* uses Shakespeare's play as its starting point.

Premiere of *Getting On* by English dramatist Alan Bennett.

English conductor **Colin Davis** becomes music director at Covent Garden Opera House, London.

Premiere in Santa Fe, New Mexico, USA, of the opera *Yerma* by Brazilian composer Heitor Villa-Lobos.

US psychedelic funk group Sly and the Family Stone release the introverted album ***There's a Riot Goin' On***.

Fog on the Tyne by folk-rock band Lindisfarne is the UK's best-selling album of the year.

Theatrical US hard-rock band Alice Cooper release the album ***Killer***.

Short shorts, or **'hot pants'**, become fashionable women's wear, not only in the summer.

Japanese fashion designer **Issey Miyake** shows his first collection in Tokyo and New York.

Belgian cyclist **Eddie Merckx** wins a record 54 races in one season.

Dutch soccer star **Johan Cruyff** is named European Footballer of the Year for the first time.

Pakistani cricketer **Imran Khan** makes his debut for Pakistan.

1972

In 1972, many stored-up problems began to turn into full-blown crises. In Britain, curbs on pay resulted in a national strike by coal miners. Owing to shortages of coal, British industry is reduced to a three-day working week. In response to the deteriorating economy, Edward Heath's government implemented its famous U-turn, abandoning confrontation with trades unions, and, to bring down unemployment, embracing collectivist expansionist policies. Also in 1972, after the shooting dead of 13 civilians by British soldiers in Londonderry, the Heath government suspended the locally elected sectarian Northern Ireland government, and commenced direct rule of the province from London. In the United States, Richard Nixon became the first US president to visit the communist government of China. There, he met the aged Chinese leader Mao Zedong. This same year Nixon secured re-election for a second term as president. By plotting the burglary of the offices of his political opponents in the Watergate Building in Washington DC during the campaign, however, he sowed the seeds of his own destruction.

Military **coup in Ghana**: General Ignatius Acheampong seizes power and bans all political activity.

The UK and Denmark leave the **European Free Trade Association** because they are about to join the European Community (EC).

 Bloody Sunday in Northern Ireland (30 Jan): 13 civil-rights demonstrators are killed in Londonderry (or Derry) by British troops.

I have always said that it is a great mistake to prejudge the past.
British Conservative politician **William Whitelaw** on being appointed secretary for Northern Ireland

---

 A seven-week **coal miners' strike** begins in the UK.

 The number of **unemployed in the UK** passes 1 million.

Unemployment in Britain today is by far the biggest single cause of avoidable human misery and suffering.
British Labour politician **Denis Healey**, speech in Parliament

---

The world's first **kidney transplant** is carried out in London.

US poet **John Berryman** commits suicide at 58 by jumping off a bridge over the Mississippi River. His 77 *Dream Songs* 1964 won the Pulitzer Prize.

US president **Richard Nixon** visits China and opens up trade relations.

The Stormont parliament is prorogued and **direct rule of Northern Ireland** from Westminster introduced. Demonstrators in Dublin set fire to the British embassy.

A **three-day working week** is introduced in the UK (Feb–March), and electricity is cut off for nine hours a day as power stations close down because of the miners' strike (which ends 28 Feb).

Jumpers, a philosophical comedy by British dramatist Tom Stoppard, opens in a National Theatre production, London, with Michael Hordern and Diana Rigg.

US National Committee on Marijuana and Drug Abuse presents the case for relaxing the **drug laws**; Nixon ignores its recommendations.

The trial of US left-wing activist **Angela Davis** begins in Berkeley, California; she is accused of supplying a weapon to Jonathan Jackson, who killed a judge at his own trial before being shot dead. She is eventually freed.

The **Parker Committee** on the treatment of terrorist suspects in Northern Ireland (reporting in March) is critical of several British practices.

A Soviet space probe manages a soft landing on **Venus**.

US space probe ***Pioneer 10*** is launched towards Jupiter. In 1983 it will leave the Solar System.

Some 5,000 people are killed in an **earthquake in Iran**.

US planes bomb **North Vietnam's** largest cities for the first time since 1968.

 Two *Apollo 16* astronauts spend three days on the Moon.

British Rail and London docks are hit by **strikes**.

Polaroid introduces a single-lens reflex camera that makes instant prints.

A **nuclear reactor** near Kassel, West Germany, comes close to meltdown and contaminates the River Weser.

The musical ***Don't Bother Me, I Can't Cope***, which uses non-original music, opens in New York and will run for more than 1,000 performances.

Ceylon becomes independent from Britain as the Socialist Republic of Sri Lanka, within the Commonwealth.

Richard Nixon is the first US president to visit the USSR.

US forces mine **North Vietnamese ports**.

Japanese Red Army guerrillas take part in Palestinian attack on **Lod airport** in Tel Aviv, Israel; 26 bystanders and two of the guerrillas are killed.

English rock group the Rolling Stones release the double album *Exile on Main Street*.

 Burglars are arrested in the headquarters of the Democratic Party in the **Watergate** building in Washington DC (17 June).

It is going to cost a million dollars to take care of the jackasses in jail. That can be arranged.
US president **Richard Nixon** on the Watergate burglars

Iraq nationalizes an important oil field but is forced to reduce production.

Andreas Baader, **Ulrike Meinhof**, and two other members of the Red Army Faction are arrested in West Germany for terrorist activities.

Drought forces the USSR to buy up a quarter of the US wheat crop.

Hurricane Agnes devastates the eastern seaboard of the USA from Florida to New York.

The **United Nations Conference on the Human Environment** is held in Stockholm, Sweden. It condemns the continued French nuclear testing in the Pacific. The UN Environment Programme is set up as a result of the conference.

The US Supreme Court rules that **capital punishment** is unconstitutional; the decision will be reversed 1975.

The musical *Grease* by Jim Jacobs opens in New York and will run for 3,388 performances.

Vocal group the O'Jays' **'Backstabbers'** typifies the Philadelphia sound created by producers Kenny Gamble and Leon Huff (released June USA, Aug UK).

Cuba becomes a member of **Comecon**, the East-bloc economic organization.

Former Belgian prime minister **Paul Henri Spaak**, one of the founders of the EC, dies at 73.

✳ There is a **dock strike** in the UK (28 July–16 Aug).

・ In the USA, *Ms* magazine is founded, edited by feminist Gloria Steinem.

US film *Superfly* is released, with a soundtrack by Curtis Mayfield.

In **Uganda**, dictator Idi Amin expels nearly 49,000 residents of Asian origin (Aug–Oct), which devastates the service industries. Most of those affected hold UK passports.

US journalists Bob Woodward and Carl Bernstein begin to connect the **Watergate** break-in to the Committee for the Re-Election of the President (CREEP) and publish their findings in the *Washington Post* (from Aug).

Norway is accepted into the EC, but its application is withdrawn after a referendum; the Norwegian government resigns.

The **Bay Area Rapid Transit** underground system opens between San Francisco, Oakland, and Berkeley, California, the first new public transport network in the USA for more than 50 years.

US television series *M*A*S*H* begins, based on Robert Altman's film. The cast includes Alan Alda and Loretta Swit.

US television series *The Waltons* begins.

Israeli forces carry out **bombing raids on Lebanon and Syria**.

The **Access credit card** is introduced in the UK.

The television series *Colditz*, set during World War II, begins in the UK.

John Betjeman is appointed Britain's poet laureate.

The musical *Pippin* by Stephen Schwartz opens in New York and will run for almost 2,000 performances.

Presidential elections in the USA are a landslide victory for incumbent Republican Richard Nixon over Democrat George McGovern.

Soviet physicist **Andrei Sakharov** joins a group pressing for civil rights in the USSR. In 1980 he will be imprisoned for criticizing Soviet policies.

US Republican politician (a Democrat until 1970) **Jesse Helms** is elected to the Senate. He will become an influential figure on the far right.

Race Relations Act introduced in the UK.

Prices and incomes freeze in the UK (Nov, until April 1973).

US poet **Ezra Pound** dies at 87 in Italy. His *Cantos* 1925–69 attempted a reappraisal of history.

Earthquake in Managua, Nicaragua, kills about 10,000 people (25 Dec).

The **Nikkei index** of the Tokyo stock market reaches 5,000.

Idi Amin nationalizes British companies in **Uganda**.

Apollo 17 carries the last US astronauts to the Moon. Eugene Cernan has an accident with his Moon buggy.

> *Let's get this mother out of here.*
> US astronaut **Eugene Cernan**, leaving the Moon on the last Apollo mission

Life magazine in the USA ceases publication, except for special issues. Television has reduced the market for photojournalism.

The Sunshine Boys, a comedy by US dramatist Neil Simon, opens in New York and will run for 538 performances.

Ferdinand Marcos, president of the **Philippines**, declares martial law, suspends the constitution, and begins to rule by decree.

Croatian nationalist **Franjo Tudjman** is imprisoned for separatist activities in Yugoslavia (until 1974).

A military regime is established in **Dahomey** (Benin) under General Mathieu Kerekou.

Sheik **Mujibur Rahman**, who led Bangladesh to independence, becomes prime minister.

Military **coup in Ecuador** ends four years of civilian government.

 SALT I accord signed by the USA and the USSR, calling for a limit on the expansion of nuclear forces.

A Labor government is elected in Australia: **Gough Whitlam** becomes prime minister.

Socialist **Michael Manley** becomes prime minister of Jamaica.

General **Carlos Romero** becomes president of El Salvador after elections.

South Africa is banned from participating in the Olympic Games because of international objections to **apartheid**.

 Black September massacre: 11 Israeli athletes are killed in Munich, at the Olympic Games, by a splinter group of the Palestine Liberation Organization.

Zaire becomes a one-party state.

Zambia becomes a one-party state.

Military **coup in Madagascar** gives more nationalistic leadership; France is made to close down its military bases on the island.

Japan regains control of the **Ryūkyū Islands**, including Okinawa, occupied by the USA since World War II.

Basic Treaty between East and West Germany (ratified 1973) normalizes relations.

The Tutsi ethnic group in **Burundi** massacre 150,000 Hutus, blaming them for the assassination of the deposed king Ntare V.

J Edgar Hoover, head of the US Federal Bureau of Investigation (FBI) since 1924, dies; born 1895.

> *Well, Hoover would have fought. He would have defied a few people. He would have scared them to death. He has a file on everybody.*
> US president **Richard Nixon** on how the late head of the Federal Bureau of Investigation would have dealt with the revelation of the Watergate break-in

French right-wing extremist **Jean-Marie Le Pen** forms the French National Front.

The world's first **Green Party** is formed in New Zealand, under the name the Values Party.

In the Central African Republic, **Jean-Bédel Bokassa** makes himself president for life.

There is an outbreak of **Cod War** between the UK and Iceland, with sporadic skirmishes between trawlers and navy vessels.

Drought and frosts in **New Guinea** cause a food shortage. The intervention of colonial administrators to feed 150,000 people for 18 months destroys traditional methods of coping with emergencies.

The **Oslo Convention** is signed by the countries bordering the North Sea (it will come into effect 1974). It restricts the dumping of waste substances in the North Sea and the NE Atlantic.

Environmentalists protest at the start of construction of a fast breeder **nuclear reactor** in Kalkar, West Germany, near the Dutch border; the plant is a joint project with Belgium and the Netherlands.

The **pound sterling** is allowed to float; it sinks.

The Bank of England replaces the **bank rate** with minimum lending rate (until 1978).

 The **Duke of Windsor** dies; born 1894. He was King Edward VIII of Great Britain and Northern Ireland Jan–Dec 1936.

This year, 468 people are killed in political violence in **Northern Ireland**.

Local Government Act reforms administrative structure in England.

Under the **UK Criminal Justice Act**, jury members need no longer be property owners.

 Diplock courts (under Lord Diplock) are introduced in Northern Ireland: they consist of a single judge and no jury, and are used to try offences linked with guerrilla violence.

Housing Finance Act raises council rents in the UK. Over 30% of British families live in council housing.

The UK **school-leaving age** is raised to 16.

Angry Brigade members are sentenced in London.

> *Undoubtedly a warped understanding of sociology has brought you to the state in which you are.*
> Judge in UK urban-guerrilla Angry Brigade case, at sentencing

The **Honda Civic** passenger car is launched.

The **Ford Granada** passenger car is launched.

Dunlop introduces **safety tyres**, which seal themselves after a puncture.

The **Bank of Commerce and Credit International** is founded.

US molecular biologist Paul Berg combines DNA from an animal virus and a bacterial virus by **gene splicing**.

Quadraphonic sound equipment is available in three incompatible systems; none of them catches on.

The **laser** is first used experimentally in sound reproduction.

Landsat 1 is launched by the USA, the first of a series of satellites used for monitoring Earth resources.

The evolutionary theory of **punctuated equilibrium** is put forward by US palaeontologists Niles Eldridge and Stephen Jay Gould. It claims that periods of rapid change alternate with periods of relative stability.

British scientist James Lovelock puts forward the theory that the Earth's living and non-living systems form an inseparable whole that is regulated and kept adapted for life by living organisms themselves; this becomes known as the **Gaia hypothesis**.

The World Health Organization finds that 0.5 million people a year worldwide suffer **pesticide poisoning**, lethal in 9,000 cases. Global pesticide use continues to increase.

France bans the use of the cancer-causing insecticides **dieldrin** and **aldrin**. The USA will follow 1976, and the EC will impose restrictions, but the chemicals continue to be sold to the Third World.

British archaeologist Richard Leakey discovers at Lake Turkana, Kenya, an **apelike skull** with some human characteristics, estimated to be about 2.9 million years old.

The largest **oil field** in the western hemisphere is discovered in Mexico.

Tanker *Sea Star* in the Gulf of Oman spills 103,500 tonnes of oil.

A Greenpeace ship repeatedly enters the zone of the Pacific where France is conducting atmospheric **nuclear tests**, and is forcibly evicted.

The US Navy closes down a **nuclear reactor** it has operated since 1962 at the McMurdo base in the Antarctic. The reactor is disassembled and, with all its waste, shipped back to the USA for burial.

It is revealed that the USA has been dumping **nuclear waste** at sea at some 50 offshore sites since 1946. Many barrels of waste have leaked.

The **Californian sea otter** becomes a protected species.

The FBI clamps down on **'phone phreaks'**, who have worked out how to make free long-distance calls, generally from telephone boxes.

The **CAT (computerized axial tomography) scan** is first used to make an image of the human brain.

A **plastic hip and thigh joint** is first used in surgery by British surgeon John Chernley.

The first widely available **pocket calculator** is produced by British electronics engineer Clive Sinclair. It is 1 cm/0.4 in thick and 12 cm/4.7 in long.

In the UK, the magazines *Gay News* and *Spare Rib* are founded.

US architect Minoru Yamasaki's **World Trade Center** in New York is (at 415 m/1,360 ft) the world's tallest building when it opens. Work on it continues until 1977.

The **Transamerica pyramidal office block** is competed in San Francisco, California.

US architect Robert Venturi publishes *Learning from Las Vegas*, an influential book advocating eclecticism in architecture and design.

The **Pentagram** design consultancy is founded in the UK.

North Korean leader **Kim Il Sung** has a colossal statue of himself erected to commemorate his 60th birthday.

British artist Nicholas Munro temporarily erects a **giant fibreglass gorilla** in the Bull Ring, Birmingham, England.

English novelist Richard Adams's first book, *Watership Down*, written for children, becomes a general cult book.

US journalist Hunter S Thompson publishes the influential *Fear and Loathing in Las Vegas*, an imaginative style of reportage, known as the 'gonzo' school and starring the author, which becomes much imitated.

The Man Died is the prison memoirs of Nigerian writer Wole Soyinka.

Russian poet **Joseph Brodsky** is expelled from the USSR. He moves to the USA and will eventually write in English as well as in Russian.

Novelist Brian Moore, born in Northern Ireland, publishes *Catholics*.

US writer George V Higgins publishes the novel *The Friends of Eddie Coyle*.

The novel *Kōkotsu no hito/The Twilight Years* by Japanese writer Sawako Ariyoshi deals with the problem of caring for ageing parents. It is a best seller in Japan.

British writer Jill Paton Walsh publishes the teenage novel *Goldengrove*.

British writer Penelope Lively publishes the children's novel *The Driftway*.

US film director Francis Ford Coppola makes *The Godfather* about the Mafia; actors include Marlon Brando and Al Pacino.

The film *Play It Again, Sam*, directed by Herbert Ross, stars Woody Allen and Diane Keaton.

Swedish director Ingmar Bergman makes the film *Viskningar och rop/Cries and Whispers*.

Le Charme discret de la bourgeoisie/The Discreet Charm of the Bourgeoisie is a French comedy of manners by the Spanish Surrealist film director Luis Buñuel.

Soviet director Andrei Tarkovsky makes the science-fiction film *Solaris*.

The musical *Cabaret*, based on the story 'Sally Bowles' by English novelist Christopher Isherwood, is filmed by Bob Fosse, starring Liza Minnelli.

Jack Nicholson stars in *The King of Marvin Gardens* by US film director Bob Rafelson.

Yves Montand and Jane Fonda star in the film *Tout va bien* by Jean-Luc Godard and Jean-Pierre Gorin, about a factory strike.

German film director Rainer Werner Fassbinder's 18th film,

Angst essen Seele auf/Fear Eats the Soul gives him an international reputation.

US singer Diana Ross stars as Billie Holiday in the biopic *Lady Sings the Blues*.

US film director Woody Allen makes the comedy *Everything You Always Wanted to Know About Sex*.

Scottish film director Bill Douglas begins a trilogy with *My Childhood*.

English director John Boorman goes to Hollywood to make *Deliverance* with John Voigt and Burt Reynolds.

British film *That'll Be the Day* makes a pop star of David Essex.

German director Werner Herzog's film *Aguirre der Zorn Gottes/ Aguirre Wrath of God* stars Klaus Kinski.

The **fringe theatre movement** is spreading; the Bush Theatre opens in Shepherd's Bush, London.

Retire! It can't be all that pleasant to devote a whole lifetime to earning a living, scavenger-like, from the dead flesh of living literature which you slaughter.
English dramatist **Arnold Wesker** addressing *The Times* theatre critic Harold Hobson

---

Premiere of English dramatist Edward Bond's *Lear*, a reworking of Shakespeare's play.

English actress **Margaret Rutherford** dies; born 1892. She starred as Miss Marple in a televised Agatha Christie crime series, and played many eccentric and formidable ladies on the stage and in cinema.

English avant-garde composer Harrison Birtwhistle writes *The Triumph of Time* for large orchestra.

In Brussels, Belgium, German soprano **Elizabeth Schwarzkopf** makes her last stage performance, in Richard Strauss's *Der Rosenkavalier*.

The opera *Hikarigoku/The Shining Moss* by Japanese composer Ikuma Dan has its premiere.

Singer and songwriter Bob Marley's album *Catch a Fire* begins the popularization of **reggae music** beyond Jamaica.

US rock singer and songwriter Lou Reed's album *Transformer* yields a rare top-ten hit, **'Walk on the Wild Side'**.

US glitter-punk rockers the **New York Dolls** make their first UK tour.

Nigerian musician Fela Kuti makes two classic Afro-beat LPs, *Shakara* and *Roforofo Fight*.

US singer and songwriter Carly Simon has her biggest hit with **'You're So Vain'**.

US fashion designer **Ralph Lauren** starts producing women's wear.

Platform shoes, an impractical form of fashion footwear originating two years earlier in Italy, reach heights of up to 5 inches (13 cm) in Britain.

Soviet ice skater **Irina Rodnina** wins the Olympic pairs competition with her partner for the first time.

US swimmer **Mark Spitz** wins a record seven gold medals in the Olympics, all in world record times.

Soviet gymnast **Olga Korbut** wins three Olympic gold medals and one silver.

US chess player **Bobby Fischer** becomes world champion when he beats Soviet grandmaster Boris Spassky in Reykjavik, Iceland.

1973

The year Britain finally joined the Common Market, 1973 marked the end of the postwar boom. In reaction to the West's support for Israel in the Yom Kippur War, the Arab oil cartel quadrupled the price of oil. In response, Richard Nixon took the dollar off the gold standard (effectively devaluing it). The impact of these events caused a world recession and began a period of high, often uncontrolled, inflation. Britain suffered more than most. The expansionist policies of the Heath government had already triggered an unprecedented inflation in wages and prices. At the end of 1973, this inflation resulted in a second miners' strike as well as a power workers' strike, the severity of which forced Britain to declare a state of emergency, curtailed television output, and imposed power cuts on millions of homes. Political initiatives over Northern Ireland resulted in a power-sharing local administration, with both Nationalist and Unionist politicians participating.

Cease-fire in the **Vietnam War**. US troops leave (Feb–March) but the bombing of Cambodia continues until Aug.

Israeli fighter planes shoot down 13 Syrian jets.

The landmark US Supreme Court case of *Roe v. Wade* upholds a woman's right to **abortion**.

If men could get pregnant abortion would be a sacrament.
US feminist **Florynce Kennedy**

Former US president **Lyndon B Johnson** dies at 64.

The **Open University** awards its first degrees.

The USA devalues the **dollar** by 10%.

General strike in **Northern Ireland**; state of emergency declared.

The **London Stock Exchange admits women** to the trading floor.

Stephen Sondheim's musical *A Little Night Music* opens in New York, to run for 600 performances.

The new **London Bridge** is officially opened.

US choreographer Twyla Tharp's ballet *Deuce Coupe* is given its premiere by the New York Joffrey Ballet.

Dark Side of the Moon by English progressive rock band Pink Floyd is released to spend more than 100 weeks in the UK and US album charts.

Red Rum wins the British Grand National horse race in record time (9 minutes 1.9 seconds).

A US Senate committee begins to investigate the **Watergate** break-in and its connection to President Richard Nixon, his staff, and supporters.

There can be no whitewash at the White House.
US president **Richard Nixon**, television address on Watergate

Value-added tax (**VAT**) is introduced in the UK.

Spanish artist **Pablo Picasso** dies at 91; his greatest influence was in the development of Cubism.

The **Vatican** releases documents showing that the Roman Catholic Church was aware during World War II of Nazi concentration camps but did not protest.

An American Indian demonstration at **Wounded Knee**, South Dakota (Feb–May), ends in a shootout with police; several Indians are killed.

The televised **Watergate** hearings begin in the USA, chaired by Senator Sam Erwin, a Democrat from North Carolina.

I welcome this kind of examination because people have got to know whether or not their president is a crook. Well, I'm not a crook.
US president **Richard Nixon**, press conference on Watergate

---

The UK Trades Union Congress organizes a one-day **strike** (1 May) against the government's pay-restraint policy; 1.6 million people take part.

The business practices of the multinational mining and trading company **Lonrho** are questioned in Parliament.

It is the unpleasant and unacceptable face of capitalism.
British prime minister **Edward Heath**, speaking in Parliament on the Lonrho affair

---

Skylab, the first orbital space station, is launched by the USA. Comet **Kohoutek** is observed by astronauts on *Skylab*.

US rock group Steely Dan release their first album, *Can't Buy a Thrill*.

Juan Perón returns from exile to reassume the presidency of Argentina.

Eámon de Valera resigns as president of the Republic of Ireland; he is 90.

A state of emergency is imposed in **Dominica** (June–Sept) in response to Black Power demands and protests against unemployment and cash-cropping.

US soul singer Al Green releases his seventh consecutive million-selling single, **'Here I Am (Come and Take Me)'**.

The **Bahamas**, islands in the Caribbean, achieve full independence from Britain, within the Commonwealth.

The **Watergate** hearings reveal that President Nixon bugged his own offices and White House phone calls, but he claims that some of the tapes are missing.

Once the toothpaste is out of the tube, it is awfully hard to get it back in.
White House aide **H R Haldeman**, speaking to a colleague about the Watergate affair

---

The UK **National Health Service** is reorganized: area health authorities are set up.

US sculptor **Robert Smithson** dies; born 1938. He is best known for *Spiral Jetty* 1970, a large structure in a landscape.

US film actor **Bruce Lee** dies at 32, having popularized the oriental martial arts in a number of action films, most of them made in Hong Kong.

Premiere of *Equus* by English dramatist Peter Shaffer at the Old Vic Theatre, London.

English dramatist Alan Ayckbourn's play *Absurd Person Singular* opens in London.

German conductor **Otto Klemperer** dies at 88.

At the end of a tour, English rock singer **David Bowie** announces his retirement but, in the event, he merely discards his Ziggy Stardust persona.

Born Paul Gadd, UK 'King of Glitter Rock' **Garry Glitter** releases 'I'm the Leader of the Gang (I Am)' followed by 'I Love You Love Me Love'; both reach No One in the UK charts.

Alvin Stardust (Bernard Jury) fronts the UK hit single 'My Coo Ca Choo'.

Richard Nixon refuses a court order to hand over the secret tape recordings.

US-backed military coup overthrows President Salvador Allende in Chile, causing his death. Political repression begins under General **Augusto Pinochet**.

In the **Cod War**, an Icelandic gunboat crew accuses a UK frigate of throwing carrots at them.

US country-rock singer **Gram Parsons** dies at 26. To fulfil his wishes, friends steal his coffin and cremate him at Joshua Tree, California.

A tennis match between Wimbledon women's singles champion **Billie Jean King** and former Wimbledon men's champion Bobby Riggs ends in victory for King.

Fourth **Arab-Israeli (Yom Kippur) War** (2–24 Oct) begins with a surprise attack by Egyptian forces across the Suez Canal, and there is fighting with Syria in the Golan Heights. Israel occupies the Gaza Strip for the third time.

The Organization of Petroleum-Exporting Countries raises **oil prices** by 70%, triggering worldwide recession, and the Organization of Arab Petroleum-Exporting Countries cuts back production.

Spiro Agnew is forced to resign as US vice president when charged with tax evasion. His replacement is Gerald Ford.

I am a Ford, not a Lincoln.
US Republican politician **Gerald Ford** on becoming vice president

Newcastle-upon-Tyne Labour councillor T Dan Smith is arrested and charged with corruption as part of the inquiry into the complex affairs of bankrupt British architect **John Poulson** and his contacts in local government and nationalized industries.

Firefighters strike in the UK.

LBC (London Broadcasting Company) and **Capital Radio**, London's first commercial radio stations, start broadcasting.

Catalan cellist **Pablo Casals** dies; born 1876.

Famine in Ethiopia has claimed hundreds of thousands of victims.

Power-station workers in the UK go on strike. A **state of emergency** is declared, with reduced street lighting and a 22.30 cut-off time for television broadcasting.

Oz magazine folds in the UK.

Paul McCartney and Wings have one of the biggest post-Beatle successes with ***Band on the Run***.

David Ben-Gurion, one of the founders of the state of Israel, dies; born 1886.

UK crisis budget cuts public spending by £1.2 billion.

Political violence kills 250 people in **Northern Ireland**, of whom 171 are civilians (Jan–Dec).

US artist **Joseph Cornell** dies at 69. He arranged objects in little boxes.

The UK, Denmark, and Ireland join the **European Community** (EC).

Here we are again with both feet firmly planted in the air.
British trade-union leader **Hugh Scanlon** on his union's attitude to the European Community

---

Coup in Afghanistan overthrows the monarchy; former prime minister Daud Khan becomes president.

British Honduras, in Central America, becomes Belize but remains under British control (until 1981).

Military **coup in Rwanda**: Juvenal Habyarimana seizes power.

Togo becomes a one-party state.

Return to civilian rule in **Turkey**, under prime minister Bulent Ecevit.

In Ireland, the **Fianna Fáil** party is defeated after 40 years in office; Liam Cosgrave forms a coalition government.

The USSR enters the **Universal Copyright Convention**.

Greece is proclaimed a republic, with Col George Papadopolous as president (he is a member of the junta that seized power 1967).

Henry Kissinger becomes US secretary of state.

Agreement between the EC and the European Free Trade Association creates a **free-trade area** of more than 300 million consumers.

The UK and France sign a treaty agreeing to trial borings for the **Channel Tunnel**.

Soviet leader **Leonid Brezhnev** visits Washington DC.

The **Polisario** nationalist movement is formed in Western Sahara.

South African Eugene Terreblanche founds the neo-Nazi Afrikaner Weerstandsbeweging (**AWB**).

Eleven African states form an organization to tackle drought problems, the Comité Permanent Inter-états de Lutte contre la Sécheresse dans le Sahel (**CILSS**).

The Caribbean Community and Common Market (**CARICOM**) is established.

The International Convention for the Prevention of Pollution from Ships (**MARPOL**) sets limits and minimum distances from shore for the discharge or dumping of sewage, toxic waste, and other waste.

The **Ecology Party**, that will become the UK Green Party, is founded.

National and regional **water boards** are set up in the UK, removing from local authorities the responsibility for water and sewerage.

The **Office of Fair Trading** is established in the UK.

The **Manpower Services Commission** quango is set up in the UK to retrain the unemployed for available work. It will undergo several name changes in subsequent decades, as unemployment continues to rise.

London's wholesale fruit and vegetable market moves from **Covent Garden** to Nine Elms, Wandsworth.

The first **genetic engineering** is carried out by US biochemists Stanley H Cohen and Herbert W Boyer. The process will have great importance in medicine and agriculture.

A new strain of high-yielding **rice**, IR-26, is developed at the International Rice Research Institute in the Philippines. Unlike its 1971 predecessor IR-20, it is resistant to grassy stunt virus and the brown plant hopper (until a new biotype of the latter emerges 1976).

The world's first **teletext** systems, Oracle and Ceefax, are introduced in the UK.

Dutch-born US astronomer **Gerard Peter Kuiper** dies; born 1905. He made extensive studies of the Solar System.

France embarks on an ambitious programme of building **nuclear reactors**; by the late 1980s 70% of France's electricity will be generated by these.

The **Hanford nuclear power and reprocessing facility** in Washington State, USA, leaks 450,000 litres of highly radioactive waste into the environment, mainly the Columbia River.

An international agreement is signed to limit the use and manufacture of polychlorinated biphenyls (**PCBs**), which are toxic and pose an environmental hazard.

The food industry in North America adopts the **bar code**, and its use begins to spread.

Arizona bans **smoking in public places**, the first state in the US to do so.

The 110-storey **Sears Tower** opens in Chicago, Illinois. At 443 m/1,454 ft it is the world's tallest building. The architects are the US firm of Skidmore, Owings & Merrill.

Soviet novelist Alexander Solzhenitsyn's *The Gulag Archipelago* is an exposé of the Soviet labour-camp system.

English-born poet **W H Auden**, one of the greatest of his generation, dies at 66 in Vienna.

US novelist Thomas Pynchon publishes *Gravity's Rainbow*.

US writer Gore Vidal publishes the historical novel *Burr*.

English writer Angus Wilson publishes the novel *As If by Magic*.

US fantasy and science-fiction writer Kurt Vonnegut publishes the novel *Breakfast of Champions*.

The erotic novel *Fear of Flying* by US writer Erica Jong is a best seller.

Irish writer **Elizabeth Bowen** dies; born 1899. Her novels include *The Death of the Heart* 1938 and *The Little Girls* 1964.

English novelist Graham Greene publishes *The Honorary Consul*, set in Argentina.

German economist E F Schumacher publishes *Small Is Beautiful*, a seminal critique of economic growth policies.

English writer J G Ballard's novel *Crash* characteristically depicts disaster as metaphor.

Japanese avant-garde novelist Kōbō Abe publishes *Hako otoko/ The Box Man* about a man who lives in a cardboard box by choice.

English children's novelist William Mayne publishes *The Jersey Shore*.

US writer Paula Fox publishes the historical novel *The Slave Dancer* for teenagers.

English novelist Alan Garner publishes the fantasy *Red Shift* for teenagers.

US fantasy and science-fiction writer Ursula Le Guin publishes *The Farthest Shore*, bringing her *Earthsea* novel sequence to a temporary conclusion.

US writer Donald Barthelme publishes a collection of Post-Modern short stories, *Sadness*.

US illustrator and writer Rosemary Wells creates *Benjamin and Tulip*, a picture book for children.

Belgian-born French anthropologist Claude Lévi-Strauss publishes the second volume of his *Anthropologie structurale/Structural Anthropology*.

US film director **John Ford** dies at 78. He specialized in Westerns but was influential beyond the genre.

French director François Truffaut makes the film *La Nuit américaine/Day for Night* about filmmaking.

US director Martin Scorsese's film *Mean Streets* stars Robert De Niro and Harvey Keitel.

Marlon Brando stars in Italian director Bernardo Bertolucci's film *Last Tango in Paris*.

Indian film director Satyajit Ray makes *Ashanti Sanket/Distant Thunder*.

Jack Nicholson stars in US director Hal Ashby's film *The Last Detail*.

US director James Bridges makes the film *The Paper Chase*, in which film and theatre producer John Houseman makes his acting debut at the age of 70 as a law professor.

Paul Newman and Robert Redford star in the Hollywood film *The Sting*.

Sidney Lumet's film *Serpico* is based on a true story of New York police corruption.

English director Nicolas Roeg makes the horror film *Don't Look Now*.

US songwriters Bob Dylan and Kris Kristofferson appear in the Western film *Pat Garrett and Billy the Kid*, with a soundtrack by Dylan.

French film director Jacques Rivette makes *Céline et Julie vont en bateau/Celine and Julie Go Boating*.

French film director Bertrand Tavernier makes his debut with *L'Horloger de Saint-Paul*.

US nostalgia film *American Graffiti* is set in 1962.

Spanish film director Victor Erice makes *El espiritu della colmena/The Spirit of the Beehive*.

US film director Woody Allen makes the comedy *Sleeper*.

English actor Roger Moore takes over as **James Bond** in the film *Live and Let Die*.

Enter the Dragon, starring Bruce Lee, is the first US-made **kung-fu film** and comes at the height of the martial-arts boom.

The Jamaican film *The Harder They Come* stars reggae singer Jimmy Cliff and depicts local gangster life.

English actor **Laurence Olivier** resigns as head of the National Theatre; he is succeeded by Peter Hall.

In the play *Not I* by Irish writer Samuel Beckett, only the mouth of the single actress is visible. Billie Whitelaw creates the part.

English dramatist and actor **Noël Coward** dies; born 1899. His comedies include *Hay Fever* 1925 and *Blithe Spirit* 1941.

English composer Benjamin Britten's opera *Death in Venice* opens at the Aldeburgh Festival, Suffolk.

English conductor **Simon Rattle** wins the Bournemouth John Player Conducting Competition at 18. He will go on to become principal conductor of the Birmingham Symphony Orchestra.

The opera *The Old Tale of the Enslaver Tarobe* by Japanese composer Yoshiya Mamiya has its premiere in Tokyo.

US guitarist **Pat Metheny** joins the jazz group led by vibraphonist Gary Burton.

The album *Brothers and Sisters* by the US Allman Brothers band begins a 50-week stay in the US charts.

US rock singer and songwriter Lou Reed releases the harrowing album *Berlin*.

The year's biggest hit and most performed song is **'Tie a Yellow Ribbon'**, initially recorded by a US group called Dawn (featuring Tony Orlando).

The Carpenters US pop duo are at the peak of their popularity, with the hits 'Yesterday Once More' and 'Top of the World'.

English pop group Roxy Music release their second album, *For Your Pleasure*, and the lead singer, **Bryan Ferry**, embarks on a solo career.

'Smoke on the Water' is a big hit for British heavy-metal group Deep Purple.

English pop singer **Elton John** releases two number-one LPs (UK and USA) and has a number-one hit with 'Goodbye Yellow Brick Road'.

The UK's most popular group of the decade, Slade, release **'Merry Xmas Everybody'** which will also be a hit single on several occasions in the 1980s.

US heavy blues-rock trio ZZ Top have their first million-selling album, *Tres Hombres*.

British philosopher and theologian **Alan Watts** dies in California; born 1915. He popularized Zen Buddhism among the Beat Generation.

Scottish world champion motor-racing driver **Jackie Stewart** wins the Canadian Grand Prix and retires.

British equestrian **Lucinda Prior-Palmer** (Lucinda Green) wins the Badminton Horse Trials for the first time.

1974

This was the year of two general elections. The continuing miners' strike, persuaded prime minister Edward Heath to call a general election on the platform 'Who governs Britain'. Heath was defeated and Harold Wilson's Labour Party was returned to power, albeit as a minority government. Wilson settled the miners' dispute and repealed the curbs on trades unions. In a second general election, Wilson won a small overall majority. During 1974, inflation soared, peaking at 25 per cent, the stock market collapsed, and there were balance of payments and sterling crises. In Northern Ireland, following a strike by Protestants, the power-sharing local government collapsed. The IRA brought their terror campaign to mainland Britain, with bombs in Birmingham, Guildford, London, and other locations, causing death and destruction. In the United States, Richard Nixon, overwhelmed by the Watergate scandal, became the first US president to resign his office. If Nixon's resignation purged the United States of one political crisis, the handover of combat capability in Vietnam to the South Vietnamese and the withdrawal of American combat troops marked the beginning of the end of another.

A **three-day working week** is introduced in the UK as a result of a negative balance of payments, the oil crisis, and the miners' pay demands.

Direct rule of Northern Ireland from Westminster ends but is reintroduced later in the year when power sharing between Protestant and Roman Catholic groups fails.

In the UK, 18 national museums and art galleries begin to **charge for admission**.

Polish-born US film producer **Samuel Goldwyn** dies at 90. His Goldwyn Pictures Corporation, founded 1917, merged 1924 into Metro-Goldwyn-Mayer.

US sex musical *Let My People Come* by Earl Wilson Jr opens in New York for a run of 1,167 performances.

Grenada, in the Caribbean, achieves independence from Britain, within the Commonwealth, with Eric Gairy as the prime minister.

Coal **miners' strike** begins in the UK.

British architect **John Poulson** is jailed for corruption.

Dissident Soviet writer **Alexander Solzhenitsyn** is exiled from the USSR.

*In our country the lie has become not just a moral
category but a pillar of the state.*
Soviet dissident writer **Alexander Solzhenitsyn**

US heiress **Patricia Hearst** is kidnapped in California by a guerrilla group called the Symbionese Liberation Army.

'**Streaking**' – dashing naked across public spaces – becomes a craze on US college campuses and spreads from there.

General election in the UK: Labour wins a majority of four over the Conservatives, though no overall majority, and Harold Wilson replaces Edward Heath as prime minister. This means the end of the coal strike (the miners receive a 35% pay rise), the three-day week, and the state of emergency. Shirley Williams is given her first cabinet post, as minister for prices and consumer protection.

In **Guatemala**, widespread political violence is precipitated by the discovery of falsified election returns.

The UK introduces a 50-mph/80-kph **speed limit on motorways**.

An attempt to **kidnap Princess Anne** in London is foiled by her bodyguards.

Military **coup in Portugal** overthrows the dictatorship (25 April). The coup leader is General Antonio Spinola, who is a moderate centrist.

Patricia Hearst is photographed by security cameras taking part in a bank robbery in San Francisco.

Contraception becomes freely available on the National Health Service in Britain.

In West Germany, chancellor **Willy Brandt** resigns when one of his staff, Günter Guillaume, is revealed to be an East German agent. Helmut Schmidt takes over as chancellor.

Gaullist politician **Valéry Giscard d'Estaing** is elected president of France after the death in office of Georges Pompidou.

India tests its first **nuclear bomb**, underground. It has been made with equipment supplied by Canada, which breaks off further nuclear co-operation.

Premiere of US musical *The Magic Show* by Stephen Schwartz; it will run for 1,859 performances.

US jazz musician and composer **Duke Ellington** dies at 74. He was one of the originators of big-band jazz.

Israel withdraws its forces from Syria, including part of the Golan Heights.

A chemical plant in **Flixborough**, Humberside, England, explodes, killing 29 people.

The first **summer solstice festival** is held at Stonehenge, Wiltshire, England.

English actor John Wood stars in the Royal Shakespeare Company's original production of *Travesties* by British dramatist Tom Stoppard.

War is capitalism with the gloves off and many who go to war know it but they go to war because they don't want to be a hero.
British dramatist **Tom Stoppard**, *Travesties*

Argentine dictator **Juan Perón** dies. He is succeeded by his third wife, Isabel Perón.

The **Greek military junta resigns**, and former premier Constantine Karamanlis is recalled from exile to lead the government. Martial law and the ban on political parties are lifted; restoration of the monarchy is rejected by a referendum.

Military **coup in Cyprus** temporarily deposes president Makarios. Turkish troops are sent to northern Cyprus, which declares itself the Turkish Federated State of Cyprus, with Rauf Denktaş as president.

The UK **Industrial Relations Act** is abolished and ACAS (the Advisory, Conciliation, and Arbitration Service) established.

The US Central Intelligence Agency recovers, from a depth of 5 km/3 mi in the N Pacific, part of a Soviet submarine that sank 1968 with **nuclear missiles** on board.

US president **Richard Nixon** resigns (9 Aug) under threat of impeachment, having been forced by the Supreme Court to release his incriminating tape recordings. Vice president Gerald Ford takes over.

I guess it just proves that in America anyone can be president.
Gerald Ford on becoming president when Richard Nixon was forced to resign

Japan launches a **nuclear-powered cargo ship**, the *Mutsu*. It has reactor trouble on its first voyage and the repairs take ten years. No further nuclear-powered ships are built in Japan.

The last issue of the British underground magazine *IT* is published.

Emperor **Haile Selassie** of Ethiopia is overthrown in a military coup and Ethiopia declared a socialist state.

President Ford pardons **Richard Nixon** to prevent further investigation of his abuse of power.

In Portugal, **General Spinola** is ousted by the left wing. The banks and large industries are nationalized.

France officially abandons atmospheric **nuclear testing**.

A 13th **satellite of Jupiter** is discovered by a US astronomer.

A second **general election** is held in the UK. Labour wins an absolute majority of three. The Scottish Nationalist Party makes large gains, winning 11 seats with 30% of the Scottish vote.

They [Labour ministers] are going about the country stirring up complacency.
British Conservative politician **William Whitelaw** during election campaign

---

The trial of the **Watergate** burglars begins in the USA (1 Oct).

The long nightmare is over.
Newly sworn-in US president **Gerald Ford** on the end of the Watergate hearings

---

The **Palestine Liberation Organization** becomes the first nongovernmental delegation to be admitted to a plenary session of the United Nations General Assembly.

The Irish Republican Army (IRA) extends its terrorist campaign to the British mainland. Five people are killed in a **Guildford pub bombing** and 17 in Birmingham. Six people are arrested.

Five **Oxford colleges abandon their all-male tradition** and allot 100 places between them to female undergraduates; other colleges will follow suit.

US poet **Anne Sexton** commits suicide at 45.

Irish rock band **Thin Lizzy** gives its first live performance.

A prize fight is held for a record sum of money between US boxers **Muhammad Ali** and **George Foreman** in Zaire. Ali regains the world heavyweight title.

Japanese prime minister **Kakuei Tanaka** resigns because of allegations of corruption. Takeo Miki is chosen as his successor.

The US **Freedom of Information Act** is passed by Congress despite a presidential veto.

Democrat **Jerry Brown** is elected governor of California.

The **Prevention of Terrorism Act** is passed in the UK, making the IRA an illegal organization and enabling police to hold suspects for seven days without charge.

US technician **Karen Silkwood** dies in a car crash. She worked in a nuclear laboratory and was about to release information about dangerous irregularities by the company. Her life and death later became the subject of a Hollywood film.

Dominica passes a law – the **Prohibited and Unlawful Societies and Associations Act** – stating that anyone wearing dreadlocks can be killed with impunity.

British aristocrat **Lord Lucan** disappears immediately after the murder of his children's nanny and is never heard from again.

A **cyclone devastates Darwin**, Australia.

Earthquake in N Pakistan kills more than 5,000 people.

Labour MP **John Stonehouse** is arrested in Australia after faking his own disappearance in Florida; he is wanted for questioning in the UK in connection with a Bangladeshi bank and will eventually be tried for embezzlement.

Golda Meir is succeeded by Yitzhak Rabin as prime minister of Israel.

Pessimism is a luxury that a Jew never can allow himself.
Israeli prime minister **Golda Meir**

Military **coup in Niger** ousts President Hamani Diori; Seyni Kountché seizes power (until his death 1987).

A **coup attempt in Bolivia** prompts a clampdown on political activity.

Mali becomes a one-party state.

The **famine in Bangladesh** claims hundreds of thousands of victims.

US president Gerald Ford meets Soviet leader Leonid Brezhnev in Vladivostok, eastern USSR, to discuss **strategic arms limitations**.

Pro-Saudi military **coup in North Yemen**.

In Rhodesia (now Zimbabwe), political opposition leaders **Joshua Nkomo** and **Robert Mugabe** are released from prison.

Malta becomes a republic.

The USA agrees to negotiate full transfer of the **Panama Canal** to Panama.

Loyalist car bombers in Dublin and Monaghan, Ireland, kill 33 and injure 300.

US Democrat politician **Michael Dukakis** becomes governor of Massachusetts (later the basis of his unsuccessful presidential campaign).

The **Irish National Liberation Army** is founded as an offshoot of the IRA.

The **Multi Fibre Arrangement** is introduced, a world trade protectionist measure limiting the quantity of textiles that the West would import from poorer countries.

The European Community **Programme of Social Action** attempts to protect the rights of migrant workers.

Jamaica introduces a **Special Works Programme** to alleviate unemployment and stimulate production.

The **'White Australia'** immigration policy is abolished.

Paid parental leave (the right of either parent to stay home with a new baby for a specified period, without loss of income) becomes available by law in Sweden. Only 2% of fathers take it in the first year.

The **FT30 index** of shares in 30 UK companies drops to 147, its lowest point since the 1950s.

The **Farakka barrage** built by India across the River Ganges near the border with Bangladesh starts a long-running dispute about entitlement to the water.

The world's deepest **oil well**, 10,941 m/3,441 ft, is drilled in Oklahoma, USA.

Ariel 5, a British satellite, makes a pioneering survey of the sky at X-ray wavelengths.

The tomb of Emperor **Shi Huangdi** is discovered in Xian, China, guarded by 10,000 life-size terracotta warriors.

Footprints of a hominid (subsequently referred to as **Lucy**), 3 to 3.7 million years old, are found at Laetoli, Ethiopia.

CLIP-4, the first computer with a parallel architecture, is developed by US multinational IBM.

The first computer **word processors** come on the market.

The Olivetti Lettera 25 **typewriter**, designed by Mario Bellini, goes into production.

The planet Mercury is weighed, measured, and mapped by US probe *Mariner 10*.

US astronomer William K Hartman puts forward the theory that the **Moon** originated as part of a larger planet that once collided with the Earth.

In particle physics, a charmed **quark** is discovered, to go with the previously known up, down, and strange quarks.

The **Airbus** is introduced, a wide-bodied passenger plane built by a European consortium.

Charles de Gaulle international airport opens in France, the third airport serving Paris.

The **Volkswagen Golf** is launched (called the Rabbit in the USA); it will become Europe's best-selling car. The designer is Italian Giorgio Giugiaro.

London's first **McDonald's** fast-food outlet opens.

The British charity War on Want begins the worldwide campaign against aggressive marketing of powdered **baby milk** in the Third World, where breast-feeding is generally safer for babies. A World Health Organization code of practice will eventually be adopted by the companies concerned.

People and *High Times* magazines begin publication in the USA.

English high-tech architect Norman Foster designs the **Sainsbury**

Centre for Visual Arts at the University of East Anglia, England (opened 1978).

Byker Wall, Newcastle-upon-Tyne, NE England, is a council estate built after consultation with the inhabitants; the architect is Ralph Erskine.

The **Prefectural Museum**, Gumma prefecture, Japan, by Japanese architect Arata Isozaki is a late Modernist building.

English poet Philip Larkin publishes the collection *High Windows*.

Sexual intercourse began / in nineteen sixty-three / –
(Which was rather late for me) – / Between the end of the
Chatterley ban / And the Beatles' first LP.
English poet **Philip Larkin**, 'Annus Mirabilis'

Zen and the Art of Motorcycle Maintenance by US novelist Robert M Pirsig is a best seller.

Canadian economist John Kenneth Galbraith publishes *Economics and the Public Purpose*.

English writer John Wain publishes a biography of 18th-century lexicographer **Samuel Johnson**.

South African novelist Nadine Gordimer publishes *The Conservationist*.

The War Between the Tates by US novelist Alison Lurie is a best seller.

US novelist Ursula Le Guin publishes the political science-fiction novel *The Dispossessed*.

English thriller writer John Le Carré publishes *Tinker Tailor Soldier Spy*.

US novelist Joseph Heller publishes *Something Happened*.

English novelist Beryl Bainbridge publishes *The Bottle Factory Outing*.

British writer Penelope Mortimer publishes the novel *Long Distance*.

US writer Virginia Hamilton publishes the children's novel *M C Higgins, the Great*.

French writer and film director **Marcel Pagnol** dies; born 1895. His work includes *Manon des Sources* 1952.

French director Louis Malle makes the film *Lacombe Lucien*.

US film director Francis Ford Coppola makes *The Godfather II* with actors Al Pacino and Robert De Niro.

US film director Martin Scorsese makes *Alice Doesn't Live Here Anymore*, starring Ellen Burstyn, Kris Kristofferson, and Jodie Foster.

US actress Sissy Spacek stars in Terence Malick's road movie *Badlands* about two teenage serial killers.

Italian director Federico Fellini's film *Amarcord* is a childhood memoir.

Senegalese film director Ousmane Sembene makes *Xala*.

Polish film director Roman Polanski casts US actors Jack Nicholson, Faye Dunaway, and John Huston in *Chinatown*.

French actor Jean-Paul Belmondo stars in *Stavisky*, a film by Alain Resnais with music by Stephen Sondheim.

Italian film director Lina Wertmüller makes the film *Travolti da un insolito destino dell'azzuro mare d'agosto/Swept Away*.

Swedish director Ingmar Bergman films Wolfgang Amadeus Mozart's opera *The Magic Flute*.

US film comedy *Blazing Saddles* is directed by Mel Brooks.

The Texas Chain Saw Massacre is the most controversial horror film of the decade.

Premiere of the trilogy *The Norman Conquests* by English dramatist Alan Ayckbourn.

English music-hall comedian Max Wall appears in a revival of John Osborne's 1957 play *The Entertainer*.

Soviet Kirov Ballet dancer **Mikhail Baryshnikov** defects in Canada and joins the American Ballet Theatre (ABT). US ballet dancer **Gelsey Kirkland** also joins ABT this year and becomes Baryshnikov's most outstanding partner.

British composer Iain Hamilton's opera *The Catiline Conspiracy* is staged by Scottish Opera.

The **Sadler's Wells Opera** company is renamed the English National Opera.

Swedish pop quartet **Abba** have their first international hit, 'Waterloo'.

Scottish pop group **Bay City Rollers** have their first UK top-ten hit, beginning a two-year spell as leading teenybop idols.

Heart Like a Wheel is US pop singer Linda Rondstadt's breakthrough album.

Good Old Boys by US singer and songwriter Randy Newman is an ironic concept album about white Southerners.

Disco music gets under way with the Florida funk sound of KC and the Sunshine Band; 'Rock Your Baby' is a US number one.

West German techno-rock band Kraftwerk make an international impact with the album *Autobahn*.

Welsh singer and musician John Cale, formerly of the Velvet Underground, makes the rock album *Fear*.

Anglo-US pop group **Fleetwood Mac** arrive at the line-up that will make them hugely successful.

English cleric **Donald Coggan** to succeed Michael Ramsay as archbishop of Canterbury.

US tennis player **Jimmy Connors** wins the men's singles titles at Wimbledon and the US Open.

US tennis player **Chris Evert** wins the women's singles at Wimbledon for the first time.

Belgian cyclist **Eddie Merckx** wins the Tour de France for the fifth time.

West Germany, captained by Franz Beckenbauer, wins the soccer World Cup.

US baseball player **Hank Aaron** sets a new record by hitting his 715th home run.

1975

In 1975, Britain began to tackle an inflation that was destroying savings, and, with massive pay hikes, creating a major instability. Pay and price curbs, together with food subsidies, began the process of control. Conservative leader Edward Heath was toppled as party leader by Margaret Thatcher who became Britain's first woman party leader, and leader of the Opposition.

The final agony of Vietnam ended, with the North Vietnamese army taking over the South and renaming the capital, Saigon, after its wartime leader Ho Chi Minh. The Irish Republican Army's terror campaign continued on the British mainland.

The UK government cancels the **Channel Tunnel** project because of escalating costs.

Adult comic book *Métal hurlant* launched in France with artwork by illustrators Jean Giraud (Moebius) and Philippe Druillet.

Margaret Thatcher becomes leader of Britain's Conservative Party.

English-born humorous novelist **P G Wodehouse** dies at 93; he spent most of his life in the USA, though his work is set in a vaguely Edwardian England.

US rock singer and songwriter Bob Dylan releases the album *Blood on the Tracks*.

King Faisal of Saudi Arabia is assassinated; he is succeeded by his half-brother Khalid.

Iraqi forces attack **Kurds** in N Iraq.

In **Portugal**, General Antonio Spinola attempts a **countercoup** against the left.

The play *Same Time, Next Year* by Canadian dramatist Bernard Slade opens in New York and will run for 1,444 performances.

In **Cambodia**, US-backed leader Lon Nol is overthrown by Pol Pot's Khmer Rouge communist forces (17 April). Prince Norodom Sihanouk is reinstated as head of state. Cambodia's capital, Phnom Penh, is forcibly evacuated.

The **Vietnam War ends** in victory of the North over the South; Saigon is taken over by the Vietcong and the last Americans are evacuated (30 April). The war has cost 1.7 million Vietnamese lives, 56,500 US lives, and 1 million killed by the US bombing of Cambodia; at a cost to the USA of $141 billion.

Chinese nationalist **Chiang Kai-shek**, president of Taiwan, dies at 87; he is replaced as Kuomintang leader by his son Chiang Ching-kuo.

UK car-manufacturer **Aston-Martin Lagonda** is sold to a US firm for £1,050,000.

Portable **bleepers** are introduced in the UK.

No Man's Land by English dramatist Harold Pinter has its premiere at the Old Vic Theatre in London, starring Ralph Richardson and John Gielgud.

US-born French cabaret artist **Josephine Baker** dies at 68.

The trial of the **Baader-Meinhof** urban guerrillas (Red Army Faction) begins in Stuttgart, West Germany. The security arrangements cost more than £2 million.

English sculptor **Barbara Hepworth** dies at 72; she created mainly abstract forms in stone or wood.

The Wiz, a musical based on the US children's fantasy novel *The Wizard of Oz*, opens in New York to run for 1,666 performances.

Mozambique, SE Africa, achieves independence from Portugal, with Samora Machel as president and Frelimo as the sole legal party. Hundreds of thousands of Portuguese settlers emigrate, leaving a population that is 90% illiterate.

The re-election of Indian prime minister **Indira Gandhi** to parliament 1971 is declared invalid because of corrupt practices.

Instead of resigning, and in the face of mounting protest demonstrations, she imposes a state of emergency.

The **Suez Canal** is reopened, having been closed since the 1967 Six-Day War between Egypt and Israel.

The US state of Minnesota enacts a law requiring all public buildings to provide **no-smoking areas**.

A referendum in the UK comes out in favour of remaining in the **European Community**.

This going into Europe will not turn out to be the thrilling mutual exchange supposed. It is more like nine middle-aged couples with failing marriages meeting in a darkened bedroom in a Brussels hotel for a Group Grope.
British historian **E P Thompson**

Proceedings in the UK **House of Commons are broadcast live** on radio for the first time. The service does not become regular until 1978.

Oil production from the British section of the North Sea begins. The British National Oil Corporation is set up to deal with it.

The island republic of **Comoros** in the Indian Ocean achieves independence from France; Ahmed Abdallah is elected to be president.

Cape Verde, in the Atlantic off W Africa, achieves independence from Portugal, with Aristides Pereira as its first president.

Military **coup in Nigeria** led by Brig Murtala Mohammad ousts Yakubu Gowon (who seized power 1966). Mohammad is in turn assassinated and replaced by General Olusegun Obasanjo.

The **Helsinki Conference on Security and Co-operation** in Europe is held in Finland (July–Aug); 35 countries participate, including the USA and the USSR.

The spacecraft *Apollo 18* (USA) and *Soyuz 19* (USSR) make a joint flight and **link up in space**.

Controversial US trade-union leader **Jimmy Hoffa** disappears; he is believed to have been murdered.

The president of Bangladesh, **Sheik Mujibur Rahman**, is assassinated (15 Aug); martial law is imposed.

Death of former prime minister and president of the Irish Republic **Eámon de Valera**; born 1882.

The Irish don't know what they want and won't be happy till they get it.
British army officer

Two US **Viking probes** are launched (Aug and Sept). They will analyse the soil on Mars and send back colour photographs 1976.

Roger Bannister's record for running a mile is broken by New Zealand athlete **John Walker**.

Papua New Guinea, SW Pacific, achieves independence from Australia.

Civil war breaks out in **Beirut**, Lebanon.

Lynette 'Squeaky' Fromme attempts to assassinate US president Gerald Ford. She is a former member of murderer Charles Manson's 'family'.

The left-wing government of **Portugal**, led by Vasco Goncalvez, resigns in favour of a centrist coalition.

US heiress **Patricia Hearst** is arrested, having joined her urban guerrilla captors.

The production of **Wolseley cars** ends in the UK.

US rhythm-and-blues and soul singer **Jackie Wilson** has a heart attack on stage in New Jersey. He lapses into a coma from which he never recovers.

Czechoslovak tennis player **Martina Navratilova** defects to the USA.

Bob Dylan begins his **Rolling Thunder Review** tour.

The age of the **pop video** begins with the success of 'Bohemian Rhapsody' by British group Queen, taken from the album *A Night at the Opera*.

Civil war breaks out in Angola, SW Africa, as the country achieves independence from Portugal, with Agostinho Neto as president. Cuban troops arrive to support the MPLA (People's Movement for the Liberation of Angola) against the US-backed UNITA and South African-backed FNLA (National Front for the Liberation of Angola), who set up rival governments.

Surinam, on N coast of South America, achieves independence from the Netherlands; 40% of the population emigrate to the latter.

The United Nations (UN) International Court of Justice rules that **Western Sahara**, NW Africa, has a right to self-determination and independence. Spain cedes Western Sahara to Morocco and Mauritania; the Polisario Front independence movement is formed to resist both countries' occupation.

The monarchy is restored in Spain on the death of dictator **Francisco Franco** at 82.

Dahomey changes its name to Benin.

Zionism is 'a form of racism and racial discrimination', according to a resolution passed by the UN General Assembly.

US pop singer Donna Summer has the first of many disco hits, produced by Giorgio Moroder in Munich, West Germany, **'Love to Love You Baby'** (Nov USA, Jan 1976 UK).

Portugal having withdrawn from **East Timor**, Malay Archipelago, the left-wing Revolutionary Front of East Timor (Fretilin), occupies the capital, Dili, calling for independence. Indonesian invasion begins; many Timorese civilians are raped or killed, and property destroyed.

I know I am recommending a pragmatic rather than a principled stand, but that is what national interest and foreign policy is all about.
Richard Woolcott, Australian ambassador to Indonesia, advocating hushing up the impending invasion of East Timor

---

A one-party communist republic is proclaimed in **Laos**.

Palestinian guerrillas take 81 hostages and kill three at a conference of the Organization of Petroleum-Exporting Countries in Vienna, Austria.

Soviet chess player **Anatoly Karpov** succeeds US grand master Bobby Fischer as world champion.

The Himalayan country of **Sikkim** is annexed by India. China does not recognize India's claim.

Start of **civil war in Lebanon** between Christians and Muslims.

Guerrillas seeking independence for the **S Moluccas** seize a train and the Indonesian consulate in the Netherlands, and take hostages.

Military **coup in Chad**; guerrilla war continues. Libya occupies the Aouzou strip of N Chad, rich in iron and uranium.

Military **coup in Peru**: Juan Velasco Alvarado is replaced by General Morales Bermúdez.

The military government of **Nigeria** announces a plan to move the capital 800 km/500 mi NE from Lagos to Abuja.

Iran becomes a one-party state under the shah.

The **Four Modernizations** programme begins in China, intended to make agriculture, industry, science and technology, and the armed forces catch up with the West by the year 2000.

In Australia, the Senate blocks the government's financial legislation. Prime minister **Gough Whitlam** declines to resign but is dismissed by governor general John Kerr, who invites Liberal politician Malcolm Fraser to form a government.

In Turkey, **Suleyman Demirel** returns to head a right-wing coalition government.

Habib Bourguiba of Tunisia is made president for life.

In **Bahrain**, the prime minister resigns and the national assembly is dissolved; the emir and his family assume virtually absolute power.

British troops are sent to **Belize** to defend the frontier with Guatemala.

The first meeting is held of **G7** (Group of Seven), the world's seven wealthiest countries: the USA, Japan, West Germany, France, the UK, Italy, and Canada.

A conference is held in Geneva, Switzerland, between the representatives of the Rhodesian government, the Rhodesian opposition, and the UK government, agreeing to move towards constitutional independence for **Rhodesia** (Zimbabwe).

The **Latin American Economic System**, a trade organization, is established.

ECOWAS (the Economic Community of West African States) is established.

The **Declaration of Ayacucho** is signed by Argentina, Bolivia, Chile, Colombia, Ecuador, Panama, Peru, and Venezuela. It is an agreement to create conditions for effective arms limitation in Latin America. The refusal of Brazil to join the discussions means that little progress is made: Brazil is the biggest Third World exporter of arms.

Vietnamese refugees flood into Hong Kong. Arriving by sea, they become known as **'boat people'**.

Israel officially accords Jewish status to **Falashim** (black Ethiopian Jews) and they begin to settle in Israel.

The **National Enterprise Board** is set up in the UK to administer government shareholdings and assist firms in trouble; among them, motor-vehicle manufacturers British Leyland and Chrysler.

UK **Sex Discrimination Act** makes it illegal to discriminate in employment, housing, or education.

The term **'microchip'** comes into use for integrated circuits.

US computer enthusiast **Bill Gates**, 19, founds the Microsoft computer-software company with his friend Paul Gardner Allen in Seattle, Washington.

Altair 880, the first **personal computer**, or microcomputer, is launched.

Nuclear medicine comes into practical use; for example, **CAT (computerized axial tomography) scans**, a sophisticated method of X-ray imaging used in diagnosis, developed by EMI in the UK.

The discovery of **encephalins**, the first known endogenous opiates (the brain's own painkillers), opens up a new phase in the study of brain chemistry.

Monoclonal antibodies are first produced in a Cambridge University laboratory, England, by Argentine-born British molecular biologist César Milstein and others.

A serious bacterial infection called **Lyme disease** is identified in Connecticut, from where it spreads across the USA.

Norway prohibits all **tobacco advertising**.

In Egypt, some 4,000 sq km/1,500 sq mi of **Nile valley farmland** has been paved over since 1955. This is greater than the amount of land brought into agricultural production by irrigation and other schemes.

The world's **tropical forest** has been reduced to 12% of the area it covered in 1950.

Browns Ferry, Alabama, the world's largest nuclear power station, has a fire that puts two reactors out of action for 18 months.

Having abandoned atmospheric testing, France begins **underground nuclear testing** on Mururoa atoll in French Polynesia.

The **European Space Agency** is founded.

A record 91.6 million vinyl **LPs** are sold this year in the UK.

Sony introduces the videocassette tape-recorder system **Betamax** for domestic use.

The world's first **viewdata** system, Prestel, is introduced by the British Post Office.

Lead-free petrol becomes available in the USA.

A railway link from central Zambia to Dar es Salaam, Tanzania, on the Indian Ocean, is completed with Chinese aid. The **Great Uhuru Railway** is 1,870 km/1,160 mi long.

The Convention on the Prevention of Marine Pollution by Dumping of Waste and Other Matter (known as the **London Dumping Convention**) comes into force. It restricts, and in the case of certain substances prohibits, the dumping of waste at sea from ships and aircraft worldwide.

US zoologist **Dian Fossey** begins the study of mountain gorillas in Rwanda.

Fewer than 50 **California condors** remain in the wild.

Braun alarm clocks, designed by Dieter Raus, are first produced in West Germany.

Television comedy series *Fawlty Towers*, with John Cleese and Connie Booth, begins in the UK.

English painter **David Hockney** is the subject of a semidocumentary film, *A Bigger Splash*, by Jack Hazan.

US Pop artist Andy Warhol collects his thoughts in the book *From A to B and Back Again: The Philosophy of Andy Warhol.?*

German-born US political philosopher **Hannah Arendt** dies; born 1906. Her books include *The Origins of Totalitarianism* 1951.

US novelist Saul Bellow publishes *Humboldt's Gift*, based on the life of US poet Delmore Schwartz.

> *History had created something new in the USA, namely crookedness with self-respect or duplicity with honour.*
> US novelist **Saul Bellow**, *Humboldt's Gift*

US poet William **Carlos Williams** dies; born 1883. He wins a posthumous Pulitzer Prize for *Pictures from Brueghel*.

US zoologist Edward O Wilson publishes *Sociobiology: The New Synthesis*, stimulating interest in the subject.

English novelist Paul Scott publishes the last volume of his Raj Quartet, *A Division of the Spoils*.

Irish poet Seamus Heaney publishes the collection *North*.

English novelist Anthony Powell publishes the last volume of his 12-volume novel sequence *A Dance to the Music of Time, Hearing Secret Harmonies*.

British writer and academic Malcolm Bradbury publishes the satirical campus novel *The History Man*.

English writer David Lodge publishes the campus novel *Changing Places*.

US rock critic Greil Marcus publishes the influential study *Mystery Train*.

US feminist writer Joanna Russ publishes the science-fiction novel *The Female Man*.

Italian film director and writer **Pier Paolo Pasolini** is murdered; born 1922.

French director François Truffaut makes the film *La Histoire d'Adèle H* starring Isabelle Adjani.

Soviet director Andrei Tarkovsky makes the film *Mirror*.

US film director, writer, and actor Woody Allen stars in his own anguished comedy *Love and Death*.

> *And if it turns out that there is a God, I don't believe that he is evil. The worst that can be said is that he is an underachiever.*
> US filmmaker **Woody Allen**, *Love and Death*

US film director Robert Altman makes the film *Nashville* about the country-music business.

One Flew Over the Cuckoo's Nest is Czechoslovak-born director Miloš Forman's film of Ken Kesey's novel, starring Jack Nicholson.

US film director Joan Micklin Silver makes the historical film *Hester Street* with Carol Kane.

Japanese film director Akira Kurosawa makes the film *Dersu Uzala* in Siberia.

US horror film *Jaws* by Steven Spielberg is a big commercial success.

Australian film director Peter Weir makes *Picnic at Hanging Rock*.

British actor Ben Kingsley stars in Shakespeare's *Hamlet*.

English dramatist David Hare's play *Teeth 'n' Smiles* opens.

British dramatist Trevor Griffiths's play *The Comedians* opens.

British dramatist Simon Gray's play *Otherwise Engaged* opens in London.

The musical *A Chorus Line* opens in New York; it will run for 6,238 performances. The composer and lyricist are Marvin Hamlisch and Edward Kleban.

Glasgow gets an opera house in the renovated Theatre Royal, which becomes the permanent headquarters of **Scottish Opera**.

Australian composer **Malcolm Williamson** becomes Master of the Queen's Music.

English composer Benjamin Britten writes his *Third String Quartet*.

Inner Light 3 for large orchestra and tape is composed by Jonathan Harvey (UK).

US jazz pianist Keith Jarrett releases the live solo album *The Köln Concert*.

Punk is foreshadowed in the USA by Patti Smith's album *Horses*, produced by John Cale.

English rhythm-and-blues band **Dr Feelgood** release their first two albums and revitalize the pub-rock scene.

British hard rock boogie band Status Quo have their first and only number one hit single **'Down Down'**.

US heavy-metal band Kiss break through with the album *Kiss Alive*.

Canadian singer and songwriter Joni Mitchell's *Hejira* is the first rock album to use Burundi drums.

US soul-music label **Stax Records** in Memphis, Tennessee, closes.

US tennis player **Arthur Ashe** wins the men's singles at Wimbledon.

English cricketer **Graham Gooch** is first capped for England.

Austrian motor-racing driver **Niki Lauda** wins the Grand Prix world championship for the first time, in a Ferrari.

1976

The collapse of British industry, a new and disturbing feature of 1970s Britain, saw the car giant British Leyland bankrupt and in public ownership. Its striking workers were unable to identify with the business and its managers seemed unable to control events. Harold Wilson resigned as prime minister to be replaced by James Callaghan. In youth culture, the optimism of the 1960s was dead, to be replaced by anarchistic punk rock, as epitomized by the Sex Pistols' 'Anarchy in the UK'. It provided marginalized, disaffected, unemployed youth with opportunities to display its anger and despair. While inflation came down, unemployment and taxes rose as government tried to tackle deteriorating public finances. Rioting in the South African township of Soweto, by school children opposed to the introduction of Afrikaans (the language of the white minority) into schools, marked the beginning of the struggle that led, nearly twenty years later, to liberation. In the United States, Gerald Ford, who had replaced Richard Nixon as president, was defeated by a Georgia peanut farmer Jimmy Carter.

Chinese prime minister **Zhou Enlai** dies at 77 and is succeeded by Hua Guofeng.

The USA vetoes a United Nations (UN) Security Council resolution calling for an independent **Palestinian state** and for Israel to withdraw from territories occupied since 1967. Israel boycotts the UN discussion and bombs Lebanon.

The food colouring **amaranth**, E123, a coal-tar dye, is banned in the USA. Soviet studies 1970 showed it to be a possible cause of cancer. It is also banned in five European countries and the USSR, but continues to be legal in the UK.

English detective-story writer **Agatha Christie** dies at 85. She created the characters Miss Marple and Hercule Poirot.

US blues singer **Howlin' Wolf** dies at 65; his commanding persona and vocal style made him one of the foremost blues performers of the Chicago school.

The Polisario Front in **Western Sahara** begins guerrilla war against Morocco and Mauritania. Polisario sets up a government in exile in Algiers, the Sahrahwi Arab Democratic Republic; Morocco breaks off diplomatic relations with Algeria.

Earthquake in Guatemala kills 23,000. This coincides with a good harvest, so aid agencies are requested not to send emergency food; nonetheless, food is sent, and the agricultural economy suffers a severe setback.

English painter **L S Lowry** dies at 88. His characteristic matchstick figures emerged in the 1920s.

The **platinum record** is introduced for US sales of 1 million albums or 2 million singles, reflecting the overall increase in volume of record sales. (In the UK, 300,000 copies of an album or 600,000 of a single earn a platinum disc.) The first platinum record is *The Eagles: Their Greatest Hits*.

US singers **Willie Nelson** and **Waylon Jennings** emerge as leaders of the 'outlaw' movement revitalizing country music.

US singer and songwriter Paul Simon tops the US chart with the song **'Fifty Ways to Leave Your Lover'**.

In the Winter Olympics in Innsbruck, Austria, **John Curry** becomes the first Briton to win an Olympic medal for ice skating when he takes the figure-skating gold medal.

Military **coup in Argentina** removes Isabel Perón: start of the 'dirty war', or violent suppression of dissent, with between 6,000 and 15,000 people made to 'disappear' – generally tortured and killed.

The MPLA gains control of most of **Angola**. South African troops withdraw but Cuban units remain.

Mozambique closes the border with Rhodesia (Zimbabwe) in protest at Rhodesian raids on guerrilla bases in Mozambique and Rhodesian support for the Renamo rebels seeking to overthrow the Mozambican government.

I don't believe in black majority rule ever in Rhodesia . . . not in a thousand years.
Prime minister **Ian Smith** of Rhodesia (Zimbabwe), broadcast speech

---

Harold Wilson resigns at 60 as leader of the Labour Party and UK prime minister. His final honours list gives rise to, as *The Times* put it, 'universal astonishment and derision'. James Callaghan is his successor.

A lie can be halfway round the world before the truth has got its boots on.
UK prime minister **James Callaghan**

In the primary elections to select the two main parties' candidates for the US presidential election, **Ronald Reagan** loses against his fellow Republican Gerald Ford in the first three states but wins a convincing enough victory in North Carolina to be a candidate in 1980.

The **pound sterling** drops below $2 for the first time, to $1.98.

Elton John becomes the first pop star after the Beatles to have an effigy in Madame Tussaud's Wax Museum in London.

Mass deportations and executions are carried out in **Cambodia**, where Sihanouk is deposed and the communist Khmer Rouge, led by Pol Pot, are in total control.

Mass demonstration in **Tiananmen Square**, Beijing, in memory of Zhou Enlai, despite official disapproval.

Indian-born US biochemist Har Gobind Khorana and his colleagues construct the first artificial gene to function naturally when inserted into a bacterial cell. This is a major step in **genetic engineering**.

Eccentric US tycoon **Howard Hughes** dies at 70. He had interests in oil, aircraft, and cinema.

The US car industry stops manufacturing **convertibles** after this year's Cadillac Eldorado. Air pollution, vandalism, and theft have reduced the popularity of soft-tops.

German Surrealist artist **Max Ernst** dies at 85. He worked in the USA from 1941.

Dirty Linen, a farce by British dramatist Tom Stoppard, opens in London.

US punk-rock band the **Ramones** release their eponymous first album.

West German left-wing guerrilla **Ulrike Meinhof** commits suicide in Stammheim Prison, Stuttgart, at 42. The trial of **Andreas Baader** and other members of the Red Army Faction continues.

German conductor **Rudolf Kempe** dies at 65.

The Republic of the **Seychelles**, in the Indian Ocean, achieves independence from Britain within the Commonwealth.

Riots in **Soweto**, South Africa, greet the ruling that the Afrikaans language must be used in segregated black schools. They are violently suppressed; 176 people are killed and 1,139 injured.

US oil billionaire **Paul Getty** dies at 83.

The UK enjoys its **hottest summer of the century** (May–Aug), with a high of 35°C in London; the drawbacks include water rationing and forest fires.

Indonesia completes its forcible annexation of **East Timor**. The UN does not recognize Indonesia's claim, and the Fretilin independence movement remains active as a guerrilla resistance army. Indonesian troops bomb villages and massacre suspected Fretilin sympathizers.

The United States wished things to turn out as they did . . . The Department of State desired that the United Nations prove utterly ineffective. That task was given to me and I carried it forward with no inconsiderable success.
Daniel Patrick Moynihan, US ambassador to the UN, on Indonesia's seizure of East Timor

---

The Chinese city of **Tangshan** is destroyed by an earthquake that registers 8.2 on the Richter scale; more than 200,000 people die.

Israeli commandos carry out a highly successful raid on **Entebbe airport**, Uganda, freeing 104 hostages held in a hijacked plane by Palestinian guerrillas.

Japanese right-wing politician **Kakuei Tanaka** is arrested for accepting bribes from the Lockheed Corporation while premier. He will remain a powerful figure behind the scenes, and will stay out of jail on appeal.

An explosion in a chemical factory in **Seveso**, Lombardy, Italy, contaminates the town with dioxin, resulting in severe skin disorders and deformed births. The factory, belonging to a subsidiary of Swiss pharmaceutical company Hoffman La Roche, has to be dismantled.

The UK ambassador to Ireland, **Christopher Ewart Biggs**, and his aide, are killed by a land mine.

Demonstrations against the construction of a fast reactor near Lyon, France, the **Super-Phénix**, are violently suppressed by riot police.

English punk bands the **Damned** and the **Clash** give their first live performances (July and Aug respectively).

The **Mexican peso** is decoupled from the US dollar and falls rapidly.

There are mass demonstrations for peace in **Northern Ireland**.

There are riots at the **Notting Hill Carnival**, London.

UK punk fan magazine *Sniffin' Glue* begins publication.

Chinese Communist Party chairman **Mao Zedong** dies at 82 (9 Sept) and is succeeded by Hua Guofeng. The faction known as the Gang of Four, who enjoyed Mao's support, try to seize power and are arrested.

In **Sweden**, for the first time since 1951, the Social Democratic and Labour Party loses a general election. A centre-right coalition is formed by Thorbjörn Fälldin.

A prominent Chilean, **Orlando Letelier**, who has criticized the Augusto Pinochet administration, is killed by a car bomb in the USA.

A **nuclear-bomb test** in the atmosphere over Lop Nur, Xinjiang province, NW China, releases radioactive contamination that can be detected as far away as the US east coast.

The UK applies to the **International Monetary Fund** for a loan of £2.3 billion to prop up the pound.

An **underground public-transport system** opens in Brussels, Belgium.

For Colored Girls Who Have Considered Suicide/ When the Rainbow Is Enuf by US dramatist Ntozake Shange opens in New York and will run for 867 performances.

Israel promises Egypt to withdraw from **Sinai**.

South Africa grants 'independence' to its internal puppet state of **Transkei**. The UN and the Organization of African States object to the arrangement.

The **pound sterling** hits a low of $1.56.

The UK **mortgage rate** is put up to 12.25% following a rise in the Bank of England minimum lending rate to 15%.

English character actress **Edith Evans** dies at 84. She is best remembered as Lady Bracknell in the 1952 film of Oscar Wilde's comedy *The Importance of Being Earnest*.

Cease-fire agreed in **Lebanon**: a Syrian-dominated Arab force is formed to keep the peace but is regarded by Christians as an occupying force.

Military **coup in Burundi** puts Jean-Baptiste Bagaza in power. He belongs to the country's dominant ethnic group, the Tutsi.

Presidential elections in the USA: Democrat **Jimmy Carter** defeats the incumbent, Gerald Ford.

> *I've looked on a lot of women with lust. I've committed adultery in my heart many times – and God forgives me for it.*
> US president **Jimmy Carter**, interviewed by *Playboy* magazine

Australian-born media magnate Rupert Murdoch buys the *New York Post*.

US photographer and artist **Man Ray** dies in Paris at 86. He was part of the Dada movement and pioneered several photographic techniques.

US sculptor **Alexander Calder** dies at 78. He invented mobiles – hanging sculptures with moving parts.

English punk group the Sex Pistols release the groundbreaking single **'Anarchy in the UK'**.

US-Canadian rock group the Band play their final concert, filmed by Martin Scorsese as *The Last Waltz* (released 1978).

English composer **Benjamin Britten** dies at 63. His work includes the operas *Peter Grimes* 1945 and *Billy Budd* 1951.

Jamaican reggae singer and songwriter **Bob Marley** is shot and injured in an assassination attempt.

Portugal holds its first free elections in 50 years; Socialist Party leader Mario Soares forms a minority government.

North and South **Vietnam** are reunited as a socialist republic.

In France, **Jacques Chirac** resigns and the centre-right politician Raymond Barre becomes prime minister.

US Central Intelligence Agency head **Richard Helms** is found guilty of perjury and is succeeded by George Bush.

China releases more than 100,000 **political prisoners**.

Jordan bans all political parties and postpones elections.

Ugandan dictator **Idi Amin** claims that large tracts of Kenya historically belong to Uganda; relations with Kenya become strained, and diplomatic links with the UK are severed.

'Cod War' between Iceland and the UK over fishing rights: there are skirmishes between fishing vessels, and Iceland breaks off diplomatic relations with Britain.

The USA announces an extension of its **exclusive fishing zone** to 322 km/200 mi (from March 1977). The USSR follows suit.

Food-price rises in Poland trigger strikes and demonstrations.

President **Ahmed Abdallah** of the Comoros is overthrown by Ali Soilih.

Trinidad and Tobago becomes a republic.

Army **coup in Uruguay** brings Méndez Manfredini to power.

Manila becomes the capital of the Philippines for the second time (Quezon City was the capital 1948–76).

Political violence in **Northern Ireland** claims 296 lives this year.

The UK is condemned by the European Commission on Human Rights for ill-treatment of people suspected of terrorist acts in **Northern Ireland**.

Former British Labour cabinet minister **John Stonehouse** is jailed for corruption and fraud.

Jeremy Thorpe, leader of Britain's Liberal Party, resigns following a series of allegations of having had a previous homosexual relationship with Norman Scott. He is succeeded by David Steel.

British Labour politician **Michael Foot** becomes leader of the House of Commons.

The **Maguire Seven** are imprisoned in the UK for possessing explosives.

In brain chemistry, **endorphins** (a type of endogenous opiates) are discovered.

The first outbreak of **legionnaire's disease** is identified when 29 die at a convention of the American Legion in Philadelphia, Pennsylvania. It is a pneumonia-like bacterial disease.

The **Toxic Substances Act** is passed in the USA, requiring chemicals to be tested for possible cancer-causing effects before being put on the market.

The European Community (EC) bans the use of polychlorinated biphenyls (**PCBs**) except in sealed equipment. PCBs are toxic when incompletely incinerated, which is what happens in a normal accidental fire.

7.5% of the **tap water** in England is found to contain lead above the EC limit; in Scotland the figure is 34.4%.

British Nuclear Fuels Ltd applies for permission to build a thermal oxide reprocessing plant (**THORP**) at Windscale (Sellafield), Cumbria.

Dutch elm disease has killed 9 million of the UK's 23 million elms since it arrived in Britain 1964.

The **Barcelona Convention** on reducing pollution in the Mediterranean is signed by 17 countries in the region.

The Anglo-French airliner *Concorde* comes into commercial

service, making a transatlantic crossing in under three hours.

British Rail's **Inter-City 125** diesel passenger train is introduced.

French car manufacturers **Peugeot** and **Citroën** merge.

The **Honda Accord** car is launched.

The world **air-speed record** is broken in a Lockheed SR-17A flying at 3,530 kmh/2,193 mph over Beale Air Force Base, California.

The **Apple computer** company is founded in the USA.

Wang Laboratories begin to make **office computers** with multiple work stations.

The **European Southern Observatory** opens a telescope at La Silla, Chile.

The surface of the planet **Pluto** is found to be covered with frozen methane.

The *Sun* overtakes the *Mirror* to become the UK's best-selling daily newspaper.

The UK gets its first female newsreader, **Angela Rippon**, for the BBC.

In London, the **National Theatre** opens its new building on the South Bank, designed by Denys Lasdun, behind schedule and £12.5 million over budget. First the Lyttelton auditorium opens and then the larger Olivier.

The UK's Tate Gallery buys the controversial piece *Equivalent VIII* by US conceptual artist Carl Andre, a row of 120 bricks.

Bulgarian-born US sculptor Christo erects a *Running Fence* across N California, 39.5 km/24.5 mi long and 5.5 m/18 ft high.

The **Alchymia design studio** is founded in Milan, Italy, propagating an early and influential Post-Modern style.

French philosopher Michel Foucault publishes the first volume of his *L'Histoire de la sexualité/The History of Sexuality*.

US novelist John Gardner publishes *October Light*.

US novelist E L Doctorow's *Ragtime* becomes a best seller.

US writer Alex Haley has a huge best seller with the novel *Roots*.

Argentine novelist Manuel Puig publishes *The Kiss of the Spider Woman*.

US novelist Marge Piercy describes a utopia in *Woman on the Edge of Time*.

Novelist Brian Moore, born in Northern Ireland, active in Canada and the USA, publishes *The Doctor's Wife*.

English writer Jan Mark publishes her first novel, the humorous children's book *Thunder and Lightnings*.

US novelist Anne Rice publishes *Interview with the Vampire*; it acquires a cult following and the sequels, many years later, are best sellers.

US novelist Ann Beattie publishes her first novel *Chilly Scenes of Winter*.

The Pleasure Garden is a historical novel for children by English writer Leon Garfield.

English writer Peter Dickinson publishes the mystical historical novel *The Blue Hawk* for children.

French writer **André Malraux** dies; born 1901. He was an active anti-fascist before World War II and a member of the Gaullist government in the 1960s.

Italian director **Luchino Visconti** dies; born 1906. His last film, *L'innocente*, is released.

US actors Robert De Niro and 14-year-old Jodie Foster star in Martin Scorsese's film *Taxi Driver*.

Italian film director Bernardo Bertolucci makes the historical epic *Novocento/1900*.

French film director Eric Rohmer makes *Die Marquise von O/ The Marquise of O*.

English director Nicolas Roeg films Walter Tevis's science-fiction novel *The Man Who Fell to Earth* with singer David Bowie as the alien.

US actor Sylvester Stallone stars as a boxer in the first film of the *Rocky* series.

Robert De Niro stars in *The Last Tycoon*, Elia Kazan's film of F Scott Fitzgerald's novel.

Italian film director Lina Wertmüller makes *Pasqualino sette bellezze/Seven Beauties* about Nazi death camps.

English dramatist David Storey's play *Mother's Day* is a black comedy.

British dramatist Howard Brenton's play *Weapons of Happiness* opens.

Premiere of the ballet *A Month in the Country* by British choreographer Frederick Ashton.

US choreographer Twyla Tharp creates the dance piece *Push Comes to Shove*.

US choreographer Merce Cunningham creates the dance piece *Squaregame*.

US composer Philip Glass's opera *Einstein on the Beach*, using the repetitive techniques of minimalism, is given its first performance in Paris.

English composer **Peter Maxwell Davies** finishes his first symphony.

British composer Robin Holloway finishes his opera *Clarissa*.

Kent Opera is founded in Canterbury, England.

US singer and actor **Paul Robeson** dies; born 1898. He played Othello in Shakespeare's play in London 1930, New York 1943, and Stratford-upon-Avon 1959.

US country-rock band the Eagles release their most successful album, *Hotel California*.

Anglo-US soft-rock group Fleetwood Mac release the hugely commercial album *Rumours*.

An inflatable pink pig, 12 m/40 ft long, flies from Battersea Power Station, London, to Kent, surprising air traffic as it ascends to 5,500 m/18,000 ft. The inflatable was being photographed for the sleeve of the Pink Floyd album, *Animals*, when it broke from its moorings.

The Royal Scam is the most commercial album by jazz-influenced US rock group Steely Dan.

US singer and songwriter Jackson Browne's album *The Pretender* is a critical and commercial success.

US rhythm-and-blues band **Mink DeVille** emerge from the New York punk and New Wave scene.

Stiff Records is founded, one of the UK's leading independent labels for the next few years.

US rock singer Bruce Springsteen climbs a fence at Graceland, Memphis, Tennessee, hoping to meet the owner, **Elvis Presley**. US rock-and-roll singer and pianist Jerry Lee Lewis also turns up at the Graceland gates, waving a gun and demanding to see Presley. Neither is admitted.

US denim production has doubled since the beginning of the decade as the fashion for **jeans** continues.

West German swimmer **Kornelia Ender** wins four gold medals at the Olympic Games in Montréal, Canada.

Swedish tennis player **Björn Borg** wins the men's singles at Wimbledon for the first time.

Romanian gymnast **Nadia Comaneci** wins three Olympic gold medals at the age of 14.

Pakistani cricketer **Javed Miandad** scores a century in his first test match.

West Indian cricketer **Viv Richards** makes 1,710 runs in the year.

English motor-racing driver **James Hunt** becomes Formula One world champion.

1977

This was the year in which Britain celebrated the silver jubilee of Queen Elizabeth II's accession to the throne. It provided the nation with an opportunity to forget inflation, economic ills, and the troubles in Northern Ireland. For a while at least, the country could be diverted in an orgy of self-congratulation at a popular reign. Street parties, and civic and national events all helped to put a gloss on a time of self-doubt, pessimism, and gloom. The Labour government, having lost its slim parliamentary majority, made a parliamentary pact with Liberal MPs sufficient to see it through the rest of the Parliament. The deterioration in Britain's economy was so bad that bankers from the International Monetary Fund were called in to bail out the country. The cuts imposed on public expenditure by the IMF went straight to the heart of Britain's health and education programmes. British Leyland appointed Michael Edwardes to restructure the whole business and turn it around.

Jimmy Carter is inaugurated as president of the USA. One of his first acts is to issue a pardon for Vietnam draft resisters and exiles.

When the president does it, that means it is not illegal.
US ex-president **Richard Nixon** justifying the Watergate affair to British television interviewer David Frost

---

Charter 77 human-rights manifesto is signed by more than 700 Czechoslovak intellectuals and former Communist Party officials.

British centrist politician **Roy Jenkins** becomes president of the European Commission.

Capital punishment resumes in the USA after a ten-year moratorium. The first to be executed is murderer **Gary Gilmore**, later the subject of a book by Norman Mailer (1979) and a song by English punk group the Adverts.

Student **demonstrations in Ghana** temporarily close down the universities.

The **USA has its coldest winter** since records began (Jan–Feb); large rivers freeze over and there is frost in Florida.

The **Roxy Club**, London, is the focus for UK punk rock and the style that soon becomes a global youth culture (Jan–April).

Sid Vicious replaces Glen Matlock as bass player with the Sex Pistols.

Keith Richards of the Rolling Stones undergoes his biggest drug search in Toronto, Canada.

The **Lib–Lab pact** begins in the UK: the Liberal Party enters into an agreement to support Labour in any vote of confidence in return for consultation on measures undertaken.

If Labour is dead in Scotland then, from now on, I shall believe in life in the hereafter.
UK prime minister **James Callaghan**, speaking in Glasgow

The UK **Annan Committee on Broadcasting** publishes its report. It recommends excluding commercials from children's programmes and the intervals between; the latter is rejected by the Independent Television Companies' Association.

English punk-rock group the Clash release their first single, **'White Riot'**.

The sentencing of members of the **Red Army Faction** triggers further terrorist acts in West Germany.

31 million litres of oil contaminates the North Sea in a **blowout at the Ekofisk oilfield**, the worst pollution incident since drilling in the North Sea began.

US composer Stephen Sondheim's musical *Side by Side by Sondheim* opens in New York.

The musical *Annie* by Charles Strouse and Martin Charnin opens in New York and will run for 2,377 performances. It is based on a 1920s comic-strip figure.

Studio 54 disco opens in New York and will be crammed with celebrities for the rest of the decade.

The **Orient Express** train makes its last journey from Paris to Istanbul, Turkey.

Television broadcasting begins in South Africa, where it has until now been considered morally corrupting.

Djibouti, E coast of Africa, achieves independence from France; its first president is Hassan Gouled Aptidon.

Elizabeth II celebrates her **silver jubilee** as Queen of Great Britain and Northern Ireland.

A public inquiry begins into the desirability of building a thermal oxide reprocessing plant (**THORP**) at Sellafield in Cumbria, N England.

Military **coup in Pakistan**: prime minister Zulfikar Ali Bhutto is overthrown by General Mohammad Zia ul-Haq, and martial law imposed.

Deng Xiaoping, who was ousted from the Politburo during the Cultural Revolution, is rehabilitated in the Chinese communist hierarchy.

New York blackout: a power cut leaves the whole city and surrounding areas without electricity for 25 hours.

The tobacco industry launches 12 new brands of cigarettes in the UK which contain a percentage of **tobacco substitute**.

Consumers fail to be persuaded that their health will benefit, and tobacco substitutes are defeated by market forces.

English New Wave rock singer and songwriter Elvis Costello releases his first album, *My Aim is True* (July; Oct USA).

US comedian **Groucho Marx** dies at 83. He was the most wise-cracking of the Marx Brothers.

US rock-and-roll singer **Elvis Presley** dies at 42 in his Graceland home in Memphis, Tennessee (16 Aug). Some 75,000 people show up for the funeral.

Laker Airways begins a cheap London–New York service called Skytrain.

English pop star **Marc Bolan** dies at 30 in a car crash.

Andreas Baader and **Gudrun Ensslin** of the Red Army Faction guerrillas are found dead in their cells.

The world's last known case of **smallpox** is reported in Somalia.

US dramatist David Mamet's play *A Life in the Theatre* opens in New York.

The **Live Stiffs** tour of the UK, comprising Elvis Costello, Ian Dury, Nick Lowe, and other Stiff Records acts, is one of the autumn's major attractions.

US disco band Chic, whose production and songwriting team will make their mark on the pop industry, release their first single, **'Dance, Dance, Dance (Yowsah, Yowsah, Yowsah)'**.

US crooner and film actor **Bing Crosby** dies at 73. His biggest-selling record was 'White Christmas'.

The third and smallest stage of the **National Theatre**, the Cottesloe, opens on London's South Bank.

The play *The Elephant Man* by US dramatist Bernard Pomerance opens in London.

The Central African Republic is renamed the Central African Empire as its dictator **Jean-Bédel Bokassa** has himself crowned in a lavish ceremony.

Chlorofluorocarbon (**CFC**) production is restricted in the USA to protect the ozone layer.

English film comedian and director **Charles Chaplin** dies at his home in Switzerland at 88.

The world of disco music and dancing is the setting for Robert Stigwood's film *Saturday Night Fever*, starring John Travolta, with a soundtrack by the Bee Gees.

US avant-garde jazz musician **Rahsaan Roland Kirk** dies at 41.

General election in India: **Indira Gandhi** is replaced as prime minister by Morarji Desai of the Janata Party. The state of emergency is lifted.

'**Red Terror**' begins in Ethiopia: thousands of people are killed by government forces.

The Congo's military ruler Capt **Marien Ngouabi** is assassinated and Col Joachim Yhombi-Opango takes over.

Menachem Begin, leader of the right-wing Likud party, is elected prime minister of Israel.

Walid Jumblatt becomes military leader of the Druse sect in Lebanon.

Egyptian president **Anwar Sadat** visits Israel and addresses the Knesset (national assembly).

I don't know whether Sadat and Begin deserve the Nobel Prize, but they both deserve Oscars.
Israeli Labour politician **Golda Meir** on the Camp David Agreements

Archbishop **Makarios III** dies; born 1913. He is succeeded as president of Cyprus by Spyros Kyprianou.

The military ruler of North Yemen Col **Ibrahim al-Hamadi** is assassinated and Col Ahmed ibn Hussein al-Ghashmi takes over.

Civil-rights leader **Steve Biko** dies in the custody of the South African police.

The **Panama Canal Treaty** is signed, setting out terms for handing over control of the US-held canal to Panama.

Tanzania becomes a one-party state.

Exiled **Zaireans** make the first of several unsuccessful attempts to invade their country from Angola.

Rhodesian-backed guerrilla army **Mozambique National Resistance (Renamo)** fights to overthrow the Mozambican government.

The revelation of coercion and malpractice in **India's birth-control programme** is a major setback to the country's efforts to reduce population growth.

Fianna Fáil returns to power in Ireland, with Jack Lynch as prime minister.

Jamaica accepts a loan from the International Monetary Fund given on conditions that include a reduction in wages in real terms by 25%.

Finnish diplomat **Martti Ahtisaari** becomes the United Nations (UN) commissioner for Namibia.

The **Second International Conference on the Environmental Future** is held in Iceland. It predicts that about 1 billion people will starve to death by the year 2000 unless there is a significant change in economic policies.

The European Community (EC) initiates a programme to combat **poverty**.

Britain's **trade deficit** reaches £1,709 million.

The **pound sterling** drops from $2.02 to $1.64 before recovering somewhat.

Unemployment in the UK reaches the decade's peak of 1.6 million.

Average real wages in the UK have fallen by 8% since 1975.

The **Bullock Report** recommends that, to increase industrial democracy in the UK, there should be workers' representatives on boards of directors of companies with more than 2,000 employees. This is not implemented.

The UK total **fertility rate** reaches its low for the decade of 1.66.

British Labour politician **David Owen** becomes UK foreign secretary.

The UK introduces an **'aid trade provision'** whereby up to 5% of overseas aid may be used to subsidize British exports.

The genetic code for **human growth hormone** is discovered.

In **genetic research**, it is discovered that the DNA of organisms more complex than bacteria contains long strings of nucleotides with no apparent function.

The first probable cases of **AIDS** are found, though the disease is not identified until 1983.

Magnetic resonance imaging (MRI), a diagnostic scanning system, is first tested by its US inventor. It yields three-dimensional images of structures within the body without exposing the patient to harmful radiation.

A nonsurgical alternative to the coronary bypass operation is discovered, involving the insertion of tiny inflatables into clogged arteries to widen them. This becomes known as **balloon angioplasty**.

The earliest known hominid to have walked upright is discovered in Africa by US palaeontologist Donald Johanson and is nicknamed **Lucy**. Lucy is an *Australopithecus afarensis* and may have been the ancestor of modern humans.

The **Alaska oil pipeline** is completed, from Prudhoe Bay to the port of Valdez.

The **Antarctic Treaty** is extended to protect the environment against commercial exploitation of mineral resources.

Greenpeace activists **stain Canadian seals with dye** to prevent them being killed for their fur.

The **UN Conference on Desertification** considers the drought crisis in the Sahel region of Africa and recommends nomadic pastoralism as the only sustainable animal husbandry.

US president Jimmy Carter commissions an **environmental study** of what the world will be like in 2000.

Saccharin is found to cause cancer in animals and its use as a sweetener begins to be phased out. It is banned in Canada and required to carry a health warning in the USA.

Smoking or Health, the third report by the UK Royal College of

Physicians, conclusively links cigarette smoking with coronary heart disease.

Anti-smoking legislation introduced in Sweden involves 16 different health warnings to be printed on cigarette packets in rotation.

Nitrites used in cured meats are also linked with cancer.

The planet **Uranus** is discovered to have rings.

The most remote **asteroid** yet discovered is found near Uranus by US astronomer Charles T Kowall. It is named Chiron.

The spacecrafts *Voyager 1* and *2* are launched by the USA; they will pass Jupiter and Saturn 1979–81.

German-born US rocket engineer **Wernher von Braun** dies; born 1912. He played an important part in the early US space programme.

The first **fibreoptic telecommunications cable** is laid, in California. Optical fibre will become the 'communications highway' of the 1990s.

Soviet icebreaker *Arktika* makes the first surface voyage to the North Pole.

Hydrothermal vents, or **'black smokers'**, are discovered in the ocean floor, through which hot, mineral-rich ground water erupts into the sea. Complex ecosystems around them live without photosynthesis.

The first successful demonstration of a **holographic film** lasts 30 seconds and can be seen by a maximum of four viewers at a time.

Sea water enters the core of a reactor at Scottish **nuclear power**

plant Hunterston-B on the River Clyde. The reactor had been shut down before the accident.

A private prosecution is brought against the UK magazine *Gay News* for blasphemous libel, and the editor is convicted.

The UK *Sunday Times* wins an appeal in the European Court against the suppression of articles on the **thalidomide** scandal (a drug that turned out to cause malformed births).

Black South Africans' favourite newspaper, the *World*, is closed down by the government and its editor imprisoned.

The high-tech **Centre Pompidou** is completed in Paris; the architects are Renzo Piano (Italy) and Richard Rogers (UK).

Russian-born US writer **Vladimir Nabokov** dies; born 1899. His best-known book is the novel *Lolita* 1955.

English novelist Margaret Drabble publishes *The Ice Age*.

Peruvian novelist Mario Vargas Llosa publishes the humorously autobiographical *La tia Julia y el escribidor/Aunt Julia and the Scriptwriter*.

German writer Günter Grass publishes the novel *Der Butt/The Flounder*.

Bulgarian-born writer Elias Canetti publishes his first volume of memoirs, *Die gerettete Zunge: Geschichte einer Jugend/The Tongue Set Free: Remembrance of a European Childhood*.

Australian writer Helen Garner publishes her first novel *Monkey Grip*.

South African novelist J M Coetzee publishes *In the Heart of the Country*.

US writer Joan Didion publishes the novel *A Book of Common Prayer*.

After a period in obscurity, English novelist **Barbara Pym** is rediscovered with the publication of *Quartet in Autumn*.

Kenya's leading writer **Ngugi wa Thiong'o** is imprisoned for his political views.

A Scanner Darkly by US science-fiction novelist Philip K Dick is a humorous treatment of his themes of paranoia, drugs, and subjective reality.

The novel *Mikkai/Secret Rendezvous* by Japanese avant-garde writer Kōbō Abe is set in a hospital and uses disease as a metaphor for civilization.

US music critic Nick Tosches examines the roots of American popular music in *Country*.

US actor and director Woody Allen stars with Diane Keaton in his own film *Annie Hall*.

The food in this place is really terrible. Yes, and such small portions. That's essentially how I feel about life.
US humorist **Woody Allen** in his film *Annie Hall*

George Lucas's Hollywood film *Star Wars* is notable for its special effects.

May the Force be with you.
Catch phrase in George Lucas's film *Star Wars*

US film director Steven Spielberg breaks box-office records with *Close Encounters of the Third Kind*.

Jane Fonda and Vanessa Redgrave star in Fred Zinneman's film *Julia*.

Indian film director Satyajit Ray uses a historical setting for **The Chess Players**.

John Gielgud, Dirk Bogarde, and Ellen Burstyn star in **Providence** by French film director Alain Resnais.

Polish film director Andrzej Wajda makes **Man of Marble**.

US film director Robert Altman makes **Three Women**.

French film director Robert Bresson releases **Le Diable probablement/The Devil, Probably**.

English dramatist **Terence Rattigan** dies; born 1911. His last play, *Cause Celebre*, is running in London. His work includes *French Without Tears* 1936 and *The Winslow Boy* 1946.

English dramatist Mike Leigh's play **Abigail's Party** is premiered on BBC 1.

The **Institute for Research and Co-ordination of Acoustics and Music (IRCAM)** is founded in Paris, under the direction of French composer Pierre Boulez, for visiting composers to make use of advanced electronic equipment.

US conductor **Leopold Stokowski** dies; born 1882.

US opera singer **Maria Callas** dies at 53. She was a lyric soprano with a gift for dramatic expression.

British composer Iain Hamilton's opera **The Royal Hunt of the Sun** is staged by the English National Opera.

German avant-garde composer Karlheinz Stockhausen writes **Sirius**.

Premiere of British composer David Blake's opera **Toussaint**.

British composer Brian Ferneyhough writes **Transit** for voices and chamber orchestra.

US rock singer Iggy Pop releases two of his best albums, *The Idiot* and *Lust for Life*, made in Berlin, Germany, and France in collaboration with David Bowie.

David Bowie's largely instrumental album *Low*, made with input from English avant-garde composer and producer Brian Eno, is early ambient techno.

US New Wave rock band Television's first album, *Marquee Moon*, receives critical acclaim.

The album *Little Criminals* by US singer and songwriter Randy Newman contains the hit single **'Short People'**.

US heavy-metal band **Kiss** have become so popular that Marvel Comics devote a special comic book to them, for two issues.

The Roman Catholic Church ceases to have **Mass said in Latin**.

Scottish footballer **Kenny Dalglish** joins the Liverpool team.

English cricketer **Ian Botham** joins the England team.

The Wimbledon tennis championships are won by **Björn Borg** (Sweden, men's singles) and **Virginia Wade** (UK, women's singles).

US writer James S Fixx publishes *The Complete Book of Jogging*, and **jogging** is the latest fitness craze.

1978

Although inflation fell below 10 per cent in Britain during 1978, curbs on wages and prices led to numerous industrial strikes and disputes by low-paid public-sector employees. These strikes and disputes, which continued into 1979, affected refuse disposal, ambulance workers, hospitals, and cemeteries. The plight of the unburied dead led newspapers to dub the period the 'winter of discontent'. In London that year, the world's first test-tube baby was born. In Germany, meanwhile, Volkswagen produced their last German-built 'Beetle'. If Britain remained sunk in economic gloom, the situation in the Middle East was substantially eased with the United States-brokered Camp David Agreement, which brought about a new relationship between Egypt and Israel after four decades of enmity.

Rioting in Qom, **Iran**, is inspired by Islamic leaders opposed to social reform.

The last **Volkswagen Beetle** is produced in Germany, but production of the model continues on other continents.

English punk band the **Sex Pistols** break up at the end of an unsuccessful US tour.

I support the Sex Pistols because this is a constructive, necessary criticism of a country which is bankrupt. England doesn't stand a chance until you have 20,000 people saying: Bugger the Queen!
US novelist **William Burroughs**

Radioactive fragments of Soviet satellite *Cosmos 954* fall on N Canada.

The play *Deathtrap* by Ira Levin opens in New York to run for 1,793 performances.

BBC Radio One refuses to play English pop singer Tom Robinson's song **'Glad to Be Gay'**.

US heavy-rock singer Meat Loaf releases the best-selling album *Bat out of Hell*.

US boxer **Muhammad Ali** loses the world heavyweight title to Leon Spinks, also of the USA, only to regain it in Sept.

Israel invades **S Lebanon**. The United Nations (UN) sets up a peacekeeping force, but to no avail.

Former Italian prime minister **Aldo Moro** is kidnapped and killed. Responsibility is claimed by the left-wing Red Brigades, although evidence of covert involvement by the Italian security services later emerged.

US tanker *Amoco Cadiz* runs aground off Brittany, France; 220,000 tonnes of oil spills into the sea.

Finland bans all **tobacco advertising** and promotion. The number of smokers drops significantly within two years, especially among young teenagers.

English New Wave rock singer and songwriter Elvis Costello releases his first album with the Attractions, *This Year's Model*.

Pro-Soviet military junta seizes power in **Afghanistan**.

Regular live **radio broadcasting** begins in the UK of the proceedings of the **House of Commons**.

Appalled by the bellowing, abuse, baying, heehawing and the rest, the nation cannot stand the shock.
UK member of Parliament **William Price** on the broadcasting of proceedings in the House of Commons

---

Television soap opera *Dallas* begins in the USA (April).

Plenty by British dramatist David Hare opens at the National Theatre, London.

The **One Love Peace Concert** in Jamaica stars Bob Marley and the Wailers, Peter Tosh, Big Youth, and others, and features an onstage handshake by prime minister Michael Manley and opposition leader Edward Seaga.

Kassinga massacre: South African forces attack a SWAPO camp in Angola and kill up to 1,000 Namibians.

Narita Airport, serving Tokyo, Japan, opens. Its construction generated intense protests by farmers and students.

Abortion becomes legal in Italy.

The UK government scraps plans to fall into line with Europe by switching to **metric measurements**.

The musical *Ain't Misbehavin'*, based on the songs of jazz pianist Fats Waller, opens in New York to run for 1,604 performances.

The leader of North Yemen, Col **Ahmed ibn Hussein al-Ghashmi**, is assassinated by agents of South Yemen; a coup in South Yemen follows; war breaks out between the two countries.

The new **US embassy in Moscow**, USSR, is found to be full of bugging devices.

An industrial dispute at the **Grunwick** film-processing works, N London (June–Nov) attracts mass picketing. The causes are dismissals, perceived racism, and refusal by the management to allow trades unions.

The musical *Evita* by Tim Rice and Andrew Lloyd Webber, based on the life of Argentine politician Eva Perón, opens in London.

Carol Hall's musical *The Best Little Whorehouse in Texas* opens in New York to run for 1,584 performances.

British rock group the Rolling Stones release the album *Some Girls*, a partial return to form.

The **Solomon Islands**, SW Pacific Ocean, achieve independence from Britain, within the Commonwealth.

Military **coup in Ghana**: Col Ignatius Acheampong is deposed by his deputy Frederick Akuffo.

Soviet dissident **Anatoly Shcharansky** is sentenced to prison in Moscow despite international disapproval.

Start of the **Nicaraguan Revolution**, led by the socialist Sandinista National Liberation Front against the US-supported right-wing dictatorship of Anastasio Somoza.

Jomo Kenyatta dies at 86; he is succeeded as president of Kenya by Daniel arap Moi.

An outbreak of disease and malformed births at **Love Canal, Niagara City, New York State**, is traced to contamination: 22,000 tonnes of poisonous chemical waste had been dumped there 1947–53, and houses then built on the site. The most heavily contaminated area is evacuated and declared a federal disaster area. The US Environmental Protection Agency begins a survey of other toxic dump sites.

US New Wave rock group **Television** split up (Aug).

The **Ellice Islands**, SW Pacific Ocean, achieve independence from Britain under their former name of Tuvalu, within the Commonwealth.

Martial law is imposed in **Iran** after mass demonstrations against the shah. The opposition to the shah is organized from France by Ayatollah Ruhollah Khomeini.

Camp David Agreements reached on peace between Egypt and Israel, and the withdrawal of Israel from Sinai. The issue of Palestinian self-government on the West Bank and the Gaza Strip remains unresolved. The agreements will be officially signed in March 1979.

Mohammad Zia ul-Haq, military ruler of Pakistan, makes himself president.

Earthquake in N Iran, registering 7.7 on the Richter scale, kills 25,000 people.

South Africa accepts in principle a UN Security Council resolution for the independence of **Namibia**, but then rejects it.

Pope John Paul I, having succeeded Paul VI, dies after being pope for only a month. His successor Karol Wojtyla becomes John Paul II, the first non-Italian pope for more than 400 years.

Ugandan forces cross into **Tanzania** but are repulsed.

English punk rocker **Sid Vicious** is charged with the murder of his girlfriend, Nancy Spungen, in New York.

Dominica, island in the E Caribbean, achieves independence from Britain, within the Commonwealth.

The UK has a **bakers' strike**.

Italian painter **Giorgio de Chirico** dies at 90. His dreamlike style was a forerunner of Surrealism.

English dramatist Harold Pinter's play *Betrayal* opens at the National Theatre, London.

Diana Rigg stars in London in *Night and Day* by British dramatist Tom Stoppard.

More than **900 people commit suicide** in Jonestown, Guyana, on the orders of their religious cult leader, Jim Jones of the People's Temple.

Vietnam launches an invasion of **Kampuchea** (Cambodia).

Algerian president **Houari Boumédienne** dies at 46 and power is transferred to Benjedid Chadli.

Israeli Labour politician **Golda Meir** dies at 80.

Mass demonstrations in Tehran, **Iran**, demand the abdication of the shah.

The spacecraft *Venus Pioneer 1* goes into orbit around Venus. It analyses the atmosphere and maps the surface by radar.

The Beloyarsk nuclear power plant near Sverdlovsk, USSR, comes close to **meltdown** in a fire, but there is no escape of radioactivity.

Albania breaks off diplomatic relations with China, calling it 'revisionist'.

Prime minister **Mario Soares** resigns in Portugal and two years of political instability follow.

B J Vorster resigns as prime minister of South Africa and is replaced by Pieter W Botha.

The **Comoros** are declared an Islamic republic after a coup, carried out by mercenaries, installs Ahmed Abdallah as president.

In **Turkey**, a deteriorating economy is accompanied by factional violence. Bulent Ecevit becomes prime minister but his coalition collapses the following year.

Ban on political activity lifted in **Nigeria**.

The Arab League commits itself to giving $250 million a year to the **Palestine Liberation Organization**.

Vietnam becomes a member of Comecon, the communist-bloc trading organization.

Coup in Mauritania; peace agreed with the Polisario Front in Western Sahara.

AZAPO (the Azanian People's Organization) is founded; it is a South African liberation movement that rejects white participation in government.

Namibian political leader Chief **Clemens Kapuuo** is assassinated. South Africa declares a state of emergency in Namibia and arrests several SWAPO leaders.

Flooding in Bangladesh affects 65,700 villages; thousands become homeless.

The **hot line** between US and Soviet heads of government becomes a satellite link.

The **'winter of discontent'** begins in the UK: inflation is around 20%, wage increases in the public sector limited to 5%, and the social contract with the unions has broken down. It is the fourth coldest winter of the century, with much snow.

That part of his speech was rather like being savaged by a dead sheep.
UK chancellor of the Exchequer **Denis Healey** on being attacked in a parliamentary debate by Geoffrey Howe

---

Lord Kagan, a British raincoat manufacturer raised to the peerage in Harold Wilson's resignation honours, is wanted for tax and currency offences and flees to Israel.

A US team makes the first **transatlantic crossing by balloon**, in the helium-filled *Double Eagle II*.

The world's first **test-tube baby** is born at a London hospital. In vitro fertilization was pioneered by English obstetrician Patrick

Steptoe and biologist Robert Edwards; the fertilized egg was then implanted in the mother's womb for a normal pregnancy.

British archaeologist Mary Leakey and colleagues discover a **fossil footprint trail** at Laetoli, N Tanzania, made by three hominids more than 3.6 million years ago.

The **tomb of Philip II of Macedon** (Alexander the Great's father) is discovered in Greece.

The **genome** (complete genetic structure) of a virus is charted, the first step towards mapping the human genome.

Human insulin is first produced by genetic engineering.

An **oncogene** (cancer-causing gene) is produced by US scientist Robert A Weinberg and others.

A study at Cornell University, USA, estimates that only 4% less food would be produced if **pesticides** were not used. The agrochemical industry maintains that the figure is 50%.

The USSR carries out 20 underground **nuclear tests**.

The inhabitants of **Bikini atoll** in the Pacific Marshall Islands are evacuated for the second time when it is discovered that their food is contaminated with radioactive material. Bikini was used as a nuclear-weapons test site by the USA 1946–63.

Soviet cosmonauts spend a record **139 days in space**.

Pluto is found to have a satellite, Charon. This means that the planet is even smaller than previously thought, because 10% of its estimated mass belongs to Charon.

Coca-Cola will be bottled and sold in China to the exclusion of its rivals, according to an agreement signed between the US multinational corporation and the communist state.

Compact discs are first demonstrated.

The Wade-Giles system of **transliterating Chinese** is superseded by the Pinyin system, officially adopted by China.

Strikes and union disputes affect publication of *The Times* and the *Sunday Times* in the UK. The papers cease to publish (30 Nov) until Nov 1979.

English dramatist Dennis Potter writes a six-play series for BBC television, *Pennies from Heaven*.

Start of UK television series *Rumpole of the Bailey*, written by English barrister John Mortimer.

The UK commercial television channel ITN gets its first female newsreader, **Anna Ford**.

British graphic designer **Jamie Reid** dominates punk-style in record sleeves and posters.

Influential English literary critic **F R Leavis** dies; born 1895. His works include *The Great Tradition* 1948.

The Virgin in the Garden is the first of a novel sequence by English writer A S Byatt.

US novelist Toni Morrison publishes *Song of Solomon*.

British novelist Timothy Mo publishes his first novel *The Monkey King*.

British writer Michèle Roberts publishes her first novel *A Piece of the Night*.

English novelist Graham Greene publishes the spy novel *The Human Factor*.

US novelist Alice Hoffman publishes her first novel *Property of*.

US writer John Updike sets his novel *The Coup* in a fictitious African country.

US novelist John Irving has a best seller with *The World According to Garp*.

English novelist J G Farrell's *The Singapore Grip* is set during World War II.

US writer John Cheever publishes the novel *Falconer*.

English writer Jan Mark publishes *The Ennead*, a satire for children on politics and religion.

British writer Anne Fine publishes *The Summer-House Loon*, a novel for teenagers.

US director David Lynch makes his first film *Eraserhead*.

French film director Claude Chabrol releases *Violette Nozière*.

US film director Woody Allen makes his first entirely serious film, *Interiors*, using Swedish director of photography Sven Nykvist.

Swedish director Ingmar Bergman makes the film *Autumn Sonata*.

Swiss director Alain Tanner makes the film *Messidor*.

The film *The Deer Hunter* by US director Michael Cimino is set against the Vietnam War.

US film director Paul Schrader releases *Blue Collar*.

Jane Fonda and Jon Voigt star in US director Hal Ashby's film *Coming Home*.

The musical *Grease*, set in the 1950s, is filmed in the USA with Olivia Newton-John and John Travolta.

Superman is a big-budget Hollywood film of the life of the comic-book superhero.

British dramatist David Edgar's play *The Jail Diary of Albie Sachs* deals with the South African political struggle.

Soviet dancer **Mikhail Baryshnikov** leaves the American Ballet Theater for the New York City Ballet.

Hungarian-born Austrian composer György Ligeti writes the opera *Le Grand Macabre*.

Opera North is founded in Leeds, Yorkshire, England.

The avant-garde classical **Kronos Quartet** (formed in Oregon 1974) arrives at the line-up with which it will become famous.

US rock singer and songwriter Lou Reed releases one of his most cynical albums, *Street Hassle*.

US punk-pop band Blondie make their commercial breakthrough with their third album, *Parallel Lines*.

The second album by US New Wave rock band Talking Heads, *More Songs About Buildings and Food*, is produced by Brian Eno.

US heavy-metal band **Van Halen** release their self-titled first album.

US singer and songwriter Bruce Springsteen releases the album *Darkness on the Edge of Town*.

US singer and songwriter Jackson Browne releases the album *Running on Empty*.

English athlete **Daley Thompson** wins the Commonwealth Games decathlon.

The soccer World Cup is won by **Argentina**.

Czechoslovak tennis player **Martina Navratilova** wins the Wimbledon women's singles title for the first time.

The opera ain't over till the fat lady sings.
US sports commentator **Dan Cook**

1979

This was a watershed year for Britain, fed up with inflation, strikes, and the 'winter of discontent'. Believing that the welfare state and collectivist economic policies had failed, the British electorate, in the general election of that year, turned to Margaret Thatcher and the Conservatives. Thatcher had fought the election on unabashed free-market principles, and became Britain's first woman prime minister. One of the first problems she had to face was a massive increase in oil prices, imposed by the oil-producers' cartel. In Ireland, the IRA murdered Lord Mountbatten of Burma, members of his family, and others in a bomb outrage. In London, a constitutional settlement of the Southern Rhodesian problem was finally approved by all parties. In Iran, meanwhile, the shah was overthrown in an Islamic revolution. The Islamic leader Ayatollah Khomeini returned from exile to establish an Islamic republic hostile to the West and to the United States.

Full diplomatic relations are opened between the **USA and China**; the USA severs its relations with Taiwan and cancels the 1954 security pact.

Islamic revolution in Iran, led by Ayatollah Ruhollah Khomeini; the shah is exiled. Thousands of opponents will be executed under Khomeini's fundamentalist regime.

The **Vietnamese invasion of Kampuchea** (now Cambodia) is completed. Khmer Rouge dictator Pol Pot is overthrown and a Vietnamese puppet government installed under Heng Samrin.

'Winter of discontent' continues in the UK: widespread strikes in the public sector badly affect essential services (strikers include lorry drivers, ambulance crews, grave diggers, rubbish collectors, British Rail and British Leyland workers).

UK prime minister **James Callaghan**, returning from a summit meeting in Guadeloupe in the West Indies, speaks dismissively to reporters of the mounting chaos. The resultant tabloid headline of 'Crisis? What Crisis?' contributes to his defeat at the polls.

'I don't like Mondays,' says US schoolgirl **Brenda Spencer** to explain why she shot and killed two classmates.

Smoking and Health, a second report by the US surgeon-general, links cigarette smoking with several different types of cancer, as well as with heart disease, lung disease, and fetal death.

US jazz musician **Charles Mingus** dies at 56. He expanded the scope of the bass as a lead instrument.

St Lucia, in the West Indies, achieves independence from Britain, within the Commonwealth.

China mounts a brief, largely unsuccessful, punitive **invasion of N Vietnam** (Feb–March). About 700,000 Chinese and Vietnamese **'boat people'** leave the country as political or economic refugees.

A major **leak of radioactive waste liquid** is discovered at the

Sellafield nuclear power complex in NW England. It is thought to have been leaking undetected since 1976 or earlier.

The humorous radio programme *A Prairie Home Companion* begins in the USA (Feb). Written by Garrison Keillor, it will form the basis of his popular books of Lake Wobegon stories.

The musical *They're Playing Our Song* opens in New York and will run for 1,082 performances.

English punk rocker **Sid Vicious** dies at 21 in New York.

A left-wing **coup in Grenada** removes prime minister Eric Gairy and puts Maurice Bishop at the head of a People's Revolutionary Government.

The British prime minister James Callaghan is forced to call a **general election** after losing a vote of confidence in the House of Commons.

Airey Neave, British shadow undersecretary of state for Northern Ireland, is killed by a bomb placed at the House of Commons by the Irish National Liberation Army.

An **accident at Three Mile Island** nuclear power plant near Harrisburg, Pennsylvania, causes a pressurized-water reactor to leak radioactive material. Fears that the reactor's core will melt down prompts the evacuation of more than 140,000 people from the area.

Cloud Nine by British dramatist Caryl Churchill opens at the Royal Court Theatre, London.

Stephen Sondheim's musical *Sweeney Todd* opens in New York.

Tanzanian troops invade **Uganda** and, aided by Ugandan dissidents, overthrow brutal dictator Idi Amin. A provisional government is set up.

The execution of deposed Pakistani prime minister **Zulfikar Ali Bhutto** triggers widespread protest demonstrations.

New Zealand teacher **Blair Peach** dies after being hit over the head by police while demonstrating against a fascist march in London.

A Soviet laboratory manufacturing biological weapons in Sverdlovsk (now Ekaterinburg) in the eastern foothills of the Urals **accidentally releases anthrax spores**, killing hundreds of people.

US punk group the Ramones star in the film parody *Rock 'n' Roll High School*.

British dramatist Brian Clark's play *Whose Life Is It Anyway?* opens in London, starring Tom Conti.

UK general election (3 May): the Conservative Party wins an overall majority of 43 seats in the House of Commons, with 44% of the vote, and Margaret Thatcher becomes prime minister.

Ian McKellen and Tom Bell star in the first production of *Bent* by US dramatist Martin Sherman at the Royal Court Theatre, London.

The mod film *Quadrophenia* is based on a 1973 album by English rock group the Who, who are also the subject of the documentary film *The Kids Are Alright*.

In **Rhodesia**, under a new majority-rule constitution (which, however, contains inbuilt protection for the white minority), Bishop Abel Muzorewa becomes prime minister. The country temporarily reverts to British colonial status, under the name Zimbabwe-Rhodesia.

Ghana has another **coup**, led by Flight-Lt Jerry Rawlings, who has three previous heads of government executed. There is a return to civilian rule the following month.

US president Jimmy Carter and Soviet leader Leonid Brezhnev sign a Strategic Arms Limitation Treaty, **SALT II**, limiting the expansion of nuclear arsenals.

Constituencies are established for the first direct elections of members of the **European Parliament**, also a Conservative victory in the UK.

Whereas 25 years ago we were an empire, now we are a colony, with the IMF running our financial affairs, the Common Market Commission running our legislation and NATO running our armed forces.
British Labour minister **Tony Benn** to the Queen

South Africa's president **Balthazar Johannes Vorster** resigns because of a financial scandal. His successor is Marais Viljoen.

The Organization of Petroleum-Exporting Countries **raises the price of oil by 50%** (Jan–June).

The **Ixtoc 1** oil well in the Gulf of Mexico spills 535,000 tonnes of oil after a blowout, the largest oil spill to date, contaminating beaches and fisheries.

US actor **John Wayne**, star of many traditional Western films, dies at 72.

The **Gilbert Islands**, in W central Pacific Ocean, achieve independence from Britain as the Republic of Kiribati, within the Commonwealth.

In **Nicaragua**, the Sandinistas depose the right-wing dictator Anastasio Somoza. The right-wing guerrilla force known as the

Contras is formed, with US backing, to overthrow the new government.

In Church Rock, New Mexico, USA, 380 million litres/100 million gallons of **radioactive water containing uranium leaks** into a river from the nuclear plant.

The first **Sony Walkman** comes on the market.

US space station *Skylab* falls to Earth, dropping debris on Western Australia.

A **collision of the tankers** *Atlantic Empress* **and** *Aegean Captain* off Trinidad and Tobago spills 270,000 tonnes of oil into the sea.

Rust Never Sleeps is the title of a soundtrack album and film documentary of a concert tour by Canadian rock guitarist and singer Neil Young.

Military **coup in Equatorial Guinea**: Teodoro Obiang Nguema Mbasago deposes his uncle Francisco Macias Nguema, who is executed, with members of his administration, for genocide, embezzlement, human-rights violations, and other crimes.

Iranian military forces attack **Kurds** within the country's borders.

British admiral **Lord Mountbatten** and three others are killed by an Irish Republican Army bomb.

Gales and rough seas cause the deaths of 15 participants in the annual **Fastnet yacht race** off the English coast.

US progressive jazz musician and band leader **Stan Kenton** dies at 67.

The excesses of Emperor **Jean-Bédel Bokassa** of the Central African Empire, including the massacre of schoolchildren refusing to wear uniform, lead to his deposition by the country's first president, David Dacko, who reintroduces a republic.

Agostinho Neto, Angola's first president, dies at 56. He is succeeded by José Eduardo dos Santos.

Arrangements for Rhodesian independence are made in London: the **Lancaster House Agreement**.

St Vincent and the Grenadines, in the West Indies, achieve independence from Britain, within the Commonwealth.

President **Park Chung-Hee** of South Korea is assassinated by the Korean Central Intelligence Agency. Martial law is imposed. Park's successor Choi Kyu-Hah will be forced to resign the following year.

The **Farabundo Martí Liberation Front**, a socialist guerrilla movement, is formed in El Salvador. A civilian-military junta deposes the president and introduces land reform.

Control of the **Panama Canal Zone** is ceded to Panama by the USA.

The musical *Sugar Babies* opens in New York and will run for 1,208 performances; the songs are by Jimmy McHugh.

The **US embassy in Tehran**, Iran, is occupied by guerrillas who take the personnel hostage.

The **US embassy in Pakistan** is attacked by demonstrators.

It becomes public knowledge that British art historian **Anthony Blunt** was a double agent; he is stripped of his knighthood.

Publication of *The Times* and the *Sunday Times* resumes in the UK after almost a year.

Amadeus, a play about the composer Mozart by English dramatist Peter Shaffer, opens at the National Theatre, London.

Off the Wall by US rock singer Michael Jackson is the first of several albums produced for him by Quincy Jones.

Soviet troops invade **Afghanistan**, installing a puppet government; the Soviet and government forces are opposed by Mujaheddin Muslim guerrilla groups.

US car manufacturer **Chrysler** is saved from bankruptcy by a government loan of $1.2 bn.

Saddam Hussein becomes president of Iraq; effectively, he has been in power since 1968.

Israel withdraws from **Sinai** (occupied since 1967).

Egypt is expelled from the Arab League for making peace with Israel.

Up to 800 people a month are killed in **El Salvador** in the army's anti-left campaign of terror.

Iranian Revolutionary Guards are sent to **Lebanon** to spread the Islamic revolution. They form the extremist organization **Hezbollah**.

Referendum in Greenland calls for self-government.

Mauritania relinquishes its claim to **Western Sahara**.

Canadian Liberal prime minister **Pierre Trudeau** loses a general election but will return to power 1980 when the minority government of Joe Clark is defeated.

US television evangelist Jerry Falwell founds the **Moral Majority movement**, an extreme right-wing political pressure group.

The **Comoros** become a one-party state, with increased federal powers.

Political parties are legalized in **Brazil** (banned since 1964).

Britain's military base on **Malta** is closed down.

The **European Monetary System** is established for the purpose of financial co-operation and monetary stability.

Mrs Thatcher is doing for monetarism what the Boston Strangler did for door-to-door salesmen.
British Labour politician **Denis Healey**, speech in House of Commons

---

Irish prime minister **Jack Lynch** resigns and is succeeded by Charles Haughey, also of the Fianna Fáil party.

Reforms in China include the establishment of 'special economic zones' in coastal enclaves, where foreign investment is encouraged.

The **Azores**, **Canary Islands**, **Cyprus**, **Iceland**, **Madeira**, and **Malta** hold their first conference under the banner of **'the strategic islands'**.

Border war between **Israel and Lebanon** continues.

Referendum is held in Scotland and Wales on devolution; Wales is opposed and Scotland not sufficiently strongly in favour to precipitate a change.

Privatization of state-run enterprises begins in the UK with **British Petroleum**.

Foreign-exchange controls are abolished in the UK.

The World Health Organization reports that **smallpox** has been completely eradicated worldwide.

The European Space Agency's satellite launcher *Ariane 1* mak its first flight.

Jupiter's satellites and rings are explored by the US probes *Voyager 1* and *2*.

The Aztec capital **Tenochtitlán** is excavated beneath a zone of Mexico City.

Fossils of **apelike humanoids** resembling E Africa's *Proconsul* are found in the Antarctic, 500 km/300 mi from the South Pole.

The **Dartmouth Dam** in the Great Dividing Range, Australia, is completed, damming the country's largest river, the Murray.

Matsushita in Japan develops a **pocket-sized, flat-screen television set**, using a liquid-crystal display.

First **crossing of the English Channel by a human-powered aircraft**, *Gossamer Albatross*, piloted by Bryan Allen.

Japan National Railways' maglev test vehicle **ML-500** attains a speed of 517 kph/321 mph. It is suspended above a track by superconducting magnets.

Sam Barrett of the USA **exceeds the speed of sound in the rocket-engined car** *Budweiser Rocket*, but his speed record is not officially recognized because of timing difficulties.

The biosynthetic production of **human growth hormone** is announced.

The USA bans the use in agriculture of **diethylstilbesterol (DES)**, a synthetic hormone given to livestock to promote growth. It has been shown to cause premature sexual development in children who have eaten the meat. The European Community (EC) will ban DES 1981, against British objections.

The World Health Organization recommends a **total ban on all tobacco advertising** and promotion.

Greenpeace activists interpose themselves between whales and whalers, and expose the illegal sale of whale meat to Japan by Iceland.

The theory is put forward by US scientist Walter Alvarez that the **extinction of the dinosaurs** was caused by a large asteroid or comet hitting the Earth 65 million years ago. The impact would have created tsunamis and raised enough dust to blot out the Sun.

British humorist Douglas Adams creates the radio series *The Hitch-hiker's Guide to the Galaxy* for the BBC, and also turns it into a book.

The Answer to the Great Question of . . . Life, the Universe and Everything [is] Forty-two.
British humorist **Douglas Adams**, *The Hitch-hiker's Guide to the Galaxy*

South African novelist Nadine Gordimer publishes *Burger's Daughter*.

Shikasta is the first of British writer Doris Lessing's *Canopus in Argos* sequence of science-fiction novels.

British writer V S Naipaul publishes the novel *A Bend in the River*.

US novelist Alison Lurie examines the childhood of some of her recurring characters in *Only Children*.

Canadian writer Margaret Atwood publishes the novel *Life Before Man*.

US novelist Philip Roth publishes the semi-autobiographical *The Ghost Writer*.

US writer William Styron publishes the novel *Sophie's Choice*.

Czechoslovak writer Milan Kundera publishes the novel ***The Book of Laughter and Forgetting***.

> *The only reason people want to be masters of the future is to change the past.*
> Czechoslovak novelist **Milan Kundera**, *The Book of Laughter and Forgetting*

Turkish novelist Orhan Pamuk publishes ***Beyaz Kale/The White Castle***, a philosophical historical novel.

French film director **Jean Renoir** dies; born 1894. His films include the antiwar *La grande Illusion* 1937.

Soviet director Andrei Tarkovsky makes the allegorical film ***Stalker***.

US director, actor, and writer Woody Allen makes the film ***Manhattan***.

Australian film director Gillian Armstrong makes ***My Brilliant Career***.

Polish film director Roman Polanski makes ***Tess***, based on the novel, *Tess of the d'Urbervilles*, by Thomas Hardy and starring Nastassja Kinski.

US film director Francis Ford Coppola makes the Vietnam War epic ***Apocalypse Now***, loosely based on Joseph Conrad's novel *Heart of Darkness*.

> *The superpowers often behave like two heavily armed blind men feeling their way around a room, each believing himself in mortal peril from the other, whom he assumes to have perfect vision.*
> US diplomat **Henry Kissinger**

German film director Rainer Werner Fassbinder makes *Die Ehe von Maria Braun/The Marriage of Maria Braun*.

Scottish film director Bill Forsyth makes his debut with *That Sinking Feeling*.

The Great Rock 'n' Roll Swindle is a tongue-in-cheek British punk documentary focusing on the Sex Pistols, directed by Julien Temple.

German director Werner Herzog's film *Nosferatu*, a reworking of the vampire theme, stars Klaus Kinski, Isabelle Adjani, and Bruno Ganz.

Australian action film *Mad Max* makes an international star of actor Mel Gibson.

US film director James Bridges makes *The China Syndrome* with Jane Fonda and Jack Lemmon, drawing attention to the danger of an accident at a nuclear power station.

Sally Field stars as a trade-union activist in *Norma Rae* by US film director Martin Ritt.

Dustin Hoffman and Meryl Streep star in *Kramer vs. Kramer*, a Hollywood film about divorce.

Rap music emerges in New York; it will become one of the dominant pop-music styles of the next decade and beyond.

English rock group **Joy Division** sign to the Factory label; both will have great influence on British rock in the following years.

The synthesizer sound of English rock musician Gary Numan pioneers **techno** in the UK, as on the album *The Pleasure Principle*.

'**Gangsters**' by the Specials is the first record released on the UK independent label 2-Tone, which pioneers a **ska revival**.

English ska-pop group Madness sign first to 2-Tone and then to Stiff Records, releasing the album *One Step Beyond*.

English musician Brian Eno produces another album for US New Wave rock group Talking Heads, *Fear of Music*.

US rock singer and songwriter **Bob Dylan** becomes a fundamentalist Christian, expressed in the songs on *Slow Train Coming*.

Spanish golfer **Severiano Ballesteros** wins the Ryder Cup and the British Open for the first time.

The fifties face was angry, the sixties face was well-fed,
the seventies face was foxy. Perhaps it was the right
expression: there was a lot to be wary about.
British journalist **Keith Waterhouse**

Seventies' Facts

unemployed as percentage of total labour force in G7 countries

	1973	1975	1979
Canada	5.5%	6.3%	7.4%
France	2.7%	4.0%	5.9%
Italy	6.2%	5.8%	7.6%
Japan	1.3%	1.9%	2.1%
UK	3.0%	4.3%	5.0%
USA	4.8%	8.3%	5.8%
West Germany	0.8%	3.6%	3.2%
G7 average	3.4%	5.4%	4.9%

UK gross domestic product

year	exports	imports	GDP £bn 1985 prices
1970	57.1	−57.1	231.4
1971	61.0	−60.2	235.0
1972	61.7	−66.1	241.4
1973	69.0	−74.0	260.0
1974	74.1	−74.7	255.8
1975	72.0	−69.4	253.7
1976	78.6	−72.7	260.6
1977	84.0	−73.7	267.3
1978	85.6	−76.6	275.4
1979	88.8	−84.0	282.8

proportion of UK population over 15* economically active

	men	women
1971	81%	43%
1976	79%	47%

* Over 16 for 1976.

distribution of wealth in UK

1971 the richest 1% own 31% of all marketable wealth
1971 the richest 10% own 65% of all marketable wealth
1971 the richest 50% own 97% of all marketable wealth
1976 the richest 1% own 24% of all marketable wealth

1976 the richest 10% own 45% of all marketable wealth
1976 the richest 50% own 95% of all marketable wealth

ITV advertising revenue

1970	£94,742,000	1975	£176,532,000
1971	£108,634,000	1976	£230,807,000
1972	£134,162,000	1977	£299,887,000
1973	£160,831,000	1978	£363,005,000
1974	£149,245,000	1979	£346,796,000

Figures are net of payments on commissions and discounts.

popular-music charts, UK singles

1970

week ending	single	artist
3–24 Jan	'Two Little Boys'	Rolf Harris
31 Jan	'Reflections of My Life'	Marmalade
7–21 Feb	'Love Grows'	Edison Lighthouse
28 Feb	'I Want You Back'	the Jackson 5
7–28 March	'Wanderin' Star'	Lee Marvin
4–18 April	'Bridge Over Troubled Water'	Simon and Garfunkel
25 April–2 May	'Spirit in the Sky'	Norman Greenbaum
9–23 May	'Back Home'	England World Cup Squad
30 May	'Question'	the Moody Blues
6 June	'Yellow River'	Christie
13 June–4 July	'In the Summertime'	Mungo Jerry
11–25 July	'All Right Now'	Free
1 Aug	'Lola'	the Kinks
8–22 Aug	'The Wonder of You'	Elvis Presley
29 Aug–19 Sept	'Tears of a Clown'	Smokey Robinson and the Miracles
26 Sept–24 Oct	'Band of Gold'	Freda Payne
31 Oct	'Black Night'	Deep Purple
7–21 Nov	'Woodstock'	Matthew's Southern Comfort
28 Nov	'Voodo Chile'	the Jimi Hendrix Experience

| 5–19 Dec | 'I Hear You Knocking' | Dave Edmunds |
| 26 Dec | 'When I'm Dead and Gone' | McGuinness Flint |

1971

week ending	single	artist
2 Jan	'I Hear You Knocking'	Dave Edmunds
9–23 Jan	'Granddad'	Clive Dunn
30 Jan–6 March	'My Sweet Lord'	George Harrison
13 March	'Baby Jump'	Mungo Jerry
20 March	'Another Day'	Paul McCartney
27 March–24 April	'Hot Love'	T Rex
1–8 May	'Double Barrel'	Dave and Ansel Collins
15 May	'Brown Sugar'	the Rolling Stones
22 May–5 June	'Knock Three Times'	Dawn
12 June	'My Brother Jake'	Free
19 June	'I Did What I Did for Maria'	Tony Christie
26 June–17 July	'Chirpy Chirpy Cheep Cheep'	Middle of the Road
24 July–7 Aug	'Get It On'	T Rex
14 Aug	'Never Ending Song of Love'	the New Seekers
21 Aug–4 Sept	'I'm Still Waiting'	Diana Ross
11–18 Sept	'Hey Girl, Don't Bother Me'	the Tams
25 Sept–30 Oct	'Maggie May'	Rod Stewart
6–20 Nov	'Coz I Luv You'	Slade
27 Nov–25 Dec	'Ernie'	Benny Hill

1972

week ending	single	artist
1–22 Jan	'I'd Like to Teach the World to Sing'	the New Seekers
29 Jan	'A Horse with No Name'	America
5 Feb	'Telegram Sam'	T Rex
12–19 Feb	'Son of My Father'	Chicory Tip
26 Feb	'American Pie'	Don McLean
4 March–8 April	'Without You'	Nilsson
15 April–6 May	'Amazing Grace'	Royal Scots Dragoon Guards
13 May–3 June	'Metal Guru'	T Rex

10–24 June	'Vincent'	Don McLean
1 July	'Take Me Bak 'Ome'	Slade
8–29 July	'Puppy Love'	Donny Osmond
5–19 Aug	'School's Out'	Alice Cooper
26 Aug–2 Sept	'You Wear It Well'	Rod Stewart
9–16 Sept	'Mama Weer All Crazee Now'	Slade
23 Sept	'Children of the Revolution'	T Rex
30 Sept	'How Can I Be Sure?'	David Cassidy
7–28 Oct	'Mouldy Old Dough'	Lieutenant Pigeon
4–11 Nov	'Clair'	Gilbert O'Sullivan
18 Nov–2 Dec	'My Ding-a-Ling'	Chuck Berry
9 Dec	'Gudbuy T' Jane'	Slade
16–30 Dec	'Long Haired Lover from Liverpool'	Little Jimmy Osmond

1973

week ending	*single*	*artist*
6 Jan	'Long Haired Lover from Liverpool'	Little Jimmy Osmond
13–20 Jan	'The Jean Genie'	David Bowie
27 Jan–17 Feb	'Blockbuster'	the Sweet
24 Feb–3 March	'Part of the Union'	the Strawbs
10–17 March	'Cum On, Feel the Noize'	Slade
24 March–7 April	'The Twelfth of Never'	Donny Osmond
14 April	'Get Down'	Gilbert O'Sullivan
21 April–19 May	'Tie a Yellow Ribbon Round the Ole Oak Tree'	Dawn
26 May–2 June	'See My Baby Jive'	Wizzard
9–16 June	'Can the Can'	Suzi Quatro
23 June	'Rubber Bullets'	10cc
30 June–7 July	'Skweeze Me, Pleeze Me'	Slade
14–21 July	'Welcome Home'	Peters and Lee
28 July–18 Aug	'I'm the Leader of the Gang'	Gary Glitter
25 Aug–1 Sept	'Young Love'	Donny Osmond
8 Sept	'Angel Fingers'	Wizzard
15 Sept	'Rock On'	David Essex

22 Sept	'Ballroom Blitz'	the Sweet
29 Sept–20 Oct	'Eye Level'	Simon Park Orchestra
27 Oct–10 Nov	'Puppy Song/Day Dreamer'	David Cassidy
17 Nov–8 Dec	'I Love You Love Me Love'	Gary Glitter
15–29 Dec	'Merry Christmas, Everybody'	Slade

1974

week ending	*single*	*artist*
5 Jan	'Merry Christmas, Everybody'	Slade
12 Jan	'You Won't Find Another Fool Like Me'	the New Seekers
19 Jan–9 Feb	'Teenage Rampage'	the Sweet
16–23 Feb	'Devil Gate Drive'	Suzi Quatro
2–9 March	'Jealous Mind'	Alvin Stardust
16–30 March	'Billy, Don't Be a Hero'	Paper Lace
6–13 April	'Seasons in the Sun'	Terry Jacks
20 April	'The Cat Crept In'	Mud
27 April–4 May	'Waterloo'	Abba
11 May–1 June	'Sugar Baby Love'	the Rubettes
8–15 June	'The Streak'	Ray Stevens
22 June	'Always Yours'	Gary Glitter
29 June–13 July	'She'	Charles Aznavour
20 July–3 Aug	'Rock Your Baby'	George McCrae
10–24 Aug	'When Will I See You Again'	the Three Degrees
31 Aug–7 Sept	'Love Me for a Reason'	the Osmonds
14 Sept–5 Oct	'Kung Fu Fighting'	Carl Douglas
12 Oct	'Gee Baby'	Peter Shelley
19–26 Oct	'Everything I Own'	Ken Boothe
2–30 Nov	'Gonna Make You a Star'	David Essex
7 Dec	'The First, the Last, My Everything'	Barry White
14–28 Dec	'Lonely This Christmas'	Mud

1975

week ending	*single*	*artist*
4–11 Jan	'Streets of London'	Ralph McTell

18 Jan	'Down Down'	Status Quo
25 Jan	'Ms Grace'	The Tymes
1–8 Feb	'January'	Pilot
15 Feb	'Please Mr Postman'	the Carpenters
22 Feb	'Make Me Smile'	Steve Harley and Cockney Rebel
1–8 March	'If'	Telly Savalas
15 March–19 April	'Bye, Bye, Baby'	the Bay City Rollers
26 April	'Honey'	Bobby Goldsboro
3 May	'Lovin' You'	Minnie Riperton
10–24 May	'Stand By Your Man'	Tammy Wynette
31 May	'Whispering Grass'	Windsor Davies and Don Estell
7 June	'Three Steps to Heaven'	Showaddywaddy
14 June	'Whispering Grass'	Windsor Davies and Don Estell
21–28 June	'I'm Not in Love'	10cc
5–12 July	'Tears on My Pillow'	Johnny Nash
19 July	'Give a Little Love'	the Bay City Rollers
26 July	'Barbados'	Typically Tropical
2–16 Aug	'I Can't Give You Anything (but Love)'	the Stylistics
23 Aug–13 Sept	'Sailing'	Rod Stewart
20 Sept	'Moonlighting'	Leo Sayer
27 Sept–11 Oct	'Hold Me Close'	David Essex
18–25 Oct	'I Only Have Eyes for You'	Art Garfunkel
1–9 Nov	'Space Oddity'	David Bowie
15 Nov	'D.I.V.O.R.C.E.'	Billy Connolly
22 Nov	'You Sexy Thing'	Hot Chocolate
29 Nov–27 Dec	'Bohemian Rhapsody'	Queen

1976

week ending	single	artist
3–17 Jan	'Bohemian Rhapsody'	Queen
25 Jan	'Glass of Champagne'	Sailor
31 Jan–7 Feb	'Mama Mia'	Abba
14 Feb	'Forever and Ever'	Slik
21–28 Feb	'December 1963 (Oh, What a Night)'	the Four Seasons
6–20 March	'I Love to Love'	Tina Charles

27 March–24 April	'Save All Your Kisses for Me'	Brotherhood of Man
1 May–5 June	'Fernando'	Abba
12 June	'No Charge'	J J Barrie
19 June	'Silly Love Songs'	Wings
26 June–3 July	'You to Me Are Everything'	the Real Thing
10 July	'Young Hearts Run Free'	Candi Staton
17 July	'The Roussos Phenomenon'	Demis Roussos
24 July–28 Aug	'Don't Go Breaking My Heart'	Elton John and Kiki Dee
4 Sept–9 Oct	'Dancing Queen'	Abba
16–30 Oct	'Mississippi'	Pussycat
6–27 Nov	'If You Leave Me Now'	Chicago
4–18 Dec	'Under the Moon of Love'	Showaddywaddy
25 Dec	'When a Child Is Born'	Johnny Mathis

1977

week ending	*single*	*artist*
1–8 Jan	'When a Child Is Born'	Johnny Mathis
15–22 Jan	'Don't Give Up on Us'	David Soul
29 Jan	'Don't Cry for Me, Argentina'	Julie Covington
5 Feb	'Don't Give Up on Us'	David Soul
12–19 Feb	'Don't Cry for Me, Argentina'	Julie Covington
26 Feb–5 March	'When I Need You'	Leo Sayer
12–19 March	'Chanson d'Amour'	Manhattan Transfer
26 March–30 April	'Knowing Me Knowing You'	Abba
7–21 May	'Free'	Deniece Williams
28 May–11 June	'I Don't Want to Talk/The First Cut Is Deepest'	Rod Stewart
18 June	'God Save the Queen'	the Sex Pistols
25 June–2 July	'Show You the Way to Go'	the Jacksons
9 July	'So You Win Again'	Hot Chocolate
16 July	'Ma Baker'	Boney M

23 July–20 Aug	'I Feel Love'	Donna Summer
27 Aug	'Angelo'	Brotherhood of Man
3 Sept	'Way Down'	Elvis Presley
10–24 Sept	'Magic Fly'	Space
1–8 Oct	'Way Down'	Elvis Presley
15 Oct	'Silver Lady'	David Soul
22 Oct	'Yes Sir I Can Boogie'	Baccara
29 Oct	'You're in My Heart (The Final Acclaim)'	Rod Stewart
5 Nov	'Yes Sir I Can Boogie'	Baccara
12–19 Nov	'Name of the Game'	Abba
26 Nov	'Rockin' All Over the World'	Status Quo
3–31 Dec	'Mull of Kintyre'	Wings

1978

week ending	single	artist
7–28 Jan	'Mull of Kintyre'	Wings
4–11 Feb	'Uptown Top Ranking'	Althia and Donna
18 Feb–4 March	'Take a Chance on Me'	Abba
11–25 March	'Wuthering Heights'	Kate Bush
1–8 April	'Denis'	Blondie
15 April	'I Wonder Why'	Showaddywaddy
22 April–13 May	'Night Fever'	the Bee Gees
20 May–10 June	'Rivers of Babylon'	Boney M
17 June–19 Aug	'You're the One That I Want'	John Travolta and Olivia Newton-John
26 Aug–16 Sept	'Three Times a Lady'	the Commodores
23–30 Sept	'Dreadlock Holiday'	10cc
7 Oct–11 Nov	'Summer Nights'	John Travolta and Olivia Newton-John
18 Nov–2 Dec	'Rat Trap'	the Boomtown Rats
9 Dec	'Do Ya Think I'm Sexy'	Rod Stewart
16–30 Dec	'Mary's Boy Child'	Boney M

1979

week ending	single	artist
7–20 Jan	'YMCA'	the Village People
27 Jan–3 Feb	'Hit Me with Your Rhythm Stick'	Ian Dury and the Blockheads

10 Feb	'Heart of Glass'	Blondie
17 Feb	'Chiquitita'	Abba
24 Feb–3 March	'Heart of Glass'	Blondie
10 March	'Tragedy'	the Bee Gees
17 March	'Oliver's Army'	Elvis Costello
24–31 March	'I Will Survive'	Gloria Gaynor
7 April	'In the Navy'	the Village People
14 April–12 May	'Bright Eyes'	Art Garfunkel
19 May	'Pop Muzik'	M
26 May	'Bright Eyes'	Art Garfunkel
2 June	'Sunday Girl'	Blondie
9 June	'Dance Away'	Roxy Music
16-23 June	'Ring My Bell'	Anita Ward
30 June–14 July	'Are "Friends" Electric?'	Gary Numan and Tubeway Army
21 July	'Silly Games'	Janet Kay
28 July	'Are "Friends" Electric?'	Gary Numan and Tubeway Army
4–25 Aug	'I Don't Like Mondays'	the Boomtown Rats
1–15 Sept	'We Don't Talk Anymore'	Cliff Richard
22–29 Sept	'Cars'	Gary Numan
6–13 Oct	'Message in a Bottle'	the Police
20–27 Oct	'Video Killed the Radio Star'	the Buggles
3 Nov	'One Day at a Time'	Lena Martell
10 Nov–1 Dec	'When You're in Love'	Dr Hook
8 Dec	'Walking on the Moon'	the Police
15–29 Dec	'Another Brick in the Wall'	Pink Floyd

popular-music charts, UK albums

1970

week ending	album	artist
3-31 Jan	*Abbey Road*	the Beatles
7–14 Feb	*Led Zeppelin II*	Led Zeppelin
21 Feb–30 May	*Bridge Over Troubled Water*	Simon and Garfunkel
6–20 June	*Let It Be*	the Beatles
27 June–11 July	*Bridge Over Troubled Water*	Simon and Garfunkel

18 July	*Let It Be*	the Beatles
25 July	*Bridge Over Troubled Water*	Simon and Garfunkel
1–15 Aug	*Let It Be*	the Beatles
22–29 Aug	*Bridge Over Troubled Water*	Simon and Garfunkel
5–19 Sept	*A Question of Balance*	the Moody Blues
26 Sept–10 Oct	*Bridge Over Troubled Water*	Simon and Garfunkel
17–24 Oct	*Paranoid*	Black Sabbath
31 Oct	*Led Zeppelin III*	Led Zeppelin
7 Nov	*Motown Chartbusters Vol. 4*	various
14 Nov–12 Dec	*Led Zeppelin III*	Led Zeppelin
19 Dec	*Motown Chartbusters Vol. 4*	various
26 Dec	*Led Zeppelin III*	Led Zeppelin

1971

week ending	album	artist
2–9 Jan	*Andy Williams' Greatest Hits*	Andy Williams
16 Jan	*Bridge Over Troubled Water*	Simon and Garfunkel
23 Jan	*Andy Williams' Greatest Hits*	Andy Williams
30 Jan–13 March	*All Things Must Pass*	George Harrison
20 March–3 April	*Bridge Over Troubled Water*	Simon and Garfunkel
10 April	*Home Lovin' Man*	Andy Williams
17 April	*Bridge Over Troubled Water*	Simon and Garfunkel
24 April	*Home Lovin' Man*	Andy Williams
1 May	*Motown Chartbusters Vol. 5*	various
8 May–19 June	*Sticky Fingers*	the Rolling Stones
26 June	*Bridge Over Troubled Water*	Simon and Garfunkel
3 July	*Ram*	Paul McCartney
10–31 July	*Bridge Over Troubled Water*	Simon and Garfunkel

7 Aug–4 Sept	*Every Good Boy Deserves Favour*	the Moody Blues
11 Sept	*Tapestry*	Carole King
18 Sept–13 Nov	*Every Picture Tells a Story*	Rod Stewart
20 Nov–4 Dec	*Imagine*	John Lennon
11 Dec–25 Dec	*Led Zeppelin IV*	Led Zeppelin

1972

week ending	album	artist
1–8 Jan	*Electric Warrior*	T Rex
15 Jan–12 Feb	*Teaser and the Firecat*	Cat Stevens
19 Feb	*Neil Reid*	Neil Reid
26 Feb–25 March	*Paul Simon*	Paul Simon
1 April	*Fog on the Tyne*	Lindisfarne
8–22 April	*Harvest*	Neil Young
29 April–6 May	*Machine Head*	Deep Purple
13 May	*Fog on the Tyne*	Lindisfarne
20 May–3 June	*Bolan Boogie*	T Rex
10–17 June	*Exile on Main Street*	the Rolling Stones
24 June–1 July	*American Pie*	Don McLean
8 July	*20 Dynamic Hits*	various
15 July	*American Pie*	Don McLean
22 July–5 Aug	*Simon and Garfunkel's Greatest Hits*	Simon and Garfunkel
12 Aug–9 Sept	*Never a Dull Moment*	Rod Stewart
16 Sept	*Simon and Garfunkel's Greatest Hits*	Simon and Garfunkel
23 Sept–7 Oct	*Never a Dull Moment*	Rod Stewart
14 Oct–11 Nov	*Simon and Garfunkel's Greatest Hits*	Simon and Garfunkel
18 Nov	*Back to Front*	Gilbert O'Sullivan
25 Nov	*Simon and Garfunkel's Greatest Hits*	Simon and Garfunkel
2–16 Dec	*Back to Front*	Gilbert O'Sullivan
23–30 Dec	*Slayed*	Slade

1973

week ending	album	artist
6 Jan–3 Feb	*Slayed*	Slade
10 Feb–17 March	*Don't Shoot Me, I'm Only the Piano Player*	Elton John

24 March	*Billion Dollar Babies*	Alice Cooper
31 March–7 April	*Dark Side of the Moon*	Pink Floyd
14 April	*Don't Shoot Me, I'm Only the Piano Player*	Elton John
21 April	*Houses of the Holy*	Led Zeppelin
28 April	*Ooh La La*	the Faces
5–12 May	*Aladdin Sane*	David Bowie
19 May	*The Beatles 1967–70*	the Beatles
26 May–2 June	*Aladdin Sane*	David Bowie
9 June	*The Beatles 1967–70*	the Beatles
16 June–7 July	*Aladdin Sane*	David Bowie
14 July	*We Can Make It*	Peters and Lee
21 July	*Aladdin Sane*	David Bowie
28 July–11 Aug	*We Can Make It*	Peters and Lee
18–25 Aug	*Now and Then*	the Carpenters
1–15 Sept	*Sing It Again, Rod*	Rod Stewart
22–29 Sept	*Goat's Head Soup*	the Rolling Stones
6–13 Oct	*Sladest*	Slade
20 Oct	*Hello*	Status Quo
27 Oct–8 Dec	*Pin Ups*	David Bowie
15–29 Dec	*Brain Salad Surgery*	Emerson, Lake and Palmer

1974

week ending	album	artist
5–19 Jan	*Brain Salad Surgery*	Emerson, Lake and Palmer
26 Jan–1 June	*The Singles 1969–1973*	the Carpenters
8–29 June	*Diamond Dogs*	David Bowie
6 July–7 Sept	*Band on the Run*	Paul McCartney and Wings
14–21 Sept	*Hergest Ridge*	Mike Oldfield
28 Sept–5 Oct	*Tubular Bells*	Mike Oldfield
12 Oct	*Back Home Again*	John Denver
19–26 Oct	*Smiler*	Rod Stewart
2 Nov	*'Gonna Make You a Star'*	David Essex
9 Nov	*Rollin'*	the Bay City Rollers
16 Nov	*David Essex*	David Essex
23 Nov–28 Dec	*Greatest Hits*	Elton John

1975

week ending	album	artist
4 Jan–1 Feb	*Greatest Hits*	Elton John
8 –15 Feb	*Greatest Hits*	Engelbert Humperdinck
22 Feb	*Greatest Hits*	Elton John
1–15 March	*On the Level*	Status Quo
22 March–5 April	*Physical Graffiti*	Led Zeppelin
12 April	*Young Americans*	David Bowie
19 April–31 May	*Once Upon a Star*	the Bay City Rollers
7–21 June	*Captain Fantastic and the Brown Dirt Cowboy*	Elton John
28 June–2 Aug	*Venus and Mars*	Wings
9–23 Aug	*The Best of the Stylistics*	the Stylistics
30 Aug–11 Oct	*Atlantic Crossing*	Rod Stewart
18 Oct	*Wish You Were Here*	Pink Floyd
25 Oct	*Atlantic Crossing*	Rod Stewart
1 Nov–20 Dec	*40 Golden Greats*	Jim Reeves
27 Dec	*A Night at the Opera*	Queen

1976

week ending	album	artist
3–31 Jan	*A Night at the Opera*	Queen
7 Feb	*How Dare You*	10cc
14–28 Feb	*Desire*	Bob Dylan
6–13 March	*The Very Best of Slim Whitman*	Slim Whitman
20 March	*Desire*	Bob Dylan
27 March–3 April	*Blue for You*	Status Quo
10 April	*Their Greatest Hits 1971–1975*	the Eagles
17 April–8 May	*Rock Follies*	soundtrack
15 May–3 July	*Abba's Greatest Hits*	Abba
10–17 July	*A Night on the Town*	Rod Stewart
24 July–18 Sept	*20 Golden Greats*	the Beach Boys
25 Sept	*A Night on the Town*	Rod Stewart
2–9 Oct	*Abba's Greatest Hits*	Abba
16 Oct	*A Night on the Town*	Rod Stewart
23 Oct	*Abba's Greatest Hits*	Abba
30 Oct	*The Who Story*	the Who
6–20 Nov	*Songs in the Key of Life*	Stevie Wonder

| 27 Nov–18 Dec | *20 Golden Greats* | Glen Campbell |
| 25 Dec | *Arrival* | Abba |

1977

week ending	*album*	*artist*
1–15 Jan	*Arrival*	Abba
22 Jan–12 Feb	*Red River Valley*	Slim Whitman
19 Feb	*Evita*	various
26 Feb–2 April	*The Shadows' 20 Golden Greats*	the Shadows
9 April	*Portrait of Sinatra*	Frank Sinatra
16 April–21 May	*Arrival*	Abba
28 May–4 June	*Hotel California*	the Eagles
11–18 June	*Arrival*	Abba
25 June	*The Beatles at the Hollywood Bowl*	the Beatles
2 July	*The Muppet Show*	the Muppets
9–16 July	*A Star Is Born*	soundtrack
23 July–13 Aug	*The Johnny Mathis Collection*	Johnny Mathis
20–27 Aug	*Going for the One*	Yes
3 Sept	*Moody Blue*	Elvis Presley
10–17 Sept	*Oxygene*	Jean-Michel Jarre
24 Sept–5 Nov	*20 Golden Greats*	Diana Ross and the Supremes
12 Nov–10 Dec	*Sound of Bread*	Bread
17–31 Dec	*Disco Fever*	various

1978

week ending	*album*	*artist*
7–14 Jan	*Disco Fever*	various
21 Jan–4 Feb	*Rumours*	Fleetwood Mac
11 Feb–25 March	*Abba the Album*	Abba
1–8 April	*The Kick Inside*	Kate Bush
15–22 April	*20 Golden Greats*	Nat King Cole
29 April–10 June	*Saturday Night Fever*	soundtrack
17 June	*Black and White*	the Stranglers
24 June–2 Sept	*Saturday Night Fever*	soundtrack
9–23 Sept	*Night Flight to Venus*	Boney M
30 Sept–2 Dec	*Grease*	soundtrack
9 Dec	*Neil Diamond's 20 Golden Greats*	Neil Diamond

16–30 Dec	*Grease*	soundtrack

1979

week ending	album	artist
7–20 Jan	*Greatest Hits 1976–1978*	Showaddywaddy
27 Jan–3 Feb	*Don't Walk, Boogie*	various
10 Feb–17 March	*Parallel Lines*	Blondie
24 March	*Spirits Having Flown*	the Bee Gees
31 March	*C'est Chic*	Chic
7–21 April	*Greatest Hits Vol. 2*	Barbra Streisand
28 April–19 May	*The Very Best of Leo Sayer*	Leo Sayer
26 May–16 June	*Voulez Vous*	Abba
23 June–7 July	*Discovery*	Electric Light Orchestra
14 July	*Parallel Lines*	Blondie
21–28 July	*Replicas*	Gary Numan and Tubeway Army
4–18 Aug	*The Best Disco Album in the World*	various
25 Aug	*Discovery*	Electric Light Orchestra
1–15 Sept	*The Best Disco Album in the World*	various
22 Sept	*Discovery*	Electric Light Orchestra
29 Sept	*Rock 'n' Roll Juvenile*	Cliff Richard
6–13 Oct	*The Pleasure Principle*	Gary Numan
20 Oct–17 Nov	*Regatta de Blanc*	the Police
24 Nov	*Greatest Hits*	Rod Stewart
1–29 Dec Dec	*Greatest Hits Vol. 2*	Abba

Grammy awards

(given by the US National Academy of Recording Arts and Sciences)

year	single of the year	artist
	album of the year	*artist*
1970	'Bridge Over Troubled Water'	Simon and Garfunkel
	Bridge Over Troubled Water	Simon and Garfunkel
1971	'It's Too Late'	Carole King
	Tapestry	Carole King

1972	'The First Time I Ever Saw Your Face'	Roberta Flack
	The Concert for Bangla Desh	George Harrison, Ravi Shankar, Bob Dylan, Leon Russell, Ringo Starr, Billy Preston, Eric Clapton, and Klaus Voormann
1973	'Killing Me Softly with His Song'	Roberta Flack
	Innervisions	Stevie Wonder
1974	'I Honestly Love You'	Olivia Newton-John
	Fulfillingness First Finale	Stevie Wonder
1975	'Love Will Keep Us Together'	Captain and Tennille
	Still Crazy After All These Years	Paul Simon
1976	'This Masquerade'	George Benson
	Songs in the Key of Life	Stevie Wonder
1977	'Hotel California'	the Eagles
	Rumours	Fleetwood Mac
1978	'Just the Way You Are'	Billy Joel
	Saturday Night Fever	soundtrack
1979	'What a Fool Believes'	the Doobie Brothers
	52nd Street	Billy Joel

UK best-selling singles

1970	'The Wonder of You'	Elvis Presley
1971	'My Sweet Lord'	George Harrison
1972	'Amazing Grace'	Royal Scots Dragoon Guards
1973	'Tie A Yellow Ribbon'	Dawn
1974	'Tiger Feet'	Mud
1975	'By Bye Baby'	Bay City Rollers
1976	'Save Your Kisses For Me'	Brotherhood of Man
1977	'Don't Give Up On Us'	David Soul
1978	'Rivers Of Babylon/Brown Girl In The Ring	Boney M
1979	'Bright Eyes'	Art Garfunkel

Pulitzer Prize for Fiction

1970	Jean Stafford	*Collected Stories*
1971	No award	
1972	Wallace Stagner	*Angle of Repose*
1973	Eudora Walty	*The Optimist's Daughter*
1974	No award	
1975	Michael Shaara	*The Killer Angels*
1976	Saul Bellow	*Humboldt's Gift*
1977	No award	
1978	James Alan McPherson	*Elbow Room*
1979	John Cheever	*The Stories of John Cheever*

Nobel Prize for Literature

1970	Aleksandr Solzhenitsyn (Russian)
1971	Pablo Neruda (Chilean)
1972	Heinrich Böll (German)
1973	Patrick White (Australian)
1974	Eyvind Johnson (Swedish) Harry Martinson (Swedish)
1975	Eugenio Montale (Italian)
1976	Saul Bellow (American)
1977	Vicente Aleixandre (Spanish)
1978	Isaac Bashevis Singer (American)
1979	Odysseus Lytis (Greek)

Motion picture Academy Awards (Oscars)

1970	Best Picture: *Patton*; Best Director: Franklin J Schaffner *Patton*; Best Actor: George C Scott *Patton*; Best Actress: Glenda Jackson *Women in Love*
1971	Best Picture: *The French Connection*; Best Director: William Friedkin *The French Connection*; Best Actor: Gene Hackman *The French Connection*; Best Actress: Jane Fonda *Klute*
1972	Best Picture: *The Godfather*; Best Director: Bob Fosse *Cabaret*; Best Actor: Marlon Brando *The Godfather*; Best Actress: Liza Minnelli *Cabaret*
1973	Best Picture: *The Sting*; Best Director: George Roy Hill *The Sting*; Best Actor: Jack Lemmon *Save the Tiger*; Best Actress: Glenda Jackson *A Touch of Class*

1974	Best Picture: *The Godfather Part II*; Best Director: Francis Ford Coppola *The Godfather Part II*; Best Actor: Art Carney *Harry and Tonto*; Best Actress: Ellen Burstyn *Alice Doesn't Live Here Anymore*
1975	Best Picture: *One Flew Over the Cuckoo's Nest*; Best Director: Milos Forman *One Flew Over the Cuckoo's Nest*; Best Actor: Jack Nicholson *One Flew Over the Cuckoo's Nest*; Best Actress: Louise Fletcher *One Flew Over the Cuckoo's Nest*
1976	Best Picture: *Rocky*; Best Director: John G Alvidsen *Rocky*; Best Actor: Peter Finch *Network*; Best Actress: Faye Dunnaway *Network*
1977	Best Picture: *Annie Hall*; Best Director: Woody Allen *Annie Hall*; Best Actor: Richard Dreyfuss *The Goodbye Girl*; Best Actress: Diane Keaton *Annie Hall*
1978	Best Picture: *The Deer Hunter*; Best Director: Michael Cimino *The Deer Hunter*; Best Actor: John Voight *Coming Home*; Best Actress: Jane Fonda *Coming Home*
1979	Best Picture: *Kramer vs. Kramer*; Best Director: Robert Benton *Kramer vs. Kramer*; Best Actor: Duston Hoffman *Kramer vs. Kramer*; Best Actress: Sally Field *Norma Rae*

Association Football

World Cup Winners		*European championships winners*	
1970	Brazil	**1972**	West Germany
1974	West Germany	**1976**	Czechoslovakia
1978	Argentina		

Boxing World Champions

Heavyweight

1970	Joe Frazier (USA)
1973	George Foreman (USA)
1974	Muhammad Ali (USA)
1978	Leon Spinks (USA)
1978	Ken Norton (USA) WBC
1978	Muhammad Ali (USA) WBA
1978	Larry Holmes (USA) WBC
1979	John Tate (USA) WBA

Cruiserweight

1979	Marvin Camel (USA) WBC

Light Heavyweight

1971	Vicente Rondon (VEN) WBA
1974	John Conteh (GB) WBC
1974	Victor Galindez (ARG) WBA
1977	Miguel Cuello (ARG) WBC
1978	Mate Parlov (YUG) WBC
1978	Mike Rossman (USA) WBA
1979	Victor Galindez (ARG) WBA
1979	Matthew Saad Muhammad (USA) WBC
1979	Marvin Johnson (USA) WBA

Middleweight

1970	Carlos Monzon (ARG)
1974	Rodrigo Valdez (COL) WBC
1976	Carlos Monzon (ARG)
1977	Rodrigo Valdez (COL)
1978	Hugo Corro (ARG)
1979	Vito Antuofermo (ITA)

Welterweight

1970	Billy Backus (USA)
1971	Jose Napoles (CUB)
1975	Angel Espada (PR) WBA
1975	John H Stracey (GB) WBC
1976	Carlos Palomino (MEX) WBC
1976	Pipino Cuevas (MEX) WBA
1979	Wilfred Benitez (USA) WBC
1979	Sugar Ray Leonard (USA) WBC

Lightweight

1970	Ismael Laguna (PAN)
1970	Jen Buchanan (GB) WBA
1971	Pedro Carrasco (SPA) WBC
1972	Mando Ramos (USA) WBC
1972	Roberto Duran (PAN) WBA
1972	Chango Carmona (MEX) WBC
1972	Rodolfo Gonzalez (MEX) WBC
1974	Guts Ishimatsu (JAP) WBC
1976	Esteban de Jesus (PR) WBC
1978	Roberto Duran (PAN)
1979	Jim Watt (GB) WBC
1979	Ernesto Espana (VEN) WBA

Featherweight

1970	Vicente Saldivar (MEX) WBC
1970	Kuniaki Shibata (JAP) WBC
1971	Antonio Gomez (VEN) WBA
1972	Clemente Sanchez (MEX) WBC
1972	Jose Legra (CUB) WBC
1973	Eder Jofre (BRA) WBC
1974	Ruben Olivares (MEX) WBA
1974	Bobby Chacon (USA) WBC
1974	Alexis Arguello (NIC) WBA
1975	Ruben Olivares (MEX) WBC
1975	David Kotey (GHA) WBC
1976	Danny Lopez (USA) WBC
1977	Rafael Ortega (PAN) WBA
1977	Cecilio Lastra (SPA) WBA
1978	Eusebio Pedroza (PAN) WBA

Bantamweight

1970	Chucho Castillo (MEX)
1971	Ruben Olivares (MEX)
1972	Rafael Herrera (MEX)
1972	Enrique Pinder (PAN)
1973	Romeo Anaya (MEX) WBA
1973	Rafael Herrera (MEX) WBC
1973	Arnold Taylor (SAF) WBA
1974	Soo-Hwan Hong (SKO) WBA
1974	Rodolfo Martinez (MEX) WBC
1975	Alfonso Zamora (MEX) WBA
1976	Carlos Zarate (MEX) WBC
1977	Jorge Lujan (PAN) WBA
1979	Lupe Pintor (MEX) WBC

Flyweight

1970	Chartchai Chionoi (THA) WBC
1970	Berkrerk Chartvanchai (THA) WBA
1970	Masao Ohba (JAP) WBA
1970	Erbito Salavarria (PHI) WBC
1972	Venice Borkorsor (THA) WBC
1973	Chartchai Chionoi (THA) WBA
1973	Betulio Gonzalez (VEN) WBC
1974	Shoji Oguma (JAP) WBC
1974	Susumu Hanagata (JAP) WBA

1970	Miguel Canto (MEX) WBC		
1975	Erbito Salavarria (PHI) WBA		
1976	Alfonso Lopez (PAN) WBA		
1976	Guty Espadas (MEX) WBA		
1978	Betulio Gonzales (VEN) WBA		
1979	Chan-Hee Park (SKO) WBC		
1979	Luis Ibarra (PAN) WBA		

Cricket

County Champions

1970	Kent	**1975**	Leicestershire
1971	Surrey	**1976**	Middlesex
1972	Warwickshire	**1977**	Kent and Middlesex
1973	Hampshire	**1978**	Kent
1974	Worcestershire	**1979**	Essex

Golf

British Open Championship Winners

1970	J W Nicklaus (USA)	**1975**	T Watson (USA)
1971	L Trevino (USA)	**1976**	J Miller (USA)
1972	L Trevino (USA)	**1977**	T Watson (USA)
1973	T Weiskopf (USA)	**1978**	J W Nicklaus (USA)
1974	G Player (SAF)	**1979**	S Ballesteros (SPA)

Ryder Cup Winners

1971	United States	**1977**	United States
1973	United States	**1979**	United States
1975	United States		

United States Open Championship Winners

1970	A W Jacklin (GB)	**1975**	L Graham
1971	L Trevino	**1976**	J Pate
1972	J W Nicklaus	**1977**	H Green
1973	J Miller	**1978**	A North
1974	H Irwin	**1979**	H Irwin

Lawn Tennis

Wimbledon champions

	Men's singles		Women's singles
1970	J D Newcombe (AUS)	**1970**	B M Court (AUS)
1971	J D Newcombe (AUS)	**1971**	E Goolagong (AUS)
1972	S R Smith (USA)	**1972**	L W King (USA)
1973	J Kodes (TCH)	**1973**	L W King (USA)
1974	J S Connors (USA)	**1974**	C M Evert (USA)
1975	A R Ashe (USA)	**1975**	L W King (USA)
1976	B Borg (SWE)	**1976**	C M Evert (USA)
1977	B Borg (SWE)	**1977**	S V Wade (GB)
1978	B Borg (SWE)	**1978**	M Navratilova (TCH)
1979	B Borg (SWE))	**1979**	M Navratilova (TCH)

Men's doubles

1970	J D Newcombe (AUS) A D Roche (AUS)
1971	R Emerson (AUS) R G Laver (AUS)
1972	R A J Hewitt (SAF) F D McMillan (SAF)
1973	J S Connors (USA) I Nastase (ROM)
1974	J D Newcombe (AUS) A D Roche (AUS)
1975	V Gerulaitis (USA) A Mayer (USA)
1976	B E Gottfried (USA) R Ramirez (MEX)
1977	R L Case (AUS) G Masters (AUS)
1978	R A J Hewitt (SAF) F D McMillan (SAF)
1979	P Fleming (USA) J P McEnroe (USA)

Women's doubles

1970	R Casals (USA) L W King (USA)
1971	R Casals (USA) L W King (USA)
1972	L W King (USA) B Stove (HOL)
1973	R Casals (USA) L W King (USA)
1974	E Goolagong (AUS) M Michel (USA)
1975	A Kiyomura (JAP) K Sawamatsu (JAP)
1976	C Evert (USA) M Navratilova (TCH)
1977	H Cawley (AUS) J C Russell (USA)
1978	G E Reid (AUS) W Turnbull (AUS)
1979	L W King (USA) M Navratilova (TCH)

Mixed doubles

1970	I Nastase (ROM) R Casals (USA)
1971	O K Davidson (AUS) L W King (USA)
1972	I Nastase (ROM) R Casals (USA)

1973	O K Davidson (AUS) L W King (USA)
1974	O K Davidson (AUS) L W King (USA)
1975	M Reissen (USA) B M Court (AUS)
1976	A D Roche (AUS) F Durr (FRA)
1977	R A J Hewitt (SAF) G R Stevens (SAF)
1978	F D McMillan (SAF) B Stove (HOL)
1979	R A J Hewitt (SAF) G R Stevens (SAF)

Rugby League

Challenge Cup winners

1970	Castleford	1975	Widnes
1971	Leigh	1976	St Helens
1972	St Helens	1977	Leeds
1973	Featherstone Rovers	1978	Leeds
1974	Warrington	1979	Widnes

World Cup winners

1970	Australia	1975	Australia
1972	Great Britain	1977	Australia

Rugby Union

International Championship winners

1970	France, Wales	1974	Ireland
1971	Wales	1975	Wales
1972	Not completed	1976	Wales
1973	England, Ireland,	1977	France
	Scotland, Wales,	1978	Wales
	France	1979	Wales

County Championship winners

1970	Staffordshire	1975	Gloucestershire
1971	Surrey	1976	Gloucestershire
1972	Gloucestershire	1977	Lancashire
1973	Lancashire	1978	North Midlands
1974	Gloucestershire	1979	Middlesex

Nobel Prize for Physics

1970	Hannes Alfvén (Sweden): magnetohydrodynamics and its applications in plasma physics. Louis Néel (France):

antiferromagnetism and ferromagnetism in solid state physics

1971 Dennis Gabor (UK): invention and development of holography

1972 John Bardeen (USA), Leon Cooper (USA), and John Robert Schrieffer (USA): theory of superconductivity

1973 Leo Eskai (Japan) and Ivar Giaver (USA): tunnelling phenomena in semiconductors and superconductors. Brian Josephson (UK): theoretical predictions in the properties of a supercurrent through a tunnel barrier

1974 Martin Ryle (UK) and Antony Hewish (UK): development of radioastronomy, particularly aperture-synthesis technique, and the discovery of pulsars

1975 Aage Bohr (Denmark), Ben Mottelson (Denmark), and James Rainwater (USA): discovery of connection between collective motion and particle motion in atomic nuclei, and development of theory of nuclear structure

1976 Burton Richter (USA) and Samuel Ting (USA): discovery of the psi meson

1977 Philip Anderson (USA), Nevill Mott (UK), and John Van Vleck (USA): electronic structure of magnetic and disordered systems

1978 Pyotr Kapitza (USSR): low-temperature physics. Arno Penzias (Germany) and Robert Wilson (USA): discovery of cosmic background radiation

1979 Sheldon Glashow (USA), Abdus Salam (Pakistan), and Steven Weinberg (USA): unified theory of weak and fundamental forces, and prediction of the existence of the weak neutral current

Nobel Prize for Physiology or Medicine

1970 Bernard Katz (UK), Ulf von Euler (Austria), and Julius Axelrod (USA): storage, release, and inactivation of neurotransmitters

1971 Earl Sutherland (USA): discovery of cyclic AMP, a chemical messenger that plays a role in the action of many hormones

1972 Gerald Edelman (USA) and Rodney Porter (UK): chemical structure of antibodies

1973 Karl von Frisch (Austria), Konrad Lorenz (Austria), and Nikolaas Tinbergen (Netherlands): animal behaviour patterns

1974	Albert Claude (USA), Christian de Duve (Belgium), and George Palade (USA): structural and functional organization of the cell
1975	David Baltimore (USA), Renato Dulbecco (USA), and Howard Temin (USA): interactions between tumour-inducing viruses and the genetic material of the cell
1976	Baruch Blumberg (USA) and Carleton Gajdusek (USA): new mechanisms for the origin and transmission of infectious diseases
1977	Roger Guillemin (USA) and Andrew Schally (USA): discovery of hormones produced by the hypothalamus region of the brain; Rosalyn Yalow (USA): radioimmunoassay techniques by which minute quantities of hormone may be detected
1978	Werner Arber (Switzerland), Daniel Nathans (USA), and Hamilton Smith (USA): discovery of restriction enzymes and their application to molecular genetics
1979	Allan Cormack (USA) and Godfrey Hounsfield (UK): development of the CAT scan

Civil wars and related battles

1970–	Cambodian Civil Wars	Communist Khmer Rouge against US-backed right wing and other groups.
1975–89	Angolan Civil Wars	Cuban-backed left and South African-backed right-wing forces.
1975–	Lebanese Civil War	Christian Phalangists, Muslim militias, Druse socialists, Syrian and Israeli interventions.
1975–	Western Sahara dispute	Partition of territory between Morocco and Mauritania rejected by Polisario separatist guerrillas.
1975–	East Timor guerrilla war	Popular resistance to Indonesian rule.
1976–92	Mozambique Civil War	Right-wing insurgence backed by South Africa.
1977–91	Ogaden secession	Somalian-backed breakaway from Ethiopia.

1977–	Sri Lanka guerrilla war	Ethnic Tamil separatist rebellion.
1978–90	Nicaraguan Civil War	US-sponsored right-wing guerrilla war to overthrow socialist government.
1979	Afghan War	Muslim guerrillas (Mujaheddin) against communist government and one another.

Some facts and figures of the decade

1970

71% of all US households contain a married couple. This will drop to 57% by 1988.

Less than 10% of the US population now live in the countryside; in 1900, only 10% lived in cities.

The infant mortality rate for the UK is 18.3 per 1,000 live births; Hungary has 35.9, the USSR 24.4, West Germany 23.6, the USA 19.8, France 15.1, Japan 13.1, the Netherlands 12.7, and Sweden 10.8.

Out of every 1,000 15–19-year-old girls in the UK, 71 have a baby.

18.7% of the UK's population is over 60 years old. 19.6% of the gross national product is spent on social security, and 5.2% of the gross domestic product is spent on education.

1971

In the UK, 75% of all household income is earned by men.

In the UK, 18% of all households consist of only one person; the trend is rising.

House prices in the UK rise by 30% this year.

There are six divorces for every 1,000 married people in England and Wales this year, and the rate is rapidly increasing.

1972

The richest 1% of Britons possess 25% of the country's wealth; the richest 10% own 51% of the wealth and earn 23.6% of all income after tax.

The Nike sports-shoe manufacturing company is founded in the USA.

The Federal Express delivery company is founded in Memphis, Tennessee; it will become a worldwide service.

1973

Unemployment in Jamaica is 22%.

Industrial output in the world's seven wealthiest countries is 180% higher than in 1950.

Public expenditure as a proportion of gross national product is 40.4% in the UK, 38.4% in West Germany, and 32.7% in the USA.

Some 269,000 people in the UK work in the coal-mining industry; 40,000 have incurable pneumoconiosis as a result.

Business sponsorship of sports and the arts in the UK comes to about £15 million, of which less than 10% is for the arts.

The abortion rate in England and Wales is 11.5 per 1,000 women aged 15–44 (in Sweden and the USA the rate is 16).

The world's energy use is derived from oil (43%), coal (25%), renewable sources (17%), natural gas (16%), and nuclear reactors (1%).

Since 1967, smoking has gone up steeply among young US girls: a 110% increase among 12-year-olds and a 75% increase among 15- year-olds.

Cigarette sales peak in the UK at more than 137 billion cigarettes sold this year.

1974

Inflation in the UK stands at 16% a year.

The price of a Mini car in the UK is now £1,000.

1975

Inflation in the UK is running at 21%.

There are 1.25 million unemployed in the UK.

The richest 1% of people in the UK own about 25% of the nation's personal wealth and earn about the same amount as is shared out between the poorest 20%.

UK government expenditure on education is 6.3% of the gross national product.

The population of the world passes 4 billion.

US multinational IBM, a leading computer manufacturer, is the world's largest company in terms of its share value.

According to the World Health Organization, 60% of people in the Third World do not have access to safe drinking water. Waterborne diseases and inadequate sanitation cause the deaths of 9–22 million children under five each year.

1976

Of all the food traded internationally, 20.2% is sold to richer countries from poorer ones, and only 11.9% from richer countries to poorer ones.

In the USA, 451 companies earn 72% of all profits.

The UK trade deficit is £1 billion. Inflation is 16.5%.

UK government expenditure as a percentage of gross domestic product is 46%; it will stay at about that level.

21% of all UK households consist of only one person, compared to 12% in 1961.

The richest 25% of UK households earn 44.4% of all income; the poorest 25% earn 0.8% of all income. The trend is towards greater inequality.

There are 108,000 police officers in England and Wales.

In England and Wales, there are ten divorces for every 1,000 married people; up from two in 1961.

50% of marriages in England are held in registry offices, a rising trend.

There are about 70,000 fax machines in the USA, and sales grow as transmission time is halved to three minutes a page.

1977

Inflation in the UK is down to 11% and falling.

92% of men and 55% of women aged 15–64 participate in the UK labour force; 71.6% of the women work in the service sector, 27.3% in industry, and 1.1% in agriculture.

12.6 million Britons are trade-union members. 144 trade unions have fewer than 500 members.

The amount of waste entering the Mediterranean Sea each year is estimated at 430 billion tonnes.

10.6 million UK households have colour television sets.

1978

The UK trade surplus is £1 billion. Inflation is at 8.3%.

The area of Brazilian Amazon rainforest that has been cut down has more than doubled since 1975, to 77,000 sq km/30,000 sq mi.

4 trillion cigarettes are sold worldwide this year, or more than $40 billion worth.

The UK government has given the tobacco industry £29.4 million in aid since 1972. The Health Education Authority has spent £2.3 million in the same period to publicize the dangers of smoking.

Since 1963, the USA has carried out a total of 399 tests in Nevada by June this year.

1979

The price of gold reaches a record $400 an ounce, up from $140 an ounce 1975.

The UK mortgage rate reaches a peak of 15%.

UK trade-union membership peaks at 13.3 million.

The unemployment rate in the Irish Republic is 7.14% and will double by 1991.

Nationalized industries in the UK account for 9% of gross domestic product and 11% of employment. (By 1993, it will have dropped to 2.5% of gross domestic product.)

Out of 635 seats in the British Parliament, only 19 are held by women.

The UK has 1.4 million unemployed, of whom 25% have not had a job for a year or more; this figure will rise to 41% by 1988.

38% of workers in the UK have earnings below the Council of Europe's 'decency threshold', and the figure is rising.

Britain's roads accommodate 14.6 million motor vehicles.

About 180 kg of plutonium has been discharged into the Irish Sea since 1968 from Sellafield, Cumbria.

There are 2,310 mishaps at the 68 nuclear power plants in the USA this year, one quarter of them due to human error.

465 ships are lost this year in collisions, a record number.

Recreational drug use by teenagers peaks in the USA, with 54.2% admitting to having taken an illegal drug in the past year.

Worldwide, about $2 billion is spent by the tobacco industry on advertising, half of it in the USA. Cigarettes have become the USA's most heavily advertised product.

The EC gives a subsidy to tobacco growers of $650 million this year.

In the USA, nearly 2 million people are employed in tobacco-related industries, which account for $57 billion of gross national product and a net balance-of-payments surplus of $2 billion.

Water consumption in the USA is 764 litres per person per day, compared with 45 litres in 1900. Industry accounts for most of the increase.

The amount of paper collected for recycling in the USA has doubled every year since 1975.

Almost half of Guatemala's tropical rainforest has been cut down since 1960; 49,000 sq km/19,000 sq mi remains.

In England, an average of 4,670 km/2,900 mi of hedgerow has been destroyed each year since 1969.

Philip Morris Incorporated acquires the Seven-Up soft-drinks company for $518 million.

Index

A REAL MAN

"I thought you cowboys took what you wanted and asked permission later," she teased him.

"Ladies aren't like strays. We can't rope 'em, wrestle 'em, and brand 'em." Finally, he smiled. "Though it might work out better if we could."

Araby laughed softly.

His expression was quick to change, and his voice took on an uncharacteristic seriousness. "Now I don't know how we cowboys measure up to those fancy dans back East, but I'll tell you this much. We don't go after something unless we really want it. . . ."

Jake untied her sash and watched her robe open over her hips and legs. The pink folds of satin parted to reveal soft ivory curves and rises beneath.

Blister-toughened hands eased inside, gently caressing her roundness. Then, becoming bolder, eager fingers began a delicious voyage into territories never before explored. . . .

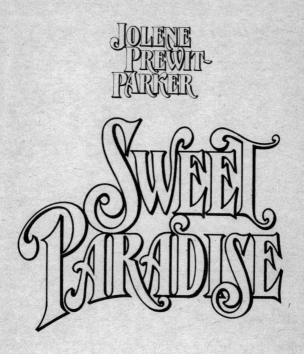

JOLENE PREWIT-PARKER

SWEET PARADISE

LEISURE BOOKS ∞ NEW YORK CITY

A LEISURE BOOK

Published by

Dorchester Publishing Co., Inc.
6 East 39th Street
New York, NY 10016

Printed in the United States of America

1

Araby Stone-Leigh sat quietly in the luxurious surroundings of the salon car, pretending to be engrossed in the latest sentimental novel. She had taken up the pose in the hope of discouraging a certain Mr. Cyril Sullivan from disturbing her. It was at the invitation of the Northern Pacific Railway executive that she was spending the last few hours of the journey in his private lounge. Much to his chagrin, however, she had deliberately assumed that the invitation extended to her friends as well, the six remaining passengers on the train.

She turned a page, just for the sake of appearance, for she hadn't a clue as to what she'd spent the last hour reading.

Her thoughts were busy elsewhere. Had she acted in haste leaving New York so suddenly? Perhaps it would have been better to wait a while before embarking on her trip west. Should she have left the city at all?

Yes! She had done the right thing! And there was no point in belaboring the issue a moment longer. Uncle Mike would have wanted her to act just as she had. *Hell fire, gal,* he would have said, *You've got to take the bull by the horn and do what has to be done!*

And just what is it that has to be done? Araby wondered sadly. What's left to do? He's gone, and nothing will bring him back.

With a heavy sigh, Araby took two letters from the back of her book and slowly unfolded the first. There was no reason to read it. She knew the contents by heart. It was from a Mr. Wallace Ford, Lawyer, of Castle Rock, Idaho. The letter was dated nearly three weeks before, May 15, 1890.

"Dear Miss Stone," it began. "It is with deepest regret that I must inform you of the death of your uncle, James Michael Stone, in a hunting accident. In accordance with the Last Will and Testament set forth by him, the ranch and all properties collectively known as Tamarack now belong to you. However, in order to claim legal ownership of said land, you must reside at Tamarack for a period no less than one month, after which the property is yours to do with as you wish, provided certain requirements are fulfilled."

Araby found herself smiling through the tears clouding her eyes. One month? Leave it to Uncle Mike to find a way of coercing her to leave New York. One month? Thirty days! It seemed a lifetime. But she'd stick it out if it killed her, not for the land, but for him. Mike undoubtedly knew she would, too.

She pulled out a second letter and debated for

a moment whether or not to open it. No, she wouldn't. Not right now. It would just make her cry. Every time she read it, she could hear Mike talking to her, telling her about the hunting trip he was planning up to Freezeout Mountain with his two stepsons and a rancher friend. What big plans he had for his annual trip to visit the family back East. He even hinted he was bringing a real cowboy with him, one that would put all her Eastern fellows to shame!

There was no doubt why Mike's legacy to her was his beloved Tamarack. He'd always sworn he'd get her to Idaho one way or another. He had known, even without her writing or telling him of her problems, that she had become disillusioned with the very existence she had strived so hard to achieve. At twenty-two, she was comfortably established as the darling of the theater world. Fans adored her, directors vied for her, and critics raved about her. So why wasn't she beside herself with happiness? Why, indeed! If only someone had told her five years ago that achieving success would be far easier than coping with it! Being talented did not necessarily guarantee peace of mind.

In fact, she couldn't remember the last time she had been truly content and at peace with herself. Mike had promised her not long ago that if she ever wanted to search deep into her soul and learn more about herself, then Tamarack was the place to do it, for there, she could truly be one with nature. And if she wanted to find a *real* man, he'd added, Idaho was the place to look.

Araby smiled at the thought. She had certainly had her fill of fancy Dans. She'd kept company with one or two gentlemen who'd almost had her convinced they were not like the rest. But it hadn't taken much time to discover that their declarations of undying love had been intended not for her, but for the character she had portrayed in her last play.

A chuckle escaped her lips. Alluring and exotic! That's how one gentleman friend had described her. That might well have been a suitable description for a dramatic heroine, but not for her. Araby Stone-Leigh might well be exotic and alluring after the make-up mistress had worked her magic with fancy powders and precious oils and creams, but without them, her cheeks were much too defined, her chin square rather than daintily round, and her mouth not shaped like a rose petal at all. Would no one ever love her just for herself? Why must they need to see someone alluring and exotic in the first place?

Perhaps Uncle Mike was right. Perhaps the only ''real'' men were out West. According to his last letter, he'd had one already picked out for her and was bringing him to New York to meet her.

''Excuse me, Miss Stone-Leigh. I do hope I'm not disturbing you,'' a man's voice interrupted.

''Oh, hello, Mr. Sullivan.''

Araby surveyed her visitor with aloof calm. It gave her great delight to address him by his surname, especially since he had implored her countless times to call him Cyril. She certainly hoped he hadn't misinterpreted her reflective smile as an invitation for him to join her.

''I do hope I'm not disturbing you, Miss Stone-Leigh,'' he said again. ''But I just couldn't resist seeking a moment of privacy with you.''

Her gaze remained cool. Did he not realize just how disturbing he was? Granted, he was a rather distinguished older man, even handsome in a rich and sophisticated sort of way. No doubt he had his pick of lady friends. There were plenty of men like him in New York. The names might be different, but they were all the same. Mr. Sullivan's manners were impecable. They were as starched and as crisp as his gray striped suit. Yet she had a feeling he was not all he seemed. There was something cold and calculating about him. Even his smile, as glossy and pearly as it was, lacked emotion.

He started to sit down beside her, but hesitated when he caught sight of her constant companion, a big fuzzy mongrel that lay stretched out across her feet. Tramp's low rumble dared him to move one inch closer to his mistress.

Masking his annoyance with a forced chuckle, Mr. Sullivan sat down in an easy chair opposite her.

"It certainly won't be much longer now," he remarked, making himself at home. "I daresay with a hot bath, a thick steak, and a soft mattress, we'll all be good as new."

"Yes, I daresay."

Perhaps he would sense her annoyance and leave her alone, but Araby doubted it.

"I believe I've told you already, Miss Stone-Leigh, I'm very familiar with Castle Rock because of my business dealings there. I would indeed be honored if you would permit me to offer my services as your guide and protector during your stay." He rolled the tip of his moustache between his thumb and forefinger, his gaze not straying far from the modest expanse of ivory flesh revealed by Araby's slightly off-the-shoulder sleeves. "Castle Rock is a far cry from the civilized world you're accustomed to," he continued. "One never knows what trying situation might be encountered there."

Araby bit her tongue. She'd love to tell him he was the only trying situation she had encountered thus far on her journey. Still, it wouldn't kill her to be polite. After all, she'd be rid of him in another few hours.

"How very kind of you to offer, Mr. Sullivan," she said, forcing a facsimile of a smile. "I shall keep that in mind . . . should the occasion arise."

With a satisfied grin, he hooked his thumbs under his arms and leaned farther back into the chair. "Day or night, my dear, I shall be at your disposal."

Araby gazed out the window at the sun-blistered plain speeding past. It was all she could do to keep from laughing. Day or night? Just what kind of a female did he take her for anyway?

Mr. Sullivan took an elegant gold cigarcase from his pocket, extracted a cigar, inhaled its aroma, obviously taking great pleasure in doing so. "You know, Miss Stone-Leigh . . . Araby . . . There's a lot of money to be made out here. I used to come to Idaho on railroad business, but now the business is mine alone. Yes, indeed, a lot of money to made here!"

Araby didn't so much as blink. She wasn't the least bit impressed.

"I trust you're staying at the Castle Rock Hotel, my dear." He struck a match to light his cigar. "One hardly expects to find such elegance as yours in such primitive surroundings."

"I've made other arrangements." Her lower lip began to twitch, just as it always did when she

12

was losing patience. From the way he leaned slightly forward in his seat, she could tell he was anticipating an explanation. But she was satisfied to keep him guessing.

"Whatever arrangements have been made for you, perhaps you might consider changing them." He drew on his cigar just the way he was studying her, long and hard. "After all there are many advantages at having a friend so close at hand. Think about it, won't you?" Smiling broadly, he reached across to give her hand a pat. Tramp's snarl cautioned him to keep his hands to himself.

"Hey, Cyril, you want a chance to win back a few of those dollars you lost last night? Blackjack? Five card draw? Your choice."

Araby breathed a sigh of relief. Thank goodness Mr. Bartell had taken it upon himself to deliver her from her predicament. The wink he shot over Sullivan's head confirmed that his interruption had not been without calculation.

"What do you say, Cyril? Feeling lucky?"

Araby's grin held. If there was one thing she had learned about Mr. Sullivan, it was that he could not turn down an invitation to gamble. There was no telling how much money he had lost already to the smooth-talking gambler from Montana. She hoped that it was his money and not Northern Pacific's that he was playing with.

Sullivan glanced in the direction of the challenge.

Araby could tell he was debating whether or not to take Bartell up on it. "Oh, please, don't let me detain you." She gave him her sweetest smile yet. "I have a feeling Lady Luck is going to smile on you."

"Her smile could be no more charming than yours, my dear."

Sullivan stood up and smoothed the front of his coat. "Please excuse me, my dear. We'll talk later. Perhaps over a quiet dinner in my hotel suite."

Her lashes swept her cheeks in feigned embarrassment. Inside, she was fuming. *Over my dead body*, she countered silently.

Araby waited until Sullivan's back was turned before mouthing her thanks to her rescuer. All things considered, Lucius Bartell was a fine gentleman in spite of his avocation. He had boarded the train the day before yesterday in Bismarck and had kept what few passengers there were still on board wonderfully entertained with card tricks and amusing, if utterly outlandish, tales of his experiences. He could very easily have passed himself off as a wealthy investor on his way to Castle Rock on business, for he was as meticulously attired as Mr. Sullivan in his fine tailored suit of small gray stripes. And he had the manners to match, though they were considerably less affected than those of the railway director. Yet, he made no secret of the fact that he was a gambler and that the purpose of his trip to Castle Rock was to relieve the miners there of proceeds from a recent gold strike. Bartell was a handsome devil as well. Those lazy blue eyes of his had undoubltedly melted many a heart. The mail-order brides on board had lavished him with attention and, Araby suspected, affection as well, and he had reciprocated by treating each of them like a grand society lady.

" 'Pears to me, Miss Araby, those gents are both stuck on you."

Smiling a gentle smile that came from the

heart, Araby looked up at the pale, blond girl who had shuffled up beside her in shoes that were several sizes too large for her feet.

'' 'Pears to me, Miss Mandy Richards, that you'd be well advised to keep your thoughts to yourself before they get you in trouble.'' Araby patted the cushion beside her. "Let's visit for a while, shall we? My book has become rather dull.''

"Just like some of the company you've been keeping, if you don't mind me saying.''

Araby glanced over to the gaming table, where Mr. Sullivan was already dabbing perspiration from his brow with his expensive silk handkerchief. "An astute observation for one so young,'' she whispered.

Mandy slid gracefully onto the plush, wine-colored cushions. Her dress looked even more tattered and frayed against the rich background, yet she wore it with simple dignity.

Araby gave the girl's bony knee an affectionate pat and watched, smiling quietly, as Mandy fussed over Tramp. She liked her young friend. Mandy was a sweet little thing, a mere wisp of a girl who was all ears and sad brown eyes. She had boarded the train in Saint Paul, half drowned from the storm and soaked to the bone. It was a wonder she hadn't caught her death. Every woman on board had taken turns nursing her through that first night. Come morning, she was fine. Little by little, Mandy's quiet apprehension had given way to girlish chatter. What a surprise they had when she announced she was going West to get married. No more being an orphan, she said. She was going to be a wife. By answering a newspaper advertisement, she had received a one-way ticket to Castle Rock, where she would find, according to the ad, "a God-fearing, hard-working Idaho man who would tend her every need."

Araby's gaze settled kindly on the girl's painfully plain features. Married? The child should be playing dolls, not having babies. She couldn't possibly be a day over thirteen, fourteen at the most. It was hard to look at her without wanting to protect her from the cruelties sure to be ahead. Even Belle and her girls, Chicago's ladies of the night turned prospective brides, couldn't resist the urge to mother her.

"Mr. Bartell tells me we'll be getting to Castle Rock along about supper time. I just can't wait, can you? You know I could hardly sleep last night for thinking about it. Could you sleep at all, Araby? I mean, what with the excitement of finally getting to Castle Rock and all?"

Legs crossed at the ankles and hands folded across her lap, Mandy did her best to copy Araby's pose.

Araby chuckled. "No, hardly at all."

Mandy peered at her through wide-opened eyes. "Say, are you really a famous actress? Mr. Sullivan said you are."

Laughing, Araby shrugged her shoulders. "A couple of people may have heard of me, providing they go to the theater, but most have no idea who Araby Stone-Leigh is and wouldn't care if they did."

Mandy curled up on the settee. "Stone Leigh. You know, I don't believe I've ever heard of anybody having two last names before."

Araby leaned down to scratch the shaggy black head nuzzling her foot. Her name frequently caused confusion. Still, it had a continental sound to it, and theatergoers loved that. "Actually, Stone is my family name. Leigh is my mother's maiden name."

Mandy smiled her approval. "I think they sound real classy together."

Araby gave her young friend's hand a squeeze. "That was the idea."

Mandy's waifish features grew very somber. "You know, Araby, you've been so nice to me, giving me that pretty red shawl of yours, taking me out to supper at that fancy cafe and giving me that money, well, I was just wondering, seeing as how you're famous and all, why'd you want to waste your time on me?" Her voice dropped into a whisper. "You're a somebody. I'm just a nobody."

Araby gave her small shoulder a gentle but firm hug. "I don't ever want to hear you talking like that again. You hear me? You are somebody! You're very special, and I think I'm very lucky to have made a friend like you."

Mandy's face lit up. Her homely features were almost pretty. "Really? No foolin'?"

"No fooling!"

"You know that money you gave me?" Mandy scooted closer, her voice lowered. "Well, I've got it tucked away in a real safe place just like you told me to do. I sewed it into my drawers. Wasn't that smart? I'm not telling nobody where it is, not even my husband—if I get one."

"What do you mean, *if*, young lady? Don't you remember what I told you about that word? Don't ever say *if*. Say *when*."

Mandy's eyes brightened. "You really think I'll find me a husband?"

17

Araby kept her smile. She hated to get her hopes up. Still, she had to do something. Mandy had had enough disappointments in her short life. "*When* you decide which one of those bachelors you want, just remember he has to have my stamp of approval first."

"I'd be such a good wife," she remarked wistfully. "And I'm not afraid to work, either. I'd work real hard to earn my keep. I may be small, but I can tote and carry as good as anybody."

"Honey, those men aren't looking for a pack mule." A hand with rings on every finger closed around Mandy's shoulders from behind. "They want a wild cat. You just remember that, and you'll get along real fine."

Araby chuckled. Belle, bless her heart, was a real diamond in the rough. She stood every bit of six feet tall and had flaming red hair with a temper to match, but underneath the tough exterior was a heart of gold. She had been delightful company ever since she boarded in Chicago, even though Mr. Sullivan had avoided Belle right from the start and had advised Araby to do the same. Traveling with Belle were her three "nieces," who like herself had mended their ways and decided to start anew in Idaho. Finding a husband was foremost on their itinerary upon arriving in Castle Rock.

Araby tried to keep a straight face while listening to Belle advising the young girl on techniques to snare a man. Finally she could stand it no longer. Poor Mandy looked as if she had swallowed her tongue.

"Now, Belle, don't you go giving Mandy the wrong idea."

"Wrong idea? Honey, that's the best advice I

can give." Belle swung her ample, pink-ruffled hips around the settee and deposited them in the chair Mr. Sullivan had occupied earlier. "If this little gal listens to me, she'll have her pick of fellows. Take it from me, honey, if you kowtow to a man, he'll run all over you. Lord knows, I've had enough of that kind in my day to be an expert."

Belle leaned forward, nearly popping the tiny pearl buttons on her blouse and all but spilling out of the ribbons and frills adorning it. "However, if you take control, all the while letting him think he's the one with the upper hand, you'll have that man right by the short . . . I mean, in the palm of your hand." She straightened back up and smoothed back a stubborn red strand that kept falling over her left eye. "Course now, to get away with it, you've got to love him up real good and let him think you'd just die without him. All the while, though, you're the one calling the shots. You know what I mean, sugar?"

"I believe I'd better think on it a little bit more." Mandy hopped up from her seat. "Right now, I need to go see if the cook has that bone he promised me for Tramp. I'll be back directly."

"You know, Belle, I don't think those Idaho men will ever be quite the same once you get into town," Araby said after Mandy's hurried departure.

Apple-plump cheeks fell down to the beauty mark painted onto her chin. "I don't care about all the men there, Araby, honey. Just one man, one very special man. Me and Mandy, we don't differ much on that account."

Araby nodded. She knew exactly what Belle meant. One very special man, a real man! Finding him had to be every woman's dream. "Don't you worry, Belle. You'll find him. I just know you will."

Belle's eyes sparked emerald fire once more. "If there ain't one for me in Idaho, then I reckon I'll just head on over to California. I hear men around San Francisco have money burning holes in their pockets." Belle gave a heavy sigh. "If worse comes to worst, I suppose me and my girls could set up shop again . . . temporarily, mind you."

The engineer sounded a series of short whistles, and the train began to slow.

Araby peered out the velvet-curtained windows. Up ahead was a wooden tank even taller than the train. "This must be the last water stop before Castle Rock." She fastened the leash onto Tramp's collar. "He knows just what those whistles mean!" She laughed when her dog jumped to his feet.

Belle fanned herself with the floppy straw hat she'd bought at the last stop. "Well, I hope they hurry. I want to look my best before I start my socializing, and that means a three-hour, hot, perfumed soak in the biggest tub I can find."

The train lunged to a sudden halt.

"You gals want to get out and stretch your legs?" Belle called out to her "nieces," who were crowded around the card-players.

"You go on, Belle," replied the redhead named Lucinda, who couldn't keep her eyes from the professional gambler.

"Guess it's just you and me." Belle reached down to give Tramp a pat. "And old faithful here."

The conductor opened the door and motioned

them back into their seats. His usually cheerful face was marred with creases and frowns. "Sorry, folks, but we seem to have ourselves a little unexpected trouble. Just stay put and nobody will get hurt."

"Trouble? What kind of trouble?" demanded Bartell.

"The less said, the better, sir. Now just keep to your seats, and we'll be on our way directly," the conductor assured them.

Araby listened to the other passengers whispering about Indians and outlaws and tried to keep her own fears under control. There was no need to worry, she told herself. The West had long been rid of the likes of Jesse James and Billy the Kid, and the sad-eyed, stooped-shouldered Indians she had seen wandering up and down the track in the Dakotas invoked pity, not fear.

Araby held tight to her purse. The barrel of her derringer poked through the beaded brocade. She had no qualms about using it should the occasion arise. Thanks to Uncle Mike, marksmanship had not been a neglected aspect of her finishing school education.

Cyril Sullivan banged his fist on the table. "Get some of the others back here!" he ordered the conductor. "I—the passengers of this train must be protected!"

Nodding, the conductor hurried out of the car, but he returned a few moments later with his hands up in the air. Standing behind him was a man whose head was covered by a flour sack. Only his eyes were visible from circles cut into the burlap. Slung low on the stranger's narrow hips was a wide belt, and the gun that should have been in the holster was in his hand.

21

"Keep calm, ladies and gents," instructed the conductor again, this time his voice quivering. "Just do as this fellow says, and everything will be fine."

"No reason for you folks to be afraid. Me and my boys, we ain't out to harm any of you. You got my word on that." The outlaw waved the conductor into a seat, then walked down the aisle, his strides long and purposeful. The jingling of his spurs was the only sound heard.

Out of the corner of her eye, Araby watched as Belle eased the rings from her fingers and slipped them down into her blouse. Odd, but she herself wasn't frightened at all. The outlaw might look threatening in his disguise, but he certainly didn't sound all that dangerous. In fact, there was something rather reassuring about his tone. She had no reason to believe he wasn't going to make good on his promise.

"If it's money you're after, mister, I can tell you right off, me and my girls here are flat broke," Belle announced, trying to make her voice sound tough. "It's taken every cent we could beg, borrow or steal to get us this much closer to our intendeds."

The intruder's eyes danced with amusement. "Your intendeds?"

Belle's girls eyed him closely. Lucinda spoke up.

"That's right," she said. "We're brides. Specially ordered, we are."

When the outlaw swept her with a long, feasting gaze, Araby realized she had just been included in the group.

"You one of those brides, too?" He walked toward her. Midway there, he hesitated and gave

22

her another long look. "Well?"

"No sir, I am most definitely not in the market for a husband!" Try as hard as she might, she could not meet his stare head-on, for fear of wilting beneath his probing gaze.

She sensed he was smiling behind the sack.

"I guess we're even, ma'am, since I'm not in the market for a wife, either." Careful to keep everyone else in his sight, he leaned over her shoulder, his cheek nearly touching hers, his breath hot on her neck. "That's not to say, though, that I wouldn't consider something a little less binding."

Suddenly, she could stand it no longer. She had to look at him. The temptation was too great to resist.

Thick black brows accented his brooding stare. His eyes arrested her, even through the mask, holding her captive. She wanted to look elsewhere, tried desperately to free herself from his penetrating gaze, but she couldn't. The longer she searched inside his eyes, the deeper she felt herself slipping under their spell. His eyes were neither blue nor green, but a strange combination of both shades. Their color was a near perfect match to the turquoise stones set deep into a wide silver wristband her uncle had given her last Christmas.

Only when Tramp rubbed against his leg did the outlaw break the spell. Keeping one eye on the passengers, the man leaned down to pat the dog. "Yours?" he asked Araby.

She nodded. He'd laugh her all the way back home if she were to tell him Tramp was the best guard dog in the Bowery. More than one male leg bore the scar of his wrath.

All at once, the outlaw straightened up and stood rigid. What hint of a smile there had been in his eyes when he was petting Tramp had disappeared. "All right, folks, off the train."

Mandy stood clutching the bone she had just brought for Tramp. Her eyes grew rounder and rounder. "You're not going to kill us, are you?"

Her question seemed to strike a soft spot in the outlaw. He shook his head slowly, his eyes nearly smiling. "No cause for you to be afraid of me, little lady. "I'm no killer. I promise you that."

The outlaw looked up suddenly, then without warning turned his crucifying glare to Bartell. "Leave it where it's at, mister. I don't have time for heroics."

Araby was confused. From the looks of it, she wasn't alone. The gambler hadn't opened his mouth. Nor had he moved a muscle. Had she only imagined the conductor quickly cutting his eyes from the outlaw to the gambler and back again a moment ago?

Bartell and the stranger locked stares. Finally, it was the gambler who looked away. Ever so slowly, he rolled up his coat sleeve, removed a tiny pistol from the holster strapped to his arm, and handed it handle-first to the outlaw.

"Thank you, sir." The outlaw emptied the bullets, then tossed it to the conductor. "Take care of this, fellow." He waved his gun at the passengers. "Everybody outside. Don't nobody else try to be a hero. In case any of you is thinking about running up front, you just remember I got my boys hid in the bush, and unlike me, they got real itchy fingers."

Araby stood up. Her lashes swept across her

cheeks every time he looked her way. It was maddening! What had happened to the spunk and spirit she prided herself on? She called to Tramp, but he refused to budge from the outlaw's side.

"Traitor," she mumbled to her dog when he was finally prodded into moving from the outlaw's side by a gentle nudge from his boot.

Belle ushered her girls out the door, then waited for Araby, who motioned her on ahead. She lingered at her seat, pretending to collect a few of her belongings, until Mr. Bartell had followed them outside.

"Hold on there, Sullivan," she heard the outlaw call out. "I believe me and you have a little unfinished business to tend to."

Araby looked up, surprised that the outlaw had called the railway official by name.

Sweat was dripping from Sullivan's red face. He patted nervously at his forehead with his handkerchief. "Unfinished business? What are you talking about? And how do you know my name?" His words were indignant, but his voice was shaky. "I demand an answer. Do you hear me?"

Araby took a few steps toward the door. Something funny was going on. Just what, she wasn't quite certain. One thing was for sure, though. This wasn't at all what she had expected a train robbery to be. Not one cent had been taken from her or her friends, and Belle had just been fooling herself to think he hadn't seen her hiding her rings.

Out of the corner of her eye, she watched as the outlaw took hold of Sullivan's arm.

"I am a director of the Northern Pacific," spouted Sullivan indignantly as he tried to wiggle out of the outlaw's grasp. "You aren't dealing with just any passenger, you understand!"

The outlaw chuckled. "For a minute there, I thought you were going to deny it."

He looked up at Araby.

Puzzled, she walked quickly out of the private salon and onto the platform leading to the next compartment. Mr. Bartell was waiting to swing her down onto the ground. Tramp followed close on her heels.

Belle hovered around her girls, fanning them with her hat and quieting their fears with words of reassurance.

There was no activity apparent at the front of the train, and as far as Araby could tell, no effort was being made to take on any water. There wasn't even a tank-keeper, as there had been at the countless other stops. Something funny was definitely going on. What, she wasn't quite sure.

Araby peered curiously into the woods bordering the track. The outlaw had said he had men hidden in the bushes. Where were they? If they were there, they were certainly well concealed, and quiet, too. The silence was deafening. They had to be there somewhere, didn't they? Surely no man in his right mind would attempt so daring a feat on his own.

Would he?

A twig snapped nearby. A cat three times the size of any she had ever seen before darted out of the shrubs, then turned up its bobbed tail and scrambled back inside the clutter of branches.

Araby's hand went immediately to Tramp's collar, but she was too late. The dog lunged out of her grasp, nearly taking her with him as he bolted after the cat. Barking as loudly as he could, he bounded into the thicket and disappeared.

"Tramp! Tramp!" She called his name over and over, but it was no use. The black, wooly mass of tangles did not return.

Araby cursed silently under her breath. One day that mongrel of hers was going to have to learn some manners. She could stand there calling his name until she was blue in the face, and he wouldn't obey, not until he was good and ready to. There was only one way to get him back—go in after him!

Dress hiked above her ankles, Araby rushed into the woods after Tramp, calling hurried explanations over her shoulder to her friends.

"Are you crazy, girl?" she heard Belle shout. "You come back here this minute!"

"I'll be fine. Don't worry. Won't take but a minute."

Araby tore quickly through the brush. Low-hanging pine branches slapped her in the face. Briars snagged her dress and prickled the tender flesh underneath the satin. Once or twice, she caught a glimpse of Tramp's shaggy form, but he was pursuing the bobcat too hotly to heed her commands.

She began to slow. Blood rushed to her head, making her dizzy. As much as she would have liked to pause for a rest, she pressed on, surprised when she didn't collapse with each exhausted step. Her feet ached. Fashionable as they were, her fancy kid shoes were no match for the sharp rocks jabbing into her soles. Her riding boots could have taken the abuse so much better. A lot of good they were doing her in the trunk!

Calling out Tramp's name over and over, she ran until there was no strength left inside her.

Still she trudged on, losing all track of time.

Tears stung her eyes. Poor Tramp! If anything happened to him, she had only herself to blame. She should have kept him on his leash. How could she have been so careless?

The wail of the train whistle brought her to a halt. Had the sound come from somewhere in the distance, or had it come from nearby? She couldn't be sure. She had heard it often enough, though, to know it signaled the train was ready to get under way.

Araby looked around her in confusion. From which direction had she come? Why hadn't she been more observant? If only she'd paid more attention to where she was going instead of blindly charging on, she wouldn't be lost now. What a mess she had gotten herself into! Thank heavens Belle and the others would alert the engineer to her disappearance. They wouldn't let the train leave without her. Once they realized she had lost her way, they'd come in after her. No need to worry, she kept telling herself.

A pitiful yelp broke the stillness of the woods.

Araby called to her dog once more.

A moment later, he came stumbling out of the bushes, fresh blood oozing from a cut on his face.

The scolding she had intended to give him was quickly forgotten. The cat's sharp claw had come within a fraction of an inch of slashing his eye.

Araby dropped down onto her knees and threw her arms around him. "Poor fellow. How could I have let this happen to you?"

Araby gulped and cautiously studied her surroundings. No doubt whatever it was that had taken a swipe at Tramp was still out there somewhere, and there was no telling how many friends it had.

She snapped Tramp's leash onto his collar—better late than never!—and stood up slowly. What about those outlaws who were supposed to be hidden away in the woods? The ones with the itchy fingers? Did they know she was there?

She gave her dog a couple of pats. "Come on, fellow. Let's get out of here."

Her pace hurried, she tried to retrace her steps back to the tracks, but everything looked the same. No pine was any different from its neighbor.

At last, the bare stretch of land beyond the thick greenery could be seen, and she headed for it.

Her heart sank. The railroad tracks were there, and the water tank, but all that was left of the train was a curl of smoke.

Araby swallowed hard. She couldn't believe what she was seeing. The train had left without her! Why hadn't they waited? Surely Belle and the others had insisted they look for her. How was she supposed to get to Castle Rock? Walk?

She threw back her shoulders with renewed determination. Yes, that was exactly what she would have to do. Castle Rock couldn't be that far away. Maybe a mile or two. Surely she could make it by nightfall. Of course, there was no telling what kind of wild animals came out at dark, no telling how many trigger-happy train robbers were lurking in the woods. No telling what . . .

"Stop it!" she shouted aloud. "Just calm down. Calm down. Everything is going to be fine. Just fine. Right, Tramp?"

Araby reached inside her purse. Her fingers curled confidently around the derringer's mother-of-pearl handle. She wasn't some helpless female afraid of her own shadow. Not Araby Stone-Leigh! Man or beast, she could deal with whatever came along!

2

A raby trudged on. Dusk was rapidly overtaking her, the sun seeming to droop lower and lower with each step she took. The amethyst and scarlet streamers that earlier had splayed across a cloudless sky of pale blue were fading slowly. Soon the hazy blush that remained would disappear, too, and darkness would envelop her. And then what? she wondered. What would she do then, if there were still no town to be found?

A cold shiver shimmered up her spine. What then? Well, when the time came, she'd just have to make out as best she could! She was going in the right direction. Of that, she was certain. After all, she had struck out behind the train's departing smoke.

Whatever had possessed those on the train to leave her out there to fend for herself? It just didn't make sense. Who had made the decision to go on without her? Finding out the answer to that was enough in itself to keep her plodding along.

Her legs felt as heavy as lead, but she couldn't give up. Somehow, she'd make it!

Araby reached down to give her dog a reassuring pat. Since Tramp's encounter with the bobcat, he had stayed close on her heels, no matter what sounds came from the bushes.

"Come on, fellow, we'll make it. Don't look so glum." Though directed at her pet, she knew her words of assurance were intended for herself as well. "And the moment we get to Castle Rock, I'm going to buy you the biggest, juciest steak I can find."

Her stomach rumbled. A big, juicy steak sounded awfully good to her. It had been a long time since noon. That greasy chicken leg she had left on her plate would sure taste good now!

The thought of food inspired her to move on, but she could not make herself go any faster than a shuffle. She was pushing herself as hard as she could. How many miles had she traveled? Four? Five? It felt like a dozen at least. Her leather high-top shoes, which were so fashionable in New York, pinched her feet unmercifully, and she could feel huge blisters festering inside the smart French heels. If she ever did reach town, it would be weeks before she walked again!

A cloud drifting low over the horizon caught the last faint rays of the sun and held them. Araby swallowed hard. Another half hour, maybe less, there would be nothing left of the day. She hoped that the Idaho moon and those million and one stars Mike had always bragged about would shed enough light to keep her from tripping over the railroad ties!

Araby listened closely to the sounds around her. Was it her imagination or was the sound of

32

howling animals coming closer? She shivered.

A few minutes later, a hazy glow flickering through the pines slowed her steps. Peering deep into the dense greenery to her right, Araby saw a thin ribbon of smoke swirling around the pines' pointed tops. She almost shouted her relief. She wasn't alone! Someone else was out there. Maybe, with any luck at all, they, too, were headed for Castle Rock.

Her enthusiasm dwindled. What if that someone turned out to be an outlaw? After all, the leader had cautioned them his friends were hidden in the bushes.

Araby gazed down the straight line formed by the railroad track. At the end, there was darkness, a darkness that would soon be coming for her. She looked back into the trees, then down the track again, debating what to do. Friend or foe, she had no choice in the matter. She had to follow the light.

Holding tight to Tramp's leash, she stepped off the tracks and cautiously made her way into the woods, taking a half dozen steps, then stopping, then starting again. Perhaps Belle had sent a search party out to find her. Of course! That had to be it!

Araby stopped short of the clearing a moment later. A lantern hung from one of the pine branches, and smouldering among a ring of rocks was the start of a fire. A spotted gray horse grazed untethered nearby. Standing in the center of the clearing, staring down at the ground with his hands stuffed in his back pockets was a cowboy. Atop his head was a high-crowned, broad-brimmed felt hat, and like all men of his trade, he wore heavy leather leggings as a protection from cactus and brush.

"I know you're out there so you might as well show your face."

Araby gulped. There had been no sound to give herself away, at least none she had heard. Even Tramp had maintained a statue-like pose similar to her own.

"Or am I going to have to come get you?"

Curses! She should have stuck to the tracks!

Araby took a step forward. A few deep breaths might well calm the rush of her nerves on opening night, but they did nothing to help now. He wasn't wearing a gun! Thank goodness for that!

Carrying her purse by its drawstrings, ready to use it for a weapon if she needed to, Araby ventured out of hiding.

"What the hell are you doing here?"

His angry outburst made her jump back. Her heart dropped. Obviously, he had not been sent to find her.

The man kicked at the ground. "Don't you know you could get yourself killed traipsing around here in the middle of the night?"

Araby drew herself up straight. Just who did he think he was talking to her like that?

"I assure you, sir, I am not traipsing around these woods merely for recreation or exercise. I am certain there are more suitable places to take an evening stroll!"

The man walked towards her with a determined stride. His gaze did not stray from her face.

Araby bit her lip to keep from saying anything. She had a feeling she had said too much already. She held tight to her dog's collar, half hoping that, given the chance, he'd pounce on the man.

34

Her hold loosened. She waited for Tramp to bark, or growl, or snarl at least, but he just sat there wagging his stub of a tail.

Araby looked up at the man approaching her. His stare forced hers to fall to the ground. She wished he would say something, anything. The waiting was almost as bad as not knowing what she was waiting for.

This is ridiculous, she thought. I am an actress, and a damned good one at that! If there ever was a time for me to put that skill to practical use, it's now!

"For your information, sir, up until several hours ago, I was sitting on the train, minding my own business, and bound for Castle Rock." With a quick, silent prayer, she slipped her hand into her purse. "It was through no fault of my own that I was forced off the train by outlaws and left out here in this God-forsaken wilderness by my own companions."

The cowboy reached down to give Tramp a pat. "Outlaws, you say? You're a mighty lucky woman to escape with your life."

When he smiled, the man was almost handsome.

His face was strong and intense and interesting. He looked eight, maybe ten years older than Araby, yet his features shouted of a wisdom not possessed by other men of his age. His cheeks were broad and hard and bore the changes of the seasons. Had he been an actor, he would have been cast to play kings, for his visage bore the dignified strength of royalty. Every detail of his appearance hinted of a fierce ruggedness, yet from the way he petted her dog, the man was not lacking in kindness. If only the fire would permit a better look into his gaze. A lot could be learned about a man from his eyes.

Araby tried not to stare, but she couldn't help herself. Never before had she met a man whose appearance intrigued her so. He was no taller than most men, yet the regal manner in which he held himself added a few extra inches. His chest looked as though it might burst right through the dark shirt restraining it. The way his muscled legs struggled against his snug trousers no doubt inspired flutters from the weaker sex. She could feel one or two herself. Now she understood why men like him prefered to be known as cowpunchers instead of cowboys. There was nothing boyish about him at all!

Her gaze drifted back up to his face. It came as no surprise that he was taking stock of her just as intently as she had been studying him. She held firm, her own stare unwavering.

She had thought herself in control of the situation, but the instant his eyes made contact with hers, searching deep into her tawny gaze, her defenses began to crumble. She'd never thought herself the kind of woman who went all jelly-kneed in the presence of a man. It had never happened before. Good heavens, she had even doubted the existence of such a male—until now.

"You can put your gun away, m'am." His voice was quiet and calming. "You won't be needing it."

Araby glanced down, surprised to discover she had unintentionally lifted the handle of the derringer out of her purse.

She wanted to speak, to explain herself, but the words would not come. How ridiculous she must look standing there with her mouth wide open! Wiping the grin, which she was certain must look silly, from her lips, Araby dropped the pistol back into her purse. She had nothing to fear from him. He intended her no harm. She could tell that the moment he spoke. His voice was firm, but gentle.

Hand held out and hoping to make amends, Araby closed the few yards separating them. "My name is Araby . . . Araby Stone." Stone-Leigh was fine for the New York stage, but it really had no place in the West.

The cowboy brushed his hands over his thighs, then took her hand and held it. His handshake was hesitant, as if he were afraid he might crush her fingers.

His smile was long and lazy. "My name's Montana, m'am. Jake Montana."

She repeated his name without saying a word. Jake Montana. Just thinking it brought a quiet smile to her lips. Jake Montana. Why, Bret Harte himself couldn't have invented a better name.

His hand, big and warm, swallowed hers whole. Hard callouses rubbed into the softness of her flesh. His roughness was not an unpleasant sensation at all. In fact, there was something rather stirring about the hands of a working man. They possessed character, real character, the kind that was achieved through sweat and toil.

Much too soon, he released his hold. Her hand felt lost and empty without his. Had he been as reluctant as she to let go? she wondered. Or was she only wishing he was?

"You shouldn't be sneaking up on somebody, m'am. Hard telling what kind of trouble you could get yourself in. You're lucky it was me and not some outlaw."

Araby smiled. She was lucky, indeed.

She took another step. The pain from inside her shoes was excruciating. She pointed to a flat-topped boulder behind him. "You wouldn't mind if I sit down for a minute or two, would you? My feet are killing me!"

He looked a bit sheepish at having forgotten his manners. "Oh, no—no, not at all. Here, let me help you."

Araby limped across the clearing. She didn't need his assistance. After all, she had gotten this far without it, but she wasn't about to tell him that. The strong hand holding on to her elbow made her feel protected and content.

She eased down onto the rock and crossed one leg over the other. Curse convention! She had to get out of those shoes!

"Here, let me." Jake knelt down in front of her and began unlacing them. She could feel strength in his hands through the leather.

He eased one shoe off, then the other.

She replied with a cry of relief. "Never again will I ever sacrifice comfort for the latest fashion!"

Without saying a word, Jake took her right foot, held it between his hands, and began massaging it with slow and easy strokes.

At that moment, fashion and comfort were the farthest thoughts from her mind. Having each curve, every rise of her foot kneaded with a lingering firmness was too much heaven to endure. Biting her lips was the only way she could keep herself from moaning in sheer ecstasy.

Strong, knowing fingers traced the shape of her ankle, then blazed a long, hot trail up her calf and back down again. Even had she wanted to object, the words would not have found their way clear of her throat. Her heart surged with each bold caress. What she was feeling was downright sinful! Her toes weren't all that was experiencing a sudden renewal of life.

"Better?"

Araby nodded. She could hardly trust herself to speak. All at once, she was aware of his looking at her in a very peculiar way. Embarrassed at the shameless pleasure she had received from his daring touch, she gracefully lifted her foot from his hold. Heaven only knew what he was thinking about her. Gracious, she didn't know what to think of herself! What kind of lady would consent to such intimate contact? Not a very well bred one, that was sure. He must think her absolutely awful! How would she ever convince him she wasn't some kind of jezebel?

Jake stood up. One foot stayed on the ground, the other rested on the rock where she was sitting. "Why don't you tell me exactly how you got here, ma'm?"

Leaning across his knee, chin in hand, Jake listened, his interest intent, as she recounted the events of the day. At the mention of Cyril Sullivan, he chuckled to himself.

"You know him?" she asked.

Jake nodded. "That I do, and believe you me, he's crookeder than any outlaw."

Mr. Sullivan a crook? The notion didn't seem all that absurd. She had pegged him right all along.

"He should have been lynched a long time ago for selling land that didn't belong to him in the first place."

She remembered how smug Sullivan had appeared when speaking of all the money that was to be made in the Idaho territory. "How did he do that?" she asked.

Jake leaned closer. Her stomach turned one somersault after another. Never had any man so affected her. She felt like a giddy schoolgirl experiencing the pangs of her first crush.

"All the railroad companies received provisional land grants from the government in exchange for extending the tracks. Northern Pacific got its share when it brought the line up here from Bismarck," Jake explained. "Now what Sullivan started doing last year was to auction off huge tracts of railroad land to the highest bidder. The only problem was that the land didn't belong to the railroad. Anyhow, he'd probably have gotten away with it if a few months back a group of homesteaders hadn't got suspicious when someone else showed up to claim land they thought was theirs. Seems like Sullivan had forgot and sold a couple of tracts twice. Anyway, the two parties involved went down to Lewiston to sort out the deed and found out neither one of them owned it. The government had already reclaimed the land and was selling it for a fraction of what Sullivan had."

"Gracious! I'm surprised he'd have the courage to show his face after pulling something like that."

Jake chuckled. "I'm sure he came out here not knowing he'd been found out. I read in the paper the other day he's having another auction on Saturday. You couldn't pay me enough money to step into his shoes. Say, did you get a good look at any of those outlaws?"

"The leader was the only one who got on the train. He said the others were standing guard in the woods.'' Araby thought long and hard. ''I really couldn't tell all that much about him. He was wearing a sack over his head.''

''How about his voice? What did he sound like?''

Araby shook her head. Back on the train she had been certain that his words, muffled as they were, would echo inside her head for a long time to come. But a few hours later, she could recall very little.

''How about his size?'' Jake edged closer. ''Was he a big man? A small man? Average?''

Those eyes. Those fascinating, mesmerizing, hypnotizing eyes. That's what she most remembered. Just like turquoise, they were. Of course, she wouldn't dare tell Mr. Montana that. He'd think her out of her mind.

''I guess he was about your height, maybe a little taller. A little heavier.'' She shook her head in frustration. ''I'm sorry; I just can't remember much about him at all.''

A soft gray fog began creeping in around her. She glanced up at the looming pines, which dwarfed them, and frowned. It didn't matter if Castle Rock were a mile away or a hundred. She'd not make it there before nightfall!

It was almost as though Jake knew what she was thinking. ''You'd be a fool to strike out for town now, seeing as how you're on foot and alone.''

His last few words gave her hope. ''Then will you take me? I'd be happy to pay you for your assistance.''

''No, m'am, I will not.'' Jake ambled on back to the fire. Tramp followed close on his heels. ''There's a thousand and one gopher holes between here and Castle Rock, and I don't aim to have my best cow-pony breaking his leg in one of them for any amount of money.''

He broke several branches under his boot and threw them into the fire.

''Oh, I see.'' Araby frowned. He certainly didn't mince any words on her account. It was obvious he had no intention of volunteering to take her to town, which left her with two choices. Either she could strike out alone in spite of his warning, or she could appeal to his chivalrous side and implore him to escort her to Castle Rock. Only a fool or someone with suicidal tendencies would head out into the darkness alone to confront whatever dangers lurked there, and she was neither. Nevertheless, while appealing to his masculine vanity might have been a viable tactic in New York, Idaho was a world apart. Men out here were different, she reminded herself. Mike had told her that. He had said no self-respecting cowpuncher would jump like a circus monkey to a woman's sweet-talking demands.

Araby sneaked a long, sweeping look at the man bent over the fire. He was no circus monkey, that was for certain. It'd take a dozen New York suitors to add up to one Jake Montana. Most likely, his only response to a woman's commands would be to lift one thick brow in amusement. She'd wager he was the one who issued the commands, and it was the women who danced attendance. Mike had been right. Cowboys made Eastern men look like mere boys in comparison.

Jake squatted at the fire, his attention not veering from the rising flames. ''What's a fancy lady from the East doing out here anyway?'' he said.

Araby sat back down on the rock. If worse came to worst, she supposed she could sit right there until sun-up. "Well, I . . .

"Say, you're not that schoolteacher Riley Saunders was bringing in for his brood of young-uns, are you? Naw, I don't reckon you are. You sure don't look like an old-maid schoolteacher to me. Every time old Riley brings in a pretty one, she up and marries some cowpoke. He swore the next one was going to be ugly as sin, and that definitely ain't you, if you don't mind me saying so."

Araby hid her smile. She didn't mind him saying so at all. What a refreshing change it was to meet a man who didn't lavish praise and flattery. His compliment was simple. She liked that. He wasn't out to impress her.

Jake walked back over to the rock and sat down a respectable distance away. "I believe you were about to tell me what brings you to Idaho." He grinned sheepishly. "Or if you'd rather, you can tell me to mind my own business."

"My uncle lives near Castle Rock." Her eyes swept the ground. "Or rather, he used to. He's dead now. I received word week before last that he was killed in some kind of a hunting accident."

"A hunting accident? Who told you that?"

"His lawyer wrote me. A man named Wallace Ford. Maybe you knew him—my uncle, I mean, Mike Stone? He owns—owned—Tamarack."

Jake reached into his shirt pocket and brought out the makings for a cigarette. For a couple of minutes, rolling it seemed the most important thing on his mind. "Yeah, I knew Mike," he said finally, his words soft and low. "Me and him went back a long ways."

Araby said nothing. She couldn't remember Mike ever talking about him, and she would surely have remembered. Jake Montana was not a name she'd be likely to forget. Then again, except for long monologues about Tamarack, Mike had never talked much about his Idaho life or his friends and family there. There was so much she had meant to ask him, so much that had been left unsaid. Now she wouldn't have the chance.

Jake struck his match on the sole of his boot and lit his cigarette. "The Cord brothers, they know you're coming?"

"Mr. Ford was the only person I wrote to. He may have told them. I don't know. Why?"

He took a long, hard drag on his smoke. "I'm not trying to meddle in your affairs, you understand, but if I were you, I'd be real watchful of Jud and Sim Cord. They're vultures, those two. The minute Mike was in the ground, they moved right in and staked their claim to Tamarack. What are you doing here now, anyway? You should have come when he was alive."

His harsh remark took her by surprise. She hadn't expected that from him.

Araby fought back the tears. There was no sense getting angry at him. He wasn't telling her anything she didn't already know. Damn! She should have come when Mike was still alive! A lot of good she would do him now.

"I'm not a vulture, Mr. Montana, if that's what you're getting at."

His hand closed around hers. "I'm sorry, Miss Stone. I didn't mean that at all. It's just that, well, I . . ." He lifted his hand quickly. "I believe

I'll have me a bite of supper. Care to join me? It's not much, but it'll get you through the night.''

''Thank you.'' Her arm was still trembling from his touch. ''That's—it's very kind of you to offer.''

Jake reached down to his saddle bag, which was resting beside the rock. He brought out a burlap sack and removed something wrapped in brown paper.

''You going to eat it or stare at it?'' he asked after handing it to her.

Araby dug into the wrapping. Inside were three huge biscuits stuffed with slabs of ham. Before she could figure out a way to slip one to Tramp without being detected, the cowboy had already thrown him one of his.

A smile tugged at her mouth. If there were the least doubt before, there was none now. She had nothing to fear from this cowboy.

They ate in silence. He made no comments, asked no questions, and whatever thoughts he had, he kept to himself. For that, she was grateful. Something about his closeness was unnerving. She didn't dare speak for fear of conveying her uneasiness in her voice. Some strange vibrations were passing between them, just as they had a moment ago when he had held her hand. Did he feel them, too? He must have. Why else would he have withdrawn his hand so quickly?

Araby tried to dismiss the questions from her mind. Perhaps she was reading too much into what was there. She concentrated instead on her supper. That wasn't hard. She had never tasted anything so delicious as the cold biscuits drenched with ham grease. French cuisine, flickering candlelight, fine china, and soft violin music could not have created a more exquisite atmosphere than the tiny campfire underneath the stars. Nor a more romantic one. Her dinner companion might only be a cowboy, but he certainly put to shame those high-browed gentlemen back home.

"So what are you doing out here in the woods, Mr. Montana?" she asked as she took her last bite.

"Just looking for strays. And the name's Jake. Seeing as how we did have supper together, I reckon we can drop the 'mister.' Agreed?"

"Agreed, but only if you call me Araby."

"Araby. That's a real pretty name. Araby."

The way his voice caressed her name when he said it made her heart skip a beat.

"Tell me, Mr.—Jake—do you work for a ranch around here?"

His hard features softened into a broad smile. "I'm from over at Cross Fork. It's just over the hill from Tamarack."

Araby returned his smile. Undoubtedly they'd meet again, and she was already looking forward to their next encounter. Perhaps by then she'd be a bit more presentable and make more of an impression—a more lasting one.

A tiny chill shivered through her, and she crossed her arms around her waist to ward off the next one. It might be as hot as Hades during the day, but from what Mike had said it could drop a good twenty degrees come sundown.

"Cold?" asked Jake.

Araby nodded. "A little."

He reached back into his saddle bag and brought out a wadded up shirt. "It ain't much, but it'll keep away the cold." He smoothed out a few of the wrinkles and held it up so she could guide her arms into the baggy sleeves.

"Thank you. Perfect fit!"

Her nose brushed against the collar. Jake's smell still lingered there. It reminded her of the woods after a heavy summer rain. There was so much comfort and security in the charcoal and evergreen scent, and the masculine feel of the rough cloth sent her insides all aquiver.

She buttoned the shirt and rolled up the sleeves to her wrist. Would she be as aware of the woodsy scent if it were Jake's arms keeping her warm instead of his shirt?

The notion all but choked her. She could hardly believe she was even thinking it.

"You planning on staying in Idaho long?"

His question jolted her back to reality. The goings-on inside her head had her all flustered. Now what had he just asked? Oh, yes, how long did she plan on staying.

"I'm supposed to stay a month."

"Supposed to?"

Araby could feel her cheeks blazing red. She didn't dare explain. He wouldn't understand her need to keep the promise she had made to Mike even though he'd never know that she had. Besides, if Jake knew the conditions of her inheritance, he'd think her only reason for coming there was to stake her claim to Tamarack. She couldn't really blame him if he did feel that way. After all, her motivation sounded suspect even to her, and she knew for a fact she was sincere.

"What I mean is that I've planned on staying a month."

"Mike told me you're an actress. Said you were the best around. He was mighty proud of you, you know."

Her eyes began to mist. "I was mighty proud of him, too."

"A month, huh?" Jake rolled himself another cigarette. "Life's a lot rougher here than in New York. Why, us cowboys have even been called uncivilized and barbaric. Reckon you can stand it out here?"

Araby laughed. Jake had sensed her lapse into depression and was doing his best to cheer her up. Uncivilized and barbaric? If only the men back East were as considerate as he was!

"Believe me, what I've seen thus far on my trip is a refreshing change from what I left behind. In some respects, New York is a lot more primitive."

Araby expelled a contented sigh. Never before had she been so much at ease with a man. Jake was so easy to talk to. He didn't give the impression at all that conversation was just a necessary prelude to whatever else he had on his mind.

"You know," she said, "I've read everything on the West that I could get my hands on—Bret Harte, Mark Twain, Erastus Beadler . . ." She didn't go on. What would a cowboy know about them?

For a moment or two, Jake made no comment. Instead, he blew smoke rings and watched as they looped one inside the other.

"I don't think *The Outcasts of Poker Flat*, or *Roughing It*, or those dime novels of Beadler's give an accurate picture of life out here."

Araby tried to hide her surprise. Somehow,

she knew she was failing miserably. "You don't?"

"Only a fool romanticizes the West. As beautiful and as challenging as it is, it's also vicious and cruel. You turn your back on it for one careless instant, and it'll kill you before you can blink." He paused long enough to take another thoughtful draw. "Believe me, I know."

"Oh." The harshness of his words stunned her, nearly as much as his familiarity with authors she had been certain must be totally unknown to him.

He could read her thoughts. "A cowboy's life is a lonely one. Sometimes the only companion I've got for days, other than cows or ole Buck here, is a good book."

Araby said nothing. It was bad enough her underestimating him. Having him know it was unbearable!

"I didn't mean to scare you," he went on. "It's just that some folks come out here expecting it to be paradise. Well, it's not, and they leave all disappointed. I just didn't want you to be one of them. That's all."

Jake hopped off the rock and went to check on his horse before she could reply.

For some reason she couldn't quite understand, she followed him and watched quietly as he stroked his horse's neck and checked the rope tethering him to a low pine branch.

They walked back to the clearing in silence. Jake offered her his hand as she stepped over a fallen log.

She took it; her heart seemed to cease its beating as he wove his fingers around hers. Her hand remained tucked inside his long after they had returned to the clearing.

They stood there, gazes focused on the fire, but neither really saw the flames.

What was the peculiar feeling overpowering her? she wondered. Whatever it was was taking full control of her senses. No hand-holding had ever incited such chaos inside her. Jake was a stranger. She'd known him only an hour, maybe less, yet it felt so much longer. She'd known some people a lifetime and never felt as close to them as she did this cowboy she knew nothing about.

His head turned.

She was powerless to keep hers from turning toward him.

The night's dark cloud prevented her from distinguishing every feature of his face, but it didn't have to be daylight to know his eyes were studying her just as intently as she was studying him. What was he thinking? Could he read her thoughts? Did he suspect she would like nothing better than to have more of him than his shirt enveloping her shoulders?

He leaned closer, so close she could have rested her head on his chest. She couldn't see his lips twitch, but she could feel them all the same. Hers trembled in response. Her mouth formed his name. Jake . . . Jake . . . But it went unsaid.

His hand tightened its hold, each finger lacing its way around hers even more possessively and with a demanding strength that stole her breath from her chest. Never had she felt so out of control.

Her head tilted back ever so slightly without her even signaling it to do so. There was no wondering why. She wanted him to kiss her—had wanted him to at least half the time she had known him, and the waiting was becoming more unbearable with each passing second. He wanted it, too. She could feel his urgency. It rivaled her own. If merely willing it to happen were enough, her wish would have already been fulfilled, and she would be drowning in his embrace.

Jake eased a half-step closer. He was only a whisper away. If her lips trembled, they would surely brush his. His breath was hot on her cheek, its potency stinging. Eyes fallen, she waited, waited for the kiss, that once-in-a-lifetime kiss she knew was about to touch her lips.

Hurry . . . hurry . . . she shouted to herself. Please, hurry. She wasn't sure how much longer she could wait. Hurry.

All at once, she was aware of her hand dropping back down to her side. It took but a moment to realize what had happened. Nothing! Her lips were left to ache, to imagine, to long for what had failed to come to pass.

Clearing his throat quietly, Jake stepped back.

Araby took two steps away. Something had happened, something that made him change his mind about taking her in his arms. But what? Had he been aware of the desire coursing through her veins like hot lava, and had that given him cause to back away? Had he found her eagerness an insult to his masculinity?

She longed to ask him, to demand an explanation, but she could not. She dared not! All that was left to do was to comply with his wishes. If he didn't want to kiss her, there was nothing in the world that could make him change his mind. Perhaps he had a wife or sweetheart waiting at Cross Fork. Perhaps he just plain didn't want to kiss her!

Araby turned away in shame. How humiliating! What on earth had come over her anyway? She was supposed to be the one who did the rejecting. How bitter to be given a dose of her own medicine! Whatever possessed her to long for the arms of a total stranger?

Could it be that Mike had been right about the Idaho air making a person do crazy things? What was the matter with her? If only she could leave for Castle Rock now! That way she wouldn't have to look Jake in the eye.

"Morning comes early around here," he said laconically, "much earlier than where you come from, I expect. We'd better get some shut-eye."

Araby whirled around, but Jake was walking away. And just where do you propose I do that? she wanted to call out after him.

A moment later, he dropped a bedroll and a blanket at her feet. Then, as if reconsidering his abrupt action, he shook them both out and spread them neatly on the ground in front of the fire.

For a moment, Araby was at a loss for words, but she really had no choice in the matter. It was better to take her chances with Jake than with the outlaws or whatever else might be lying in wait for her between there and Castle Rock. Considering what had just happened, or rather hadn't happened, there was certainly no need to worry about him forcing himself on her. But having to come face to face with him in daylight, to have him look her in the eye knowing how eagerly she had awaited his embrace, was almost enough to start her walking that minute.

Once again she cautioned herself not to let pride get the best of her. Better to be embarrassed than dead! Besides, just because sensitive feelings had been hurt was no reason, as Mike would say, to go off half-cocked.

Araby glanced down at the bedroll, then back to Jake as he added more scraggly limbs to the fire.

"It will be just fine. Thank you."

She wasn't quite sure exactly what it was she was supposed to do now. There was no ladylike way to deposit herself on the mat, at least not while he was watching her.

She leaned over the fire, pretending to warm herself and postponing what was sure to be the most awkward of maneuvers. Jake mumbled something under his breath about checking on Buck.

Araby waited until he had faded into the darkness before hiking her dress up to her knees and sitting down with a plop. Thank heavens bustles had just gone out of vogue! With one of those contraptions on, she'd have never managed!

Listening for returning footsteps, she stretched out under the cover, and when she heard them, quickly pulled the saddle blanket up above her chin. The smell, a mixture of horse and sweat, nearly gagged her, but she was determined to stiffle her cough if it killed her! Even with the roll separating her from the earth, the ground was much harder than she had expected. Rocks jabbed mercilessly in her flesh. She turned from side to side trying to get comfortable. It was useless. Come morning she'd be riddled with holes and bruises. At least she was safe and not at the mercy of some lunatic!

Jake dropped a poncho less than a yard away, then sat down beside it. "Comfortable?"

"Yes. Thank you." She tried to sound convincing, but she could hear the quaver of uncertainty in her voice. Just what was he doing so close? Surely . . . He couldn't possibly . . . no, he wasn't going to bed down only a few feet away.

He flipped his cigarette into the fire, gave a heavy yawn and a good stretch, and lay down.

Good Lord! He intended to do just that! He was going to sleep right next to her. The least he could have done was to see to it the fire was between them. A gentleman would have most definitely done so. No, a gentleman would not have, at least not the majority of the so-called gents in New York. She'd have been fighting them off long before now.

Araby held her breath. Surely he could hear the rumbling inside her chest. There was no way to quiet it, not as long as he was only an arm's length away. Jake rolled over onto his side.

" 'Night."

Only when his breathing slowed did she dare give him so much as a sidelong glance. At least he had the decency to turn his back!

Hands behind her head, cushioning it from the ground, Araby stared up into the heavens. Nights like these were few and far between in New York. The stars were like tiny diamonds upon a plush expanse of black velvet. How insignificant she felt in comparison, a tiny speck in the vastness encompassing the earth. Was that what Mike had meant when he said the West had a way of humbling a man? It didn't care if you were an actress, a banker, or a rancher—if you were going to survive, you had to make it on your own.

She smiled up into the boundless blackness

above her. No doubt Mike was looking down on her that very minute. He had gotten her to Idaho at last, and she'd stay the required month—but not to fulfill the provisions of his will. No, she'd do it strictly for him. She'd make him happy and proud of her, even if he were with her only in spirit.

Her eyes grew heavy. Sleep was coming much more easily than she had anticipated. Another few minutes and she'd be drifting into a peaceful slumber. She couldn't remember the last time she had felt so much at peace with herself and with her surroundings.

The howl of some kind of wild animal pierced the silence.

Araby hugged the bedroll tighter. Her gasp stuck in her throat, and she was determined that was where it was going to stay! She'd rather lie there scared out of her mind than have Jake Montana think her a whimpering female.

Another wail, this one even more mournful, screamed through the dense blackness. It sounded nearer than the last. Even Tramp had crawled closer to the bedroll.

She pulled the blanket over her head, clutching the corners tightly. The horsey smell didn't matter nearly as much as what was prowling around the brush. As a little girl, when she was afraid of sounds in the dark, she'd dive under the covers reasoning that if she couldn't see the bogeyman, then it couldn't see her. Somehow, such a notion was not nearly as reassuring now as it had been then.

"No reason to be afraid. Just a coyote."

Araby eased her head out of hiding. "Don't worry about me." Big round eyes stared into the night. Did coyotes attack people? she wondered. "I don't scare easily."

Was his reply a chuckle or a snore? She couldn't be sure.

One arm around her dog, she closed her eyes and held them shut tight. Where had she read that wild animals never ventured close to the fire? Maybe in one of those dime novels, the ones Jake had been so quick to criticize.

A little while later, Araby reached out to push Tramp away. Those shaggy ringlets of his were about to make her sneeze.

Her eyes came open instantly. That was no dog she was nudging! Damnation! It was Jake! What was he doing next to her? How dared he! Why, she had a good mind to . . .

She felt the cool ground underneath her. What had happened to her bedroll? Oh, no! Please don't let it be true. The bedroll was empty. She was the one who had encroached on his territory and not the other way around. What could he be thinking, with her all snuggled up to him and one arm flung around his chest? If only the ground would open up and swallow her whole that very minute!

Her breathing eased. Thank heavens, he was asleep. If only she could slip her arm out from around him without rousing him. She prayed he was a sound sleeper. If not, she was going to have a hard job convincing him of her innocence.

Eyes squinting and her chin wrinkled down to her throat, she eased her head back from his shoulder.

His snore cut off in mid-sound.

Araby froze. Her heart thumped her chest. He was going to wake up. She just knew he would.

Oh, what had she gotten herself into now? How would she ever explain what she was doing practically on top of him? Whatever the excuse he'd never believe it. She could hardly believe it herself.

He finally completed his snore after what seemed an hour's wait.

Arm free at last, Araby rolled back onto her bedroll, nearly squashing Tramp on the way, and expelled a quiet sigh of relief. Thank heavens he was a sound sleeper. She cringed at the thought of what could have happened had he been aware of her predicament. She'd have died a hundred deaths at once. He'd never believe it had been an accident. Never in a million years . . .

"How'd you sleep?"

Araby came awake with a start, then relaxed. Thank goodness it was Tramp after all who had been the recipient of her cuddles in the night. Had she really been sidled up to Jake in her sleep, or had she only dreamed it? After the kiss she had so yearned for last night never materialized, it stood to reason that she might have fantasized about it in her dreams. Wanting him to hold her was one thing, but taking matters into her own hands was something entirely different. It had to have been a dream! Yes, of course that was all it was. A dream.

She sat up and began massaging the crick in her neck. She smiled cheerfully.

"Very well, thank you, and you?"

She eyed Jake suspiciously. It must have been a dream. Otherwise he wouldn't have asked so casually about her night's sleep.

Soft shades of crimson and gold broke across the sky and filtered through the tree tops to the clearing. How tranquil the sky was! There was not a cloud in sight. Every tree, every mountain peak seemed to be paying homage to the beginning of a new day.

The aroma of fresh-brewed coffee rallied her to her feet. It was all she could do to keep from moaning in discomfort as she folded up the blanket and bedroll and placed them on the rock. There wasn't one joint in her body that didn't pain her. Everything ached! One look at her and Jake would know it, too. Oh, for a tub overflowing with hot, perfumed suds!

He handed her a bent tin cup. His eyes were cast elsewhere; his expression was as emotionless as stone. "Here, drink this. You look like you could use some."

"Thanks." She frowned into the cup of steaming black liquid. She didn't need Mr. Montana to remind her she looked a wreck! She knew that herself. But what was she supposed to do about it? She could hardly freshen up when her trunk was in Castle Rock.

Araby took a sip of the coffee. Forcing it down took every bit of will power she could summon. She'd have liked nothing better than to have spit it out onto the ground. It might be the absolute vilest coffee she'd ever tasted, but she'd smile and swallow it. She may even have a second cup. She was darned if she'd let him see she felt worse than he said she looked!

"It may be a little too strong for your liking."

She forced another swig. "Oh, no, not at all." She nearly chocked on her words—or the coffee? "It's just the way I like it." There! She'd show him she wasn't some city-slicking greenhorn!

Whistling for Tramp to join her, she

wandered over to the flat-topped boulder and sat down. There was no question about it. Jake was deliberately ignoring her. Why? She'd tried her best to be pleasant, even after he had turned away from her, and that was a lot more than could be said about him! She could deal with rejection— but it would be a lot easier if she knew what had caused it.

No, it was best that things had worked out the way they had. One kiss would have led to another, then another, and there was no telling how awkward and complicated it would all have become.

She combed her fingers through her tangled curls. What a sight she must be. If she weren't so tired and sore, she might have laughed.

She started to take a mirror from her purse, then decided against it. There'd be plenty of time later for fussing and primping. Maybe if Jake saw her at her best, he'd kick himself for not kissing her. She hoped so! She could almost kick him herself!

Damn him! He hadn't looked her way once this morning. He was probably counting the minutes until he'd be rid of her. Well, she'd show him. The minute she finished her coffee, miserable tasting though it might be, she'd get right out of his way.

Pretending to be interested in everything surrounding her except him, Araby watched from the corner of her eye as he led his big spotted gray into the middle of the clearing, where he saddled him.

She tried desperately not to be so affected by his presence, but the stirrings inside her made it impossible to deny what she was feeling. With the sunlight playing atop his head, his hair was even thicker and shinier. His features were wild and rugged, just like the land, and something about him was drawing her closer and closer. Last night, the force of his thigh and the power contained in the narrowness of his hips were distinct, but now they were downright blatant! Tonight, those commanding details would return to haunt her sleep—if she could sleep at all for thinking about him.

"You 'bout ready? It's high time we were breaking camp." Jake cinched the girth tighter. "It's nearly six o'clock."

Araby kept her groan to herself. Six! Why, she couldn't remember the last time she'd been out of bed before ten.

"Gracious me, the day's half gone," she couldn't resist remarking. Curse him! The least he could do was look at her when he was addressing her.

Jake attached the bedroll and a pair of saddle bags to the saddle. "Won't be much out of my way to swing on by town."

She was tempted to tell him not to bother, just to head her in the right direction and she'd find her own way to Castle Rock. But she held her tongue. Maybe taking her to town was his way of trying to make amends. Who could figure out cowboys anyway?

"Thank you, Jake. That's kind of you to offer."

He replied with a shrug of his broad shoulders.

Had she imagined it, or had the gruffness vanished from his voice? Why should his acting like a bear upset her so?

Her back turned to him so that he would not see her wince, Araby gently guided her shoes onto her feet and laced the ties as loosely as she could. She took one step, then another. It hurt, but the pain wasn't unbearable. Besides, if she put her mind to it, she could tolerate anything, even a moody cowpuncher.

Jake stomped out what few hot embers remained of the fire, then gave a curt nod in her direction.

She took that to mean they were leaving.

"Come on, Tramp."

She walked across the clearing, her dog close on her heels. Before she knew what had happened, Jake had picked her up and and swung her onto the saddle. The pressure from his hand squeezing her waist robbed her of all strength. She hadn't even the energy to question his action.

"I don't mind walking," she finally managed, not wanting to seem weak in front of him.

"You might not, but your feet will."

Jake took hold of the reins and walked on ahead, leading his horse. "You don't have to worry about old Buck. He doesn't have a mean bone in him. Do you, fellow?"

The horse nuzzled Jake's chest in reply.

Araby grinned to herself. What would Mr. Jake Montana say if she were to tell him she'd take a spirited mount over a placid one any day? Soon, she'd just have to show him!

The sun was already shining with a vengeance by the time the woods were behind them and a long, narrow and dusty trail stretched out in front for as far as the eye could see.

Gaze not wavering from the trail, Jake explained that the way they were going to Castle

Rock was a little farther but the terrain a lot easier to cross.

Her questions were answered with long, detailed explanations, but nothing could make him look up at her. After a while, she stopped worrying about it. No matter where he cast his eyes, just being with him was very pleasant. Nor did she mind the long gaps when neither of them offered a word. A lot could be said in silence, and she could sense his thoughts were of her, just as hers were of him.

Sitting tall and proud in the saddle, Araby took in her surroundings. Up until now, the word Idaho had just been the name of a territory somewhere in the far-away West. Suddenly, it had become very real, very awe-inspiring.

The land held a wild, rugged beauty that could be claimed by no other place she had ever visited. The Dakotas and Montana were lonely and bleak in comparison, with their windswept plains and charred forests. But Idaho was different. It was fascinating. So vibrant! So full of life! How had Mike described it? Oh, yes—"the most grand, the most wonderful, the most romantic, and the most mysterious part of the domain enclosed within the nation." He hadn't been exaggerating after all.

Everything around her was so green, so crisp—and oh, so beautiful! The air smelled of grass and pine. Mountains higher than clouds surrounded the valley, protecting it like a fort from intruders. No wonder the land had been named 'Ee-dah-how' by the Shoshone. It truly was the 'gem of the mountain.'

The body of water to the east of the ridge had to be Lake Coeur d'Alene. Mike's description could fit no other place. Surrounded by a forest of heaven-high pines, the lake really did look like a sapphire set amid a circle of emeralds.

Without warning, Jake stopped dead in his tracks.

"What's wrong?" asked Araby.

He motioned for silence.

Buck lifted his head, nostrils flaring and ears standing at attention.

Even Tramp was alert.

"Listen," Jake whispered.

At first, Araby heard nothing. Then the faint roll of thunder drummed across the valley.

She started to tell Jake she had heard it, too, and to ask him what it was, but one glance at him and she knew he wouldn't hear a word she was saying. He was hardly breathing. His look was dazed.

Finally, he looked up at her. "Wild horses. They must be over on Harrison flats about now. Won't be long." He was grinning from ear to ear like a child on Christmas morning.

His smile was contagious. "What wild horses? What won't be long?" Her eyes finally latched on to his and held them tight.

The wild horses were quickly forgotten. Now she knew why he had avoided looking her in the eye. She couldn't believe what she was seeing, but the proof was right there in front of her.

If she were to hold her bracelet up to his face, the blue-green stones would be an almost perfect match to the turquoise of his eyes!

3

Jake's fascination with the wild horses was temporarily forgotten, and his excitement turned to puzzlement as he eyed Araby suspiciously. "Something wrong?"

Araby was quick to collect herself and mask her thoughts with a flutter of her lace handkerchief across her forehead. "I'm just a little warm. That's all."

"Hate to tell you this, m'am, but come noon it's going to be a lot hotter than this."

Araby fanned herself harder. Right now the sun's blaze, miserable as it was, was the least of her worries. The heat she could cope with. The identity of her traveling companion was another worry entirely.

Jake Montana couldn't be the outlaw, could he? No, of course not. He was a cowpoke. Or so he said. Surely it was just a coincidence that both men had eyes the color of turquoise!

She chanced another hurried look at his face.

There was no mistake about it! Those were definitely the eyes of the train robber. That cowpoke and the bandit were one and the same. She'd stake her life on it.

Araby swallowed hard. She certainly hoped she didn't have to!

"Are you all right?" Jake asked. "You're not going to faint, are you?"

She couldn't force herself to meet his gaze for fear of giving herself away. "I'm fine. Just fine," she quickly assured him. "You were right. It's the sun. I suppose it will take some getting used to after all."

"That it will."

Araby gave him another smile. Whatever she did, she mustn't let on that she knew—not as long as she didn't know how he'd react if he figured out she knew who he really was!

"The first thing you ought to buy yourself when you get to Castle Rock is a sunbonnet." His back to her, Jake led Buck on. "You'd better keep your face covered, or the sun will make you an old woman in no time. And you'll be needing some sensible shoes, too." Jake walked on at a quickened pace. "And some dresses other than fancy party frocks. You might look real stylish where you come from, but out here, folks dress for the weather. Why, they'd think you're crazy as a bat stepping out in some get-up like what you got on."

Araby held her tongue. What that cowboy needed was a lesson or two in how to talk to a lady. Granted, her traveling suit might not be all that appropriate for the wilds of Idaho, but had its impracticality been all Jake had noticed? She had turned many heads wearing that "get-up."

Obviously he was not a man who was easily impressed.

"Any more suggestions?" she couldn't resist asking.

"That about does it. If I think of anything else, though, I'll tell you."

"Yes, I'm sure you will."

She regretted her curt remark the moment it was out and would gladly have retracted it had the damage not already been done. The way his shoulders tensed and his head shot up made it perfectly clear that he had not only been offended but insulted as well.

Curses! Such glibness might not raise an eyebrow in New York, but it definitely did not belong out in the wilds of Idaho. Uncle Mike had told her cowboys were a breed of men like no other. Obviously outlaws were cut from the same mold.

Jake walked on. Anything else he had to say was directed at his horse.

When they stopped beside a creek to fill the canteen, Araby decided it was time to make amends. After all, outlaw or not, he had shown nothing but kindness to her.

"Tell me about the wild horses," she asked.

Jake knelt by the stream and threw some water onto his face. Araby cooled down the same way and replied to his disapproving glances with a smile.

"Not much to tell. Every summer all the wild horses come down from the mountain." His voice took on an uncharacteristic softness. "The herd's led by a big stallion that's as black as the devil's soul. Many a man has tried to capture that animal and failed. He's outsmarted them all."

Araby listened, mesmerized as much by his voice as by his story, as he told her of the mighty stallion. From his vivid description, it was easy to imagine the spirited, fighting leader with his glossy coat and rippling muscles standing alert and proud, then at the first sign of danger bunching all his mares together and thundering away with manes and tails flying in the wind.

"Foks say he's more demon than animal. They say he breathes fire and comes straight from hell." Jake laughed. "Course you can't blame the old boy for being mean, not when every cowboy in the territory is out to get a rope around him."

"You want him, too, don't you, Jake?"

"I'm a patient man. I can wait as long as need be."

Once again, she found herself wondering if there was some hidden meaning to what he said, and once again she had to caution herself not to try second-guessing him.

Hurriedly, Jake shifted his stare from the wet ringlets curling across her forehead to the direction they were heading.

"You 'bout ready to get going? Town's just beyond that last stand of ponderosa."

Araby nodded. Was she just imagining it, perhaps trying to will it to happen, or had he almost lifted his hand to brush the damp ringlets from her cheeks? No! Thoughts like that were dangerous, too dangerous.

She called to her dog. "Come on, Tramp. Let's go, fellow."

Jake helped her back up into the saddle. The hands spanning her waist were firm and sure. There would be time later for him to discover that Uncle Mike had taught her to be a superb horsewoman. For the time being, she would enjoy his assistance.

To her surprise, he swung up in front of her. "You don't mind, do you?"

It was all she could do to keep her heart from pounding right out of her chest.

"Mind? Goodness no. If anyone should be walking, it should be I."

He took her arms and wrapped them around his waist. "You just hang on tight."

Araby smiled into his broad shoulders. She certainly didn't have to be told twice!

When the scattered buildings that made up the town of Castle Rock appeared just ahead, Araby found herself wishing it was all a mirage, an illusion perhaps brought on by the blazing sun. But she knew it was not.

Jake slowed Buck's trot. "Didn't mean to scare you."

Araby was about to tell him that he hadn't scared her at all. In fact, she couldn't remember enjoying a ride more. Galloping through the tall grass with her hair streaming out behind her and the breeze fanning her cheeks, she had felt as free as the wind. What on earth had ever given him the impression that she was afraid?

Just then, the tingling sensations shooting through her arms made her realize exactly what it was that gave him that idea. Her arms weren't just wrapped around his waist. They were locked around it! No wonder he had thought she was frightened out of her wits and holding on for dear life. A clinging vine couldn't have attached itself any more firmly!

"Seeing as how you'll be out here a while, you might as well learn which end of the horse is which," Jake said when she had untangled herself. "I could help you some if you like. It's only a hop, skip and jump out to Tamarack from where I am. I could come by now and then if you don't have any objection."

"Why, thank you, Jake. I'd certainly appreciate that."

Araby swallowed hard. She'd never been the kind of woman who pretended to be something she wasn't just to catch a man's interest. In fact, women like that made her furious. Still, she had a feeling that if she told Jake she could ride better than most men, she'd scare him off. It really shouldn't matter at all what he thought of her, but it did.

"Yes, m'am. We'll find you a nice, gentle little mare, and you'll be right at home in the saddle in no time."

Araby returned his smile. She'd just have to put her acting skills to work and convince him that she was a fast learner.

Castle Rock was just as Mike had described— a dirt-road Main Street lined on both sides with pine buildings. The town had sprung up quickly, an oasis in the wilderness for miners, lumbermen and cattlemen anxious for a taste of civilization in an untamed land. New York it wasn't, but there was still something very appealing about its lack of fancy airs. Mike had loved it there. Araby was sure she would, too.

They rode into town slowly. Araby was conscious of the curious stares and whispers directed at them. Jake tipped his hat to those who called out to him while he pointed out the sights along the way to her.

Araby felt quite at home in Castle Rock. The

names of the storefronts and the services they offered were not at all unfamiliar—Pernod Hardware, Linstrum Butcher Shop, Grimestead Shoe and Harness, Widow Morgan's Cafe, Billy Bob's Saloon, Fisher's General Store.

She had heard a lot about Fisher's. It sold everything from hairbows to rifles, foodstuff to mining gear. If old Gus didn't have what a customer wanted, he'd get it, and if he couldn't get it, it wasn't to be bought anywhere. Or so Mike had said.

Even without going inside, she knew that in the center of the store stood a huge iron stove, the square box type, with a door at one end for shoveling in wood. Scattered around it were a dozen or so straight-back chairs, where the men folk gathered to talk business and swap tall tales. The signal that it was time for them to go home so Gus could close up shop was the appearance of the broom and dustpan on the counter top.

"And down at the end of the street is the Ruby Rose."

Araby didn't have to ask why the rambling clapboard house with its big front porch and massive stone columns was separated from the rest of the buildings by a respectable distance.

"Don't guess Mike ever mentioned much about Ruby's place."

Araby could all but hear him smile. "Oh, quite the contrary. I've heard enough stories about Ruby's to fill a book."

Jake's surprised "Oh" goaded her on.

"A little bit of heaven on earth. I believe that was how Mike described it. Why, I'm as anxious to meet Ruby as I am to see Tamarack."

"You'll get your chance," Jake told her as he

71

spurred Buck in that direction. "The Ruby Rose is the closest thing to a hotel we got. Chances are your trunks were taken there."

"Do you know where I might find Wallace Ford? I wired him I was coming, and I'd like to let him know I'm here."

"You won't find him in Castle Rock," Jake told her. "At least, not for another week or so. He's over at Clewiston doing some politicking. From what I hear, the territory of Idaho is about to become a state."

Jake halted in front of the Ruby Rose. "Reckon this is where me and you part company, m'am." He swung out of the saddle and helped her down. "A funny little fellow named Hamstring will be coming in from Tamarack tomorrow for supplies. Just tell him who you are, and he'll take you back out with him."

Araby was grateful her skills as an actress helped her hide her disappointment. It'd be no bother, she was certain. After all, he himself had said Tamarack was only a hop, skip and jump away from where he lived.

"Well, thanks for your trouble, Jake."

"Shucks. Wasn't no trouble at all, m'am." Jake gave Tramp another hearty pat. "You watch out for those bobcats, fellow." He hopped back on his horse. "Maybe later, if I can find the time . . . I mean seeing as how . . .

"Yes?"

He jerked up the reins. "I'd better be getting back to rounding up those strays before some rustler finds them."

Araby forced her smile to stay put. Whatever it was he had been about to say he had apparently decided to keep to himself. Could he have been about to suggest that they meet that evening? She supposed she never would know for sure.

"Thanks again."

Jake gave a nod, then turned the horse around and headed back through town.

From the porch of the Ruby Rose, she watched as Jake rode away from her. Outlaw or not, she'd never met a man like him. Her stuck-up lady friends back East would never approve of him, but one look into those big, lusty eyes of his, and they'd be dropping like flies all up and down Fifth Avenue.

Jake stopped to talk to some man, and Araby squinted into the sun to see who. How odd. It was the conductor from the train. From the way they were laughing and slapping each other on the back, one would have thought they were old friends. Maybe they were. If it had been Jake who robbed the train, and she was dead certain it was, then the conductor had undoubtedly been in on it, too. Come to think of it, that conductor had been extremely calm in the face of such danger.

Oh well, whether Jake was a bandit, a cowboy, or both, there was no denying that he was one very intriguing character. Not even the most talented of playwrights could create a hero like him!

Araby smoothed back her hair, brushed the dust from her skirt as best she could, then turned the ivory knob on the carved oak door. Mike's description and outlandish tales about the Ruby Rose seemed tame beside the opulence that greeted her when she stepped inside the plush foyer.

An elaborate crystal chandelier hung from a ceiling decorated with paintings of naked cupids and rosy nymphs frolicking amid intertwining vines and flowers. A grand staircase with a gilded balustrade curved gracefully up to the second floor. Fancy little cages filled with brightly plumed birds hung from limbs of exotic trees that were growing in huge Mexican urns. A long brass bar with pictures of galloping horses etched into it stretched along one wall. Hanging behind the bar was a portrait of a platinum-haired beauty from an era gone by. Red velvet settees and chaises were scattered throughout the salon. Inconspiciously placed among them were gaming tables with big, comfortable wing-back chairs.

Araby saw Mr. Bartell already settled in at one of the tables and cheerfully dealing cards to a nervous-looking cowboy who kept looking over his shoulder. Mr. Sullivan had made himself at home in one of the plump, cushioned sofas with stacks of papers spread out around him.

Belle came running across the room, arms spread wide and pink boa flapping behind her.

"Araby! Araby! Thank God you're alive! I've been worried sick about you. I just knew you were lying out there somewhere, dead."

The big redhead held on tight and wouldn't let go.

"Those outlaws, they didn't . . . they didn't harm you, did they?"

It took Araby a moment to catch her breath after Belle's bear-hug greeting.

"There's not a thing wrong with me that a good, hot soak won't cure," she assured her friend.

Belle was near tears. "I have been so worried about you! Truly I have. I told that idiot Sullivan not to leave you stranded out there in that God-forsaken wilderness, but do you think he'd listen to me? Not on your life. All he cared about was getting into town so he could send the Sheriff after his precious money."

Araby took her friend by the arm and led her to one of the settees. The former madame's concern for her well-being really was very touching.

"Now, Belle, just calm down. I am fine. I promise you."

"But last night . . . all alone in the dark. How did you manage?"

Beginning with Tramp's encounter with the bobcat, Araby recounted the day's events, describing in great detail the cowboy whose campfire she had shared. There was no need to reveal her suspicion that the cowboy who befriended her and the train robber were one and the same.

"Jake Montana! That's some name. Sounds like some cowboy." Belle repeated his name again. "Sounds like just the kind of fellow I'm looking to meet up with. Handsome?"

Araby felt her cheeks crimson.

Belle slapped her on the knee. "I knew it. I knew it. You don't have to go looking for a man. They come looking for you."

"Shhh. Not so loud."

"Well, where is this cowboy of yours?" Belle whispered. When do I get to meet him? You think he's got a friend? An older friend, maybe? One that's looking for a good-hearted girl?"

"Whoa! One question at a time." Araby giggled along with her friend. "He's gone back out to gather stray cows. He may be back in town tonight, and I don't know if he's got a slightly older friend, but I'll be happy to find out."

Belle made a sour face.

Araby turned around to see why. Too late. Mr. Sullivan had already come up from behind and kissed her cheek.

"Araby, my dear, I am so happy you are all right. I can't tell you how worried I've been."

Araby moved closer to Belle.

"Why, I thought you were on the train," Mr. Sullivan said, smiling. "I had no idea you had wandered off. Otherwise I never would have insisted we go on ahead."

"Liar," whispered Belle, gritting her teeth.

Mr. Sullivan reached for Araby's hand, but a snarl from Tramp made him back away.

"Sheriff Otter is out looking for you at this very minute," he told her. "I'd have gone along, too, but he was adamant that I stay here. So many reports to complete for the railroad. You understand, don't you?"

"I understand perfectly well, Mr. Sullivan." Araby's smile was anything but friendly. Mr. Sullivan quickly excused himself.

"I guess you put that pompous ass in his place," Belle said. "As long as somebody had to be robbed, I sure am glad it was him."

Araby was curious. "What happened?"

"Oh, that's right. You don't know, do you?" Belle fanned herself with the end of the boa. "Why, the robber made him open his lock-box and count out ten thousand dollars and not one penny more. Why, Lucius said there was a couple of hundred lying on the poker table, and he didn't even touch that. And I hear that there was a whole lot more than ten thousand dollars in the train's safe, and the robber didn't blink twice at that. Pretty strange way for a robber to behave, don't you think?"

Araby nodded. "It sounds as if the robber knew exactly who he wanted to rob before he boarded the train."

"Couldn't happen to a nicer fellow," Belle snarled in Sullivan's direction. "Turnabout's fair play. Isn't that what they say?" She held out her hands and admired her collection of rings. "Ruby—she's the lady that owns this place—told me there's a lot of folks around here who'd love to put a bullet in Sullivan. Seems like he took some people around here real good by selling them land that wasn't his to sell, then when they found out they didn't own the land, Sullivan there refused to give them their money back. He got away with about ten thousand dollars. I don't know why he'd ever show his face around these parts again, do you?"

Araby shook her head. Belle's information matched what Jake had told her already. Mr. Sullivan had indeed been singled out. Surely it was no coincidence the amount of money taken from him was the exact same sum he had swindled from the townspeople. Served him right! Araby had a feeling that those people he had swindled would soon be reimbursed. Jake was no ordinary robber. He was the Robin Hood of the West. Legends would undoubtedly spring up about him.

"There you go gazing off into space again." Belle fluttered her boa in Araby's face. "Why, if I didn't know better, I'd think you were dreaming about that cowboy of yours." Her high-pitched giggles brought her closer. "Tell you what, honey. You can have that cowboy. Just let me at that train robber. Did you see those eyes? My, my!"

Araby smiled. My, my! She couldn't have

described them better herself!

Araby watched as, a moment later, a tall, stately older woman glided down the stairs.

"That's Ruby," Belle informed her. "Nicest lady you'd ever want to meet." She stood up and waved. "I sure wish I'd met up with her twenty years ago. Now, she knows how to run a place like this with style. Ruby, come over here. There's somebody I want you to meet."

Head held high, the owner of the Ruby Rose made her way toward them with slow, dignified steps. Somehow the woman in the simple grey skirt and high-necked blouse wasn't quite what Araby had envisioned from Mike's stories. True, Ruby was indeed striking with that thick mass of platinum curls, but for some reason, she had expected someone with much more flair and much less distinction. She certainly had not expected some grand dame of society, which was exactly what Ruby reminded her of. Why, in New York, Ruby might easily be mistaken for a refined lady who moved in all the better circles.

Araby stood up. She'd been looking forward to this for a long time. Ruby was—had been—very special to Mike. She always wondered why Mike hadn't married her instead of the woman he did.

Ruby interupted Belle's introduction. "You don't have to tell me who this is. I'd know Mike Stone's niece anywhere." Her somber expression softened. "Araby, dear—at last. I have been looking forward to this for a very long time. I only wish the circumstances could be different."

Araby smiled. She was certain she had detected a bit of an English accent. Hadn't Mike said something a long time ago about her being a countess or a duchess or some member of English nobility? Yes, she believed he had.

"My uncle spoke often of you, and with such great affection that I feel as if I know you, Mrs. . . .

"Just call me Ruby, dear. Do sit down. Let's chat a while, shall we?"

"You wouldn't believe what she's been through, Ruby," said Belle when they were seated. "Why, if it wasn't for some cowboy named Jake Montana, Lord only knows what might have happened to our little Araby."

Araby was certain she had caught a glimmer in Ruby's eyes at the mention of Jake Montana.

"Really, Belle, believe it or not, I can take care of myself." She leaned down to pat her dog. "And you forget how protective Tramp is. He doesn't let anybody male within ten feet of me."

"I'm afraid Belle had cause for alarm, dear," Ruby told her. "After all, there is a reason Easterners refer to our part of the nation as the Wild West."

Belle stood up and straighted her boa. "If you ladies will excuse me, I believe I'll run along upstairs and freshen up so I'll be ready for those ranchers and miners and lumbermen you were telling me about, Ruby. Araby, darling, see you later. Ta-ta, ladies."

Ruby took Araby by the hand. "Your uncle was so proud of you, dear. Why, from the time you were knee-high, it was always Araby this and Araby that and did I tell you that Araby can do such and such better than anyone else. Oh, my dear, he adored you. Why, he couldn't have loved you any more had you been his own daughter. Mike was a wonderful man. He will most assuredly be missed by all of us." Ruby blinked quickly, then glanced away. "Senseless cuss," she said softly. "I told him not to go on that cursed hunting trip with the Cords, but no, he wouldn't listen to me."

For a moment, it seemed that the ever-so-composed features were about to crumble.

Araby reached for her hand. The ivory flesh was satin smooth.

A quick sniff, and Ruby was calmed. "At least we have our memories." She smiled at Araby for the longest time. "I truly am pleased to meet you at last. Mike spoke so often of his family back East. Why, he lived for the summers when he could make the trip home."

Araby squeezed Ruby's hand. "You were part of that family, Ruby. Mike never wrote unless he said something about you."

"I was a friend, my dear. A very close and loving friend. I could never have been more no matter how hard we both pretended otherwise."

This time Ruby made no effort to blink back the tears. "Oh, dear, I promised myself that there'd be none of this sentimental nonsense, and now look at me."

Araby was at a loss for words. She knew exactly what Ruby had meant by never being more to Mike than a very close friend. But she was certain it had been Ruby and not Uncle Mike who placed the restrictions on their relationship. Mike loved Ruby. He made no secret about it. Her past wasn't the least bit important to him. How sad it was that he was never able to convince her of that.

Ruby made another effort to compose herself. "You know, Araby dear, sitting here with you makes me feel very old. It's almost as though I've watched you grow up through Mike's eyes. Why, it seems like only yesterday he was telling me about taking you for pony rides in the park." She brushed back the hair around Araby's cheeks and studied her every feature. "Who would ever have thought that little girl with braids and skinned knees would grow up to be so beautiful, and so famous?"

Ruby gave her knee another pat then stood up. "We truly do have so much to talk about, my dear, but all in good time. Right now, you look as if you could use a rest."

She motioned to the black man behind the bar. "Felix, go upstairs and ask Gloria to fix up the room next to mine. And take up Miss Stone-Leigh's trunks, please. I believe they were left out back."

Once again, she touched Araby's cheek, her fingers lightly lingering on her face. "Why don't you stop by my apartment for tea at four. We'll talk more then."

"I'd like that, Ruby. Very much."

Araby watched her walk gracefully away. Poor Ruby. How sad it must be to have loved a man for all those years and never to have married him.

Mr. Bartell laid his cards down on the table just then and made his way across the room to meet her.

"You don't know how relieved I was when you walked in," he told Araby. "That damned Sullivan told me you were on the train, and I didn't know he'd left you behind until we got here. Glad to see you're all right." Harsh lines furrowed his forehead. "I heard some cowboy brought you in. He didn't do anything to harm

81

you, did he?''

''Oh, no. No. He was a gentleman.''

She could tell Lucius wanted to give her a hug, but he kept his arms at his sides.

''So how's business?'' she asked him. ''Is it as good as you heard it was?''

''Better.'' He leaned closer. ''Never have seen so many men so anxious to get rid of their money. Why, their month's wages is just burning holes in their pockets. They got to spend it, even if it means losing to some slick card-dealer like me.''

''Better you than somebody else, right?''

Lucius motioned for Felix to bring him a drink. ''I sure wish I knew who that train robber was. I'd like to shake his hand. I really appreciate him leaving all that payroll money in the safe so I could get my chance at it. Hey, me and Belle are going out tonight to celebrate. You wouldn't want to come with us, would you?''

Her smile was genuine. She really liked the gambler, but only as a friend. She had a feeling he could be a real heart-breaker.

''Why, Lucius, I'd be disappointed if you didn't ask me.''

He kissed her hand, then gave a low bow. ''You have just made me one very happy man, my dear. As a matter of fact, if I weren't too old to change my ways, a gal like you could make me think twice about this gambling life.''

''What? And disappoint all these cowpokes? Why, they'd never forgive me if I took you away from it. Where else would they find someone as fascinating as you to give their money to?'' Araby did her best to make light of the remark, even though she suspected he was dead serious.

''Good point,'' he agreed. ''Now if you will

excuse me, my dear, I believe I have another visitor at my table. Until tonight, Miss Stone-Leigh.''

"Until tonight, Mr. Bartell.''

Araby kicked off her shoes and fell across the patchwork bedspread the moment she got to her room. Giggles and hushed whispers roused her from her nap some time later. Too tired to lift her head, she opened one eye and saw two of the girls who had been lounging in the salon earlier pouring pitchers of water into a big wooden tub that had somehow appeared in her room while she was napping.

She was about to ask them to be a little quieter when she realized they were talking about her.

"She don't look much like an actress to me,'' remarked the one with long blond curls. "Maybe she looks better when she's made up and gets her hair done.''

"Not so loud, Lilly. You'll wake her up.''

"No wonder she's so tired. I mean, how would you feel after spending the night with Jake Montana. Lucky her!''

"Shhh. You better not let Belle hear you talk like that about Mike Stone's niece. She'd kick your fanny out of here so fast you wouldn't know what hit you.''

Lilly slumped against the wardrobe and watched her friend do all the work. "Wouldn't matter none with me. I've been thinking about leaving anyway. But if you dare say a word about it, Mae, I'll call you a liar.''

"Now, honey, don't you be getting your hopes up, you hear me? Just because Clay Tillis wants you to save it all for him and not let nobody else come around doesn't mean he wants to marry you."

"Maybe not, but when I get through with him he'll be begging me to go to the preacher."

Mae gave her friend a sad look.

"Say, you think Montana will come back tonight? What Clay don't know won't hurt him."

Mae sprinkled some powders into the water. "He probably will, seeing how it's pay day and all."

Lilly primped in front of the mirror. "I sure wouldn't charge him. Don't think any of the girls would."

"Shhh. You're gonna get me and you both in hot water if you don't keep that voice down."

Lilly gave a haughty toss of her head in the direction of the bed. "She's dead to the world. Don't blame her. I'd sell my soul to share Jake's bedroll."

"Yeah, well, you better talk to Lena Cord about that."

"Lena? What does she have to do with Jake?"

"I hear they been stepping out behind Sim's back."

Lilly's mouth dropped open. "You don't say."

"That's what I hear." Mae grabbed hold of her arm. "Now come on and let's get out of here before she wakes up."

"Lena and Jake. How do you like that?" Araby heard Lilly remark as the door closed softly behind them.

Araby rolled over but made no effort to get up. Instead she stared up at the ceilng. Jake Montana and a married lady? He certainly hadn't struck her as the type to go sneaking around with somebody else's wife.

Araby frowned. Then again, how was she supposed to know exactly what kind of a man he was? Only one thing was certain. No other man had ever intrigued her so much.

She stretched her legs and sighed. So what if he were seeing someone else? That certainly didn't mean he couldn't be friends with her as well. After all, fate hadn't made their paths cross for nothing.

Just the thought of their next meeting gave her the strength to spring up out of bed. She had so much to do! And right now, that tub of hot suds looked very inviting. And after a long soak, she'd get out her journal and write down everything that had happened since the day before. Why, what she had to say about a cowboy named Jake Montana would be enough to fill every page of the leather-bound volume.

4

Araby stood at the top of the grand staircase and surveyed the hurried activity below. Lilly, Mae, and the rest of the girls, all bare-shouldered, black-stockinged, and wearing row upon row of red ruffles and plumed tiaras, scurried in and out of the salon making final preparations for the evening's gala festivities. Felix was polishing the bar's brass railing and telling Tramp about an old dog he used to have. Tramp had made himself right at home. Ruby had given him full run of the place. He even had his own bowl behind the bar and a stack of steak bones to choose from.

Araby started slowly down the stairs. It wouldn't be long now before the Ruby Rose was jammed with customers. According to Ruby, word had spread like wildfire that women in search of men had arrived from back East, and miners, loggers, and ranchers who were in the market for wives would be sure to come courting at sundown. Pay day was always the most profitable time of the month for Ruby, but whenever husband hunters came to town, business boomed.

After spending the last two hours with Ruby in her suite munching petit-fours and sipping dainty cups of tea poured from a silver teapot, Araby could well understand Mike's affection for the proprietress of the most famous house of ill repute west of the Mississippi. Ruby's real name was Suzanna Balmoral, Lady Balmoral. She and her penniless husband, Lord Balmoral, had ventured from England many years before to seek their fortunes in the West. Lord Balmoral had died after the first winter, leaving his wife to manage as best she could. Her ties with her aristocratic past were broken the day she buried her husband, and Lady Balmoral ceased to exist. Instead, she took the name of her husband's favorite gem, a ruby, as her own name. What happened between that time and two decades later when Ruby had become a successful businesswoman had gone unmentioned, and Araby had not dared to ask about it. Ruby only told her that the worst Araby could possibly imagine would not even begin to compare with the hardships she had to endure in those early years. Ruby had indeed made her own way, and through it all had managed to maintain her cool dignity. Mike always bragged that Ruby was one hell of a woman, and now Araby knew why.

Waiting for her at the bottom of the stairs was Lucius Bartell. When she greeted him with a smile and a cheerful "good evening," he took her hand and kissed it.

"You, my dear Araby, are a vision of loveliness. These gents are going to be inconsolable when they find out you're not in the market for a husband. Of course, they should be able to figure it out on their own that you wouldn't have to cross a country to find a husband. I daresay you've had more than your share of offers from those Eastern fellows.''

His flattery always brought red to her cheeks. ''I do believe you've missed your calling, Lucius. Why, I've had leading men who weren't nearly so eloquent with words. You really should have been an actor.''

Once again he bowed with great decorum. ''I shall be whatever you want me to be, lovely lady.''

Araby was anxious to change the topic of conversation to something a little less personal. ''You're very cheerful. I have a feeling you've emptied the pockets of every cowboy miles around.''

He flashed her one of his most charming grins. ''I never empty a man's pockets. At least not entirely. I always leave him enough to fill his belly and get a place to lay his head.''

''A gentleman through and through.''

Araby looked anxiously around the room as Lucius escorted her to the parlor where Belle was waiting with her ''nieces'' and Mandy. They all looked as demure, in their high-necked party dresses with girlish ruffles and frills and sitting on the settees all prim and proper, as ladies waiting for their gentlemen callers. She hadn't really expected to find Jake there. Still, she was disappointed when he was nowhere around. No matter! She'd only wanted to thank him again for his kindness.

Araby couldn't help laughing aloud at herself.

And just who did she think she was fooling? Thanking him wasn't all she had in mind. The last time she saw him she had looked a mess! Her traveling suit had been all wrinkled and dusty, and her hair resembled a rat's nest more than the latest stylish coiffure. A long, luxurious soak in a tub filled with lilac bubbles had taken away all of the grime and most of the aches of her long journey, and she had taken great care in choosing just the right outfit for the evening. After several changes and much deliberation, she'd finally decided upon a cream silk-faille reception dress that was decorated with Italian point lace and seed pearls. Its pale color made a striking contrast to the fiery color of her hair. She couldn't remember the last time she had set out to impress any man. Then again, Jake Montana was not just any man. Who'd have thought a cowboy could be so intriguing? Just thinking about those turquoise eyes and the way they seemed to stare right through her made her go all weak-kneed.

Just as he had promised, Lucius bought them all the finest meal Widow Morris' cafe had to offer—big, thick steaks, potatoes fried in onions, fried squash and okra, and double helpings of cherry cobbler. Belle and her nieces attacked their food with the same unabashed enthusiasm as they put into flirting with every man who stepped into the cafe. Mandy tried hard to imitate Araby's table manners, then finally gave up the dainty portions and wolfed down everything on her plate and accepted seconds.

Between mouthfuls, Belle and the girls discussed the kind of man they each wanted, but as far as Araby could tell, as long as the prospective suitor could walk, talk, and breathe reasonably well he would fit the bill just fine. Belle, who had received what she considered expert advice from Ruby, reckoned that there were close to five hundred men for every one woman in Idaho. While that might have been a slight miscalculation, the pickings were plentiful indeed, and for once in their lives, Belle and the girls would be wooed and courted like any proper lady back East. Marriage would give them respectability, and Araby suspected that was all any of them ever wanted.

She was worried about Mandy though. The girl was hardly more than a child, a babe in the woods. She was much too young to be saddled with children and a husband who was insensitive to her needs—or worse still, one who beat her black and blue. Belle and the girls could take care of themselves, but poor, sweet Mandy needed someone to take care of her. If only there was some way she could help.

When they returned to the Ruby Rose, a group of cowboys had already gathered around the poker table, and Lucius quickly excused himself.

Every eligible bachelor in the Idaho Territory—and a few other territories besides, Araby decided—had found his way out of the mines, the fields, and the logging camps. Hair slicked back, boots with a spit-polish shine, they all looked awkward and uncomfortable in their Sunday-go-to-meeting clothes. Most of the men looked like honest, hard-working fellows, but a few of them had faces like bulldogs and dispositions to match. Those were the ones who could break any woman's spirit as well as her neck, Araby knew. Even Belle, with her quick fist and fast talk, backed away from that lot.

Lucinda and her two "sisters" were the belles of the ball and loved all the attention they were getting. Lounging on the settees like queen bees, they were surrounded by suitors. Ruby's girls didn't seem to begrudge them the attention. After all, the gents who were rejected needed a few hugs and kisses to heal their wounded pride, and Lilly, Mae, and the rest were all too happy to provide such affection for a price.

Belle had hardly closed her mouth since walking back into the Ruby Rose. "Lordy me, I don't think I've ever seen so many men in one place. There's a lot of money to be made out here. I don't think Ruby would mind a little small scale competition. Maybe me and her could work out a deal." She surveyed the salon in awe. "Let me see—twenty fellows a night times—"

"Belle!"

"Only joking, Araby. My mind's made up. I ain't turning back. From now on it's cooking supper, scrubbing floors and going to church socials. Now, that don't sound so bad, does it?"

Araby agreed. "It doesn't sound bad at all."

A giant of a cowboy boldly strutted up to them with his thumbs hooked in his belt.

"All right, missy. Let's get right down to basics."

Araby winced. She certainly hoped she wasn't the missy he was addressing. His breath could fell trees, and what few teeth he had were stained yellow from tobacco.

"I'm looking for a woman," he went on. "I got me an eight-hundred-acre spread up in the hills, and a good herd of beef to boot. You keep a good house, and I won't lay the strap to you. Fair enough?''

Araby tried not to giggle. "Sorry, but I'm not in the market for a husband."

Squinted eyes studied her every feature. "Then what'll it cost me to take you upstairs?"

Belle shoved him away, nearly sending him sprawling over the bar. "You ain't got that much money, mister. Now why don't you just take those fine propositions and mosey on out of here."

The cowboy stumbled back with his fists up. "Yeah, says who?"

"Says me. That's who." A short, skinny fellow in a red vest and matching felt hat pushed him out of the way. "You heard the lady, Dooley. Now move it."

"If'n it wuz anybody but you, Charlie, I'd flatten them." Dooley stooped down and whispered loud enough for everyone in the room to hear. "They ain't husband hunting, and they ain't looking to take a trip upstairs, neither.

"Good-bye, Dooley."

"You're just wasting your time," Dooley stuttered as he stumbled away.

"Charlie Pepper," said the little man, "at your service, ladies." He tipped his old felt hat first to Belle, then to Araby. "Don't mind old Dooley. He's not half bad when he's sober." He scratched his grizzled chin while Belle made the introductions. "If you don't mind my asking, ladies, if you're not looking for husbands—and from the looks of you two you wouldn't have to look far—what are two beautiful sisters doing out here? Why, you belong in a fancy restaurant sipping champagne out of satin slippers."

Belle gave Araby a poke in the ribs. "Did you

hear that? He thinks we're sisters." She took hold of Charlie's arm and held on tight. "My friend's not looking for a husband, but I am, and I do declare if you're not just about the most handsomest man I ever did see."

Charlie seemed to grow a foot. "I'd be plum tickled, Miss Belle, if you'd take a turn in the moonlight with me."

With a wink, Belle was off. Her schoolgirl giggles echoed through the salon.

"Do you believe in love at first sight?" Araby heard Charlie ask Belle.

Araby chuckled softly. She had a feeling her redheaded friend had just found her knight in shining armor, even if he did only come up to her chin.

Araby settled comfortably onto one of the settees in the back and watched the musical revue staged by Ruby's girls. With Felix at the piano, the girls sang and danced and performed funny skits for the patrons of the Ruby Rose. Word had spread quickly among the clientele that she was Mike Stone's niece. The few men who did approach her for reasons other than expressing their condolences were put in their place by warning growls from Tramp. Throughout the evening, she kept one eye on the door, hoping every time it opened that Jake Montana would step inside. He was undoubtedly the only cowboy in the territory who wasn't at the Ruby Rose. What Mae had said earlier about him and some married woman still weighed heavily on her mind. Of course, it wasn't any of her business what he did and with whom. Still, she had very little control over the fact that she found him very attractive . . .

"Hello, Araby."

Araby looked up to find Jake standing tall and proud beside her and holding his hat in his hands. He wasn't dressed up in his Sunday best like most of the other men, but his black trousers and starched shirt looked as if they had been cut and made to form. Not even Araby, who could turn tears off and on at whim, could hide the surprise written all over her face.

"Why, Jake. I didn't see you come in."

Curses! What an utterly stupid thing to say. Now, he'd know she had been looking for him.

"I thought you'd still be out rounding up strays."

"Some of the other fellows relieved me for a while. You mind if I sit down?"

"Oh, no, of course I don't mind. Please do." She was about to tell Tramp there was no need for any growling, but when she reached down to grab hold of his collar, he was snoozing peacefully and not the least bit put out by this particular intruder.

Jake sat down at the end of the settee and rolled a cigarette. "I'd have been here a lot sooner, but Sheriff Otter had a few questions he wanted to ask me about the train robbery. Seems like he thinks I did it."

Araby looked him straight in the eye. She knew the identity of the robber as well as he. "Didn't you tell him you were out hunting strays?"

"He didn't believe me." Jake rolled his cigarette between his thumb and forefinger but did not light it. "Me and him, we don't see eye to eye about most things. I expect he'll be asking you questions before long."

"He's already questioned the others." Araby then told him of her supper conversation with Lucius, Mandy, and Belle and her girls. "All anyone could remember was that the train robber wore a flour sack over his head. No one could agree on his size or even the color of his shirt. The conductor was positive he had two guns in his holster, and poor Belle swore he was carrying a rifle in one hand and a hunting knife in the other."

"How convenient. For the outlaw, that is."

"Yes. Seems like he had a very sympathetic audience." Tawny eyes bore deep into his turquoise ones. "Is it true the outlaw stole back the money Sullivan had swindled from some settlers?"

Jake didn't bat an eye. "I wouldn't know about that, m'am."

Araby followed Jake's gaze, then, to see a man coming toward them with a long, slow stride. Even had his vest not borne a silver star, she'd have had no trouble picking out the Sheriff from the description Belle gave. Sheriff Otter's name did him justice, for with his short, blunt head and round face fringed with whiskers, an otter was just what he looked like.

"Hello, Montana. I figured you'd be too busy rounding up those strays to come to town partying. Or was it rustling you were up to yesterday?"

"No, Sheriff, you were right the first time. I was rounding up strays." Jake stretched out his legs and leaned back into the cushions. "A man can get hanged for rustling."

"A man can get hanged for robbing the train, too." The Sheriff tipped his hat to Araby. "M'am,

Horace Otter's my name. I'm the sheriff of Castle Rock."

"Hello, Sheriff. I'm pleased to meet you. I'm—"

"Oh, I know exactly who you are, m'am. I make it my business to find out about everybody coming and going in my town. I believe you're the only passenger on the train that I haven't talked to, and I have some questions I'd like to ask you. Privately."

Araby paid no attention to the harsh look he threw Jake. Even a stranger could sense there was bad blood between those two. "I am so pleased to meet you at last, Sheriff. My uncle Mike spoke often of you and what a fine job you do keeping law and order in Castle Rock."

"I'm pleased to hear that, m'am. Your uncle was as fine a man as they come. I was mighty sorry about what happened to him." He gave Jake another frown.

Jake sat unflinching. Araby had a feeling he knew she wouldn't give him away. How could she? After all, he had befriended her, and if he had indeed stolen from Sullivan to give back to the people he had swindled, then Jake deserved a reward, not a jail sentence.

"Now, about that train robber, Miss Stone-Leigh."

"You know, Sheriff, had it not been for Mr. Montana here, I might still be trying to find my way to Castle Rock, and with a gang of outlaws on the loose, I'd probably have never made it here."

"Yes, m'am, but—"

"You have no idea, Sheriff, what an absolutely terrifying ordeal that was, to be out in the wilderness alone." Araby gave a heavy sigh.

"Why, I'm lucky to have gotten out of there alive."

"Yes m'am, I can understand what a horrible experience you had. However, if Mr. Montana here will leave us alone, I'd like to ask you a few questions."

"Why, Sheriff, Mr. Montana is just the finest gentleman I have ever met. I owe him my life. Castle Rock is lucky to have such an outstanding citizen."

The Sheriff's impatience was starting to show. "About this robbery, m'am."

Araby gave him her most genial smile. "Of course, Sheriff. Ask away. I'm as anxious as you that these criminals be apprehended."

The Sheriff raised a bushy brow in Jake's direction.

Jake gave a curt nod. "Reckon I'll pay a visit to Felix."

Araby folded her hands demurely in her lap. "Just what is it you'd like to know, Sheriff? I'll certainly try to be as much help as I can."

The Sheriff pulled up a chair and stradled it. "The man that robbed the train, what did he look like?"

"Well, you understand I couldn't see his face for that flour sack." Finger tapping her chin, she pretended to be deep in thought. "All I remember is his eyes, and those were the meanest eyes I've ever seen. They were dark . . . almost black . . ." She shivered. "It makes me tremble just to think about them. The whites were all red and bloodshot, like he'd been on a real long drunk. Let me see now. Oh, yes, his eyebrows were real bushy, and I think he may have had a beard because he kept scratching his chin, though mind you, I can't say for sure.''

The Sheriff let out a loud sigh. ''Go on, Miss Stone-Leigh. Anything else?''

Araby smoothed the folds of her skirt. ''I am sorry, Sheriff Otter, but that's all I remember.''

The Sheriff glanced over at the bar where Jake was laughing with one of Ruby's girls. ''You sure there's nothing else you care to tell me, Miss Stone-Leigh?''

She was too busy watching Jake to hear the Sheriff's question. Did all of the girls at the Ruby Rose feel about Jake the way Lilly did? She couldn't help but wonder how many visits he'd made up that grand staircase.

''Oh, I'm sorry, Sheriff. I was just concentrating, trying to remember more. If I think of anything else, I'll be sure to write it down so I won't forget to tell you. You will catch him, won't you Sheriff?''

Another scowl was sent in Jake's direction. ''Oh, I'll catch him all right. I got a noose all ready to slip over his head.''

Araby shivered, this time for real.

''Something wrong, Miss Stone-Leigh?''

She shook her head. ''I was just thinking about those horrible eyes, Sheriff. They'll haunt my sleep for many nights to come.''

The Sheriff tipped his hat and excused himself. Araby watched as he walked straight over to Cyril Sullivan and motioned him outside.

''We're even now, Jake Montana,'' she told him when he sat back down beside her.

Blue-green eyes danced with mischief. ''Even? What are you talking about?''

''You know what I'm talking about. You helped me out of trouble last night, and I just returned the favor." Arms crossed, she sat back in the plump cushions and studied him long and hard. He truly was like no other man she had ever come across.

"Care to see what an Idaho full moon looks like, Miss Stone-Leigh?"

"I'd like that very much, Mr. Montana."

Jake stood up and offered her his arm. "Then shall we?"

Araby took hold of his arm thinking that she might never let go.

Belle and Charlie were about to come inside when they stepped out onto the porch.

"Why, you must be Jake Montana!" Belle seized his arm and gave him a hug. "I'd know you anywhere. Just let me thank you personally for rescuing my good friend here. Who knows what awful happenings might have befallen her had you not been there to save her."

Jake chuckled. "I have a feeling that anybody who tangled with this little lady would live to regret it. Charlie, how you doing? I don't believe I've ever seen you looking better."

"Me and Belle, we just got ourselves engaged," announced Charlie proudly. "Belle Pepper. Has a nice ring to it, don't it?"

Jake and Araby agreed, laughing.

"Oh, Belle, I'm so happy for you," said Araby, squeezing her dear friend's hand. "But isn't this all kind of sudden?"

"Sudden? Heck no," interupted Charlie. "Why, I been waiting for this gal all my life, and now that I've found her I'm going to tie her down before she can get away."

Belle beamed. "Ain't he just the most romantic thing you ever saw?" She hugged her intended closer. "My knight in shining armor. I knew I'd find him out here."

Charlie elbowed Jake. "I told her all I had was a little shack and a couple of pack mules and a dried up old mine, and you know, this woman said she'd love me even if we had to live in a tent. What do you think about that?"

"I think you got yourself quite a woman, Charlie," Jake told him. "You better hang on to her."

"Oh, I am. I ain't giving her a chance to change her mind. She said yes, and I'm not letting her back out."

Belle blushed like a schoolgirl. "You don't have to worry about me backing out. No siree. From now on it's me and you, Charlie Pepper. For better or worse, till death do us part."

"We just went and woke up the preacher." Charlie gave his bride to be a peck on the cheek. "We'll be tying the knot just as soon as the reverend can stand sober. You folks will come, won't you?"

"We wouldn't miss it for the world," Araby assured him.

"Your friend Belle certainly is in for the surprise of her life," Jake remarked as they strolled down the street. "An old shack and a couple of mules ain't all Charlie Pepper's got. Why, he's one of the richest men in the whole territory. He can sniff out gold a hundred feet under."

Araby smiled into the night. It was about time Belle found a little happiness, and she had a feeling Charlie had been looking for it just as long.

Castle Rock could have been no brighter had

all the streets been lined with gaslamps. Mike had told her the moon was fuller and brighter out in Idaho than anywhere else in the world, and now she knew exactly what he had meant. The Idaho moon truly was like no other, and there was no one else she'd rather be seeing it with than Jake.

Jake kept a respectable distance as they strolled down the street in silence. Occasionally, he reached for her arm but took it only long enough to guide her over a rut or up a step. More than once she found herself wishing—praying— that his hand would linger just a little longer. If Mike hadn't already warned her that cowboys were quick to shy away from any woman who took matters into her own hands, she might have been tempted to take his arm and hold on. She had a feeling Jake would have no use at all for a woman of the world. Still, she couldn't picture him with a cowering, simpering female, either. What kind of a woman was this Lena Cord, any- way? Had she not been able to keep a late-night rendezvous with Jake, and was that the reason he had decided to come to town? She wished that she were that reason!

"You're mighty quiet." Jake stopped to roll another cigarette. "What's on your mind?"

"You are." Her boldness surprised even her.

Jake seemed amused in an uncomfortable sort of way. "Me? Why, I must be just about the dullest fellow you ever met."

"Dull? Quite the contrary, I assure you." She studied his face closely. The moonlight made those scars and creases even more fascinating. "My uncle promised me cowboys were a cut above the Eastern man. Now, I see what he meant."

Araby held her breath. Perhaps she had been too brazen. She half expected Jake to take off running in the other direction.

"You and Mike were real close, weren't you?" Jake asked, sadly shaking his head. "I still can't believe he's gone."

"No, neither can I." The thought of Mike staring down from heaven at them that very moment with that "I told you so" grin on his face made her remember all the good times they had shared. She smiled. "Mike was like a second father to me."

"Mike was closer to me than my own father," Jake said, his voice softening.

Araby sat down on the bench in front of Fisher's. Jake stood over her, one leg propped up on the bench and an arm folded over it.

"If it wasn't for Mike, I'd probably be ten feet under by now with a bullet hole in my back," Jake revealed. "I used to be a bounty hunter. I'd go out looking for men who had a price on their head and bring them back dead or alive. I let them be the judge of which. Sooner or later, the odds were bound to catch up with me. I have Mike to thank for turning me around."

His grave expression gave way to a smile. "Of course, if Sheriff Otter gets his way, I'm liable to be belly-up myself before long."

"He really hates you, doesn't he?"

"Naw. He thinks he does, but he doesn't. Not really." Jake's grin widened. "Reformed or not, I'm still a gunslinger in his book."

"Well, in my book, you are one fine man . . . for what that matters," she added hurriedly.

"It matters a lot what you think."

"Oh."

Araby waited for him to say more, but he didn't. Instead, he gazed out into the night deep in thought. She watched his every move, caring little whether or not he was aware of her close scrutiny. How would his lips feel on hers? she wondered. And those powerful arms, with their muscles straining against his shirt—would they crush her when he held her close?

Jake's chuckle was low and throaty. "You know, I'm not usually much of a talker, but Mike told me so much about you, I just feel like I know you." His smile grew wider. "I was going back East with Mike the next time he went for a visit. He told me he was going to show me the sights."

Araby smiled. She had thought as much all along, and she knew that one of those sights would be Mike's niece! Leave it to Uncle Mike to try his hand at matchmaking. Well, she had to give credit where it was due. Mike had done a fine job picking out a man for her.

"You're smiling," Jake said softly. "You're even prettier when you smile."

His turquoise stare held her captive long before he pulled her to her feet and imprisoned her in his arms.

Araby didn't know what to say. What should she say? That the moment she had been longing for had finally come? No, he'd think her too bold, for sure. Then again, why did she have to say anything? After all, talking was not exactly what either of them had on their minds.

Jake stared deep into her eyes, as if searching for some hidden message.

Araby was certain the look in her eyes spoke all that needed to be said. She whispered his name, and he hers, and the next moment their noses touched and their eyes melted together.

Jake brushed his lips across hers, hesitant at first, as if he weren't quite certain what her reaction might be. Then when she flung her arms around his neck and stood up on tip-toe to meet him, he eagerly sought her mouth and drank thirstily from the sweetness within.

Each kiss lifted her higher and higher off the ground. Mike had been right again! Those fellows back East were mere boys in comparison. She'd never known a real man. Few had gotten so far as a kiss on her cheek, and those who had dared to try for more were quickly put in their place. More than one overzealous suitor had been turned away with her hand print on his cheek. But Jake was different, and what she was feeling at that moment was different as well. Her whole being pleaded with him to go on and on and never stop. She'd offer no resistance. What woman would shun such a man? Certainly not one in her right mind!

Lips parting wider, she beckoned him inside.

Someone moaned softly. Araby wasn't sure who it was. Perhaps it was both of them together.

She felt herself slipping deeper and deeper under his spell. Never had she dreamed one kiss could possibly invoke such bliss.

Jake stepped away abruptly. "Sorry. I didn't mean to . . ."

"There's no need to be sorry about anything." Araby closed the distance between them. "If I had had any objections, I can assure you I would have voiced them by now."

His cheeks blazed red.

Araby was certain they were a reflection of her own. Discomfort or embarrassment could not have caused that sudden flush, nor could the sultriness of the night. The excitement of the moment had raised both their temperatures more than just a few degrees.

Jake made no effort to continue where they left off. "It's getting late. We ought to be going."

"Of course." Araby did her best to hide her disappointment, but just when she needed it most, her theatrical skill failed her. "I wouldn't want to miss Belle's wedding."

As they made their way back to the Ruby Rose, Araby was aware of walking much more slowly. And there was no wondering why. This was one night she wanted to last forever! She would savor those magical moments they had shared for the rest of her life. At last she had found a real man, the kind of man she had thought existed only in writers' creative imaginations, and now that she had found him, she didn't want to let him go even for a minute. She'd traveled across a nation to get to him. Now all she had to do was figure out was how to keep him!

Charlie and Belle's wedding was short and sweet. Just the basics, Charlie kept telling the preacher. The "I do's" were exchanged in the salon amid cheers and applause. Even the gambling stopped momentarily in honor of the occasion.

Belle could not have been happier had the hammered horseshoe nail Charlie slipped onto her finger been a band of diamonds. Considering what Jake had told her earlier, Araby had a feeling it would soon be just that.

Throughout the ceremony, Jake kept a firm grip on her arm. His hold was not without a hint of possessiveness. When another cowboy eyed her, he made sure the cowpoke knew just who she was with. That didn't bother Araby in the least. What did give her cause for concern, however, were her own thoughts. There was no telling what may have happened had Jake not put an end to their romantic interlude in front of Fisher's. She would have offered no resistance, no matter how out of control the situation might have become. No doubt he had sensed as much. Could it be that her willingness had put him off? Or perhaps thoughts of someone else had distracted him.

Mae's remarks about Jake and that married woman came back to haunt her once again. Maybe Jake wasn't the marrying kind. Maybe he preferred to get involved with women who were already married, women he could love and leave, with no commitment.

Araby could feel her blood boil. Curses! Why did the thought of him with another woman, married or not, send her into a tizzy? What he did was his business! Why should she care?

Once again, she reminded herself that she was in Idaho for one month. Thirty more days to go! That was hardly enough time to get unpacked, much less to develop any kind of a romantic involvement.

While waiting their turn to congratulate the newlyweds, Araby made use of every opportunity to study Jake's face. Why settle for stolen glances here and there? After all, his was the face that would fill her dreams for many nights to come, and she wanted to make sure every detail, even down to the hardly noticeable sprinkling of tiny freckles across his nose, was accurately recreated in her bedtime imaginings.

Belle came to her, arms outstretched and choking back the tears. "Oh, Araby, never in my life have I been as happy as I am right now. My Charlie was worth the long wait. He loves me, Araby. He honest and truly loves me."

Araby hugged her friend. "Who says dreams don't come true?"

Jake gave Charlie a playful punch in the belly. "You ole cuss. You ought to be ashamed of yourself, dragging this fine woman off to live in that shack."

"Our shack," Belle piped up. "And by the time I get through fixing it up, our little home will be just as grand as any palace. You just wait and see."

Charlie returned Jake's punch. "If you had any gumption about you, Montana, you'd be tying the knot, too. It's time you settled down. You been running wild too long!"

"Break open your finest champagne, Ruby!" Charlie bellowed. "The drinks are on me, in honor of this momentous occasion."

"But Charlie, darling," whispered Belle. "Champagne for all these people will cost a fortune."

"Hush up, sweetie pie. This is my wedding, and I aim to do it up right." He hugged her close and gave her another kiss. "Remind me to have a little chat with you about our finances later."

Belle snuggled close to her new husband. "Whatever you say, dear."

Araby smiled to herself. Why, Belle sounded almost matronly!

It was well after midnight before Felix pushed back from the piano and the fellows who had been strumming and fiddling called it a night. Any romantic fantasies Araby might have entertained about Jake waltzing her into the night had been just that—a fantasy. Light on his feet he definitely was not. That cowboy had not been joking when he warned her he had two left feet. Her toes would most likely be black and blue from the point of his boots jabbing in. But what did that matter, when in his arms she had truly found paradise on earth? She could have danced all night with him, even with all ten toes broken.

Long before she was ready to say her goodbyes to her cowboy hero, the Ruby Rose was closing down. Except for Felix and the few girls left downstairs to tidy up, she and Jake were the only ones left standing.

"I reckon it's time to, uh—to say good night." Jake stood at the bottom of the stairs, hat in hand and his fingers nervously skimming the rim.

Araby nodded. Never before had she been the least tempted to invite a man to her room. Never—until now. What was it about that slow-talking cowboy that made her want to throw caution to the wind and experience firsthand that torrid passion her friends whispered about?

"Good night, Jake," she said with a soft sigh.

Neither of them moved an inch from where they were standing, Jake on the bottom step and she on the first step up.

What was it, indeed. No man had ever made such a lasting impression on her. No man! And now to let some cowboy make her swoon and flutter . . . just what was coming over her? Perhaps that magical Idaho air Mike was always bragging about really was clouding up her good senses.

"I told you about the wagon coming in from Tamarack tomorrow, didn't I?" Jake asked.

Araby nodded. He had told her more than once. Just the sound of his voice lulled her into a mellowness she'd never before experienced.

"The name of the man coming in is Hamstring, and he usually arrives at Fisher's about eight," she said, just to let him know she hadn't forgotten one detail.

"Ole Hamstring can be an ornery cuss, but pay him no mind. You just smile at him a time or two and those dimples of yours will melt him in no time."

She wondered if her dimples had melted Jake, but she didn't dare ask. All she could do was mumble, "I'll remember that."

Jake let out another labored breath. "I—I guess I'll be talking to you soon. It wouldn't be out of the way to drop by Tamarack and check in on you. Make sure you got everything you need." One shoulder turned, but the other stayed where it was. "One more thing. Jud Cord can be a handful at times. If he gives you any trouble, you just send one of the boys for me, and I'll put him in line real fast."

"Thanks, Jake. I'll keep that in mind." Araby's smile remained locked in place. No doubt Jake could make the devil himself walk the straight and narrow.

"Well . . ."

"Well . . ." Jake made no effort to go.

Araby could sense he didn't want to say goodbye any more than she did. Still, someone had to make the move.

His hand reached out for her without warning.

Araby surprised herself, and him, by taking hold.

"I better walk you up to your room," he told her as he stepped up to where she was standing. "Just to make sure you don't have any surprise visitors waiting for you. Some of the fellows—well, when they get all liquored up, they go a little crazy, and I wouldn't want one thinking you were one of Ruby's girls. I mean, I'll walk you up if you don't mind."

"No, no, I don't mind at all. It's very kind of you to offer."

Araby held tight to his arm with one hand while the other laced its fingers through his. Who said knights in shining armor could only be found in fairy tales?

Tramp was curled up at the foot of the bed.

"One of the girls must have let him in," she said softly, not really knowing exactly what it was that should be said during such moments.

Jake stood just inside the doorway while Araby, at his direction, checked behind the dressing screen, under the bed, and inside the wardrobe closet.

Tramp wouldn't have let anyone in, she thought, keeping her smile to herself, but there was no point in telling Jake that. It was rather nice having someone so concerned about her well-being.

"No one here but Tramp," she announced after looking in all the places Jake had suggested and a few others besides to delay his parting a little longer.

"Good. You never know what to expect from some of these cowpokes." He stepped back out into the hall. "Oh, about tonight. Thanks."

Araby returned his grin. She knew he wasn't referring to either the stroll or the company, and she knew he knew, too. Sheriff Otter had needed her eyewitness account before he could lock Jake up, and when he failed to get a positive identification from her, he had no choice but to let Jake remain a free man. Oh dear! She hoped gratitude wasn't the only reason behind his kindness—or his kisses.

She leaned against the door, wishing his departure might be delayed still a moment longer. "Your secret is safe with me," she assured him. "If the rest of the townspeople knew, they'd think you were a hero. I know I do."

"A hero? I been called a lot of things, but never that." His eyes held tight to hers. "I better go now, or I won't be going at all."

Araby swallowed hard. If only she had the courage to tell him what was in her heart.

She watched as he walked slowly back down the hall. At the top of the stairs, he turned back around and gave her a final wave and one last lazy grin.

"Don't forget to lock the door," he reminded her.

"I won't. Good night, Jake."

" 'Night, Araby."

Even before she slipped into bed, she knew that this would be one night when sleep would take its time coming. And when she finally did fall under its spell, there'd be no wondering whose face would fill her dreams. He hadn't wanted to leave any more than she had wanted him to go. Most other men would have taken advantage of the situation, but not him. Not Jake

Montana. He might be a cowboy, but he was a gentleman through and through! Why, already she was counting the minutes when next they would meet. Perhaps tomorrow . . .

5

With waves and smiles and promises to Ruby that she would be back later in the week for another long chat, Araby headed down the street towards Fisher's General Store early the next morning. Felix had already taken down her trunks and left them at the store. It was sad leaving Mandy, even though Araby knew she would be seeing a lot of her young friend. The girl's future was no longer unsettled. Sharing the same fear that she had regarding Mandy, Ruby had offered her a job as housekeeper of her private suite. Mandy was thrilled with the arrangement. Not only was she to receive room and board and a small salary, but Ruby was going to teach her how to read and write and cipher as well. All had worked out for the best. Ruby would have a friend, and Mandy would have her own guardian angel.

At eight o'clock sharp, the Tamarack supply wagon pulled up in front of the general store.

True to Jake's description, the driver was an ornery little man who was none too grateful for the company on the way back, especially when he found out the dog that had jumped onto the flour sacks was a passenger as well. But his attitude changed quickly when he found out that Araby was Mike Stone's niece, and the fuzzy black mutt he kept cursing turned out to be the infamous Tramp.

Although it was hot and dusty and uncomfortably bumpy, the ride from Castle Rock to Tamarack was one of the most pleasant journeys Araby had ever taken. Hamstring turned out to be one of the most entertaining characters she had ever come across. A character! That was exactly what he was. What fun an actor would have portraying him. He was a short man, his whiskered chin barely even with her shoulder. His belly drooped low over a blood-splattered apron, and the yellow suspenders he kept popping did nothing to keep his trousers from slipping below his hips. On his head he wore an old straw hat that was full of holes—holes made by Injun arrows, or so he said. Looking her straight in the eye, Hamstring told her the reason he had no hair was because he'd been scalped—not once, but twice!

The Saint Joseph River, or the Saint Joe as it had been affectionately dubbed by the settlers, ran alongside the road. Bunches of yellow belles, pale blue forget-me-nots, violets and lillies grew wild on its banks. Willow withes fanned the water, and underneath the overhanging branches, trout could be heard jumping to the surface.

Riding alongside the river left her with a feeling of having passed this way before. Mike had written such vivid descriptions of the river that lazily zig-zagged through the gently rolling meadows that she felt she knew every inch of the road. The river had been named by Jesuit missionaries and had long been referred to as "the gentle river" by Indians and settlers alike. To the Indians who had traveled up and down it in their dugout canoes, the river possessed mystical powers. Many tales were created to explain why trees and mountains and birds flying upside down were seen in its crystal waters.

A flat-bottomed skiff carrying a farmer and his young sons passed them on their way into town. Hamstring explained that the skiff was used by many of the homesteaders instead of wagons to transport provisions back to their farms. He also told her about the *Lottie Mae*, a big paddlewheel steamer that carried mail and supplies all the way up to the Canadian border. On Sundays and holidays, it became an excursion boat for picnickers and sightseers.

A little farther upstream, Araby saw an Indian brave paddling a dugout canoe up one of the many streams that flowed into the river. With him was a squaw, and on her back was a cradleboard. When Hamstring called out to him, the brave turned around and raised his hand in friendship.

Araby waved back. They were not so different from any other family.

"Listen," Hamstring told her a little while later. "That's nature's music."

He identified each sound of the melody for her—the cry of the wild loon, the shriek of the hawk, the coyote's yip, the cougar's snarl, the fawn's bleat, and the bugle-like noise made by the old bull elk.

"Do you know what that is?" Hamstring asked as something slapped against the water. "That's a beaver building its dam. Now that nobody's trapping no more, there's a whole slew of those little critters all up and down the river."

"Tell me as soon as we cross onto Tamarack land," Araby said.

He threw back his head and bellowed out a laugh that echoed all along the razor-back ridges on the other side. "Why, we been on Tamarack soil ever since we left Castle Rock. As far as you can see, and then some, that's Tamarack. You see that stand of pines up there? Well just beyond that is the house." His tone grew somber. "Things just ain't the same there now that Mike's gone."

Araby nodded. It wouldn't be the same for her, either. If only she'd come out to visit him last summer, or the one before that! But no, she had to play the leading lady in every production. Too late had she realized the stage would still be there long after she was gone. If only she had listened to Mike and come when he had begged her to. If only . . .

No, there was no point in punishing herself. The past couldn't be changed. She'd live the rest of her life regreting some of the decisions she had made, but at least she had to come to Tamarack to pay her last respects. Mike would have appreciated that.

"You know much about the Cord brothers?" Hamstring asked.

"No, but their names keep popping up." Ruby had been the first to warn her about Jud, the elder of the two, then Jake. From the sound of it,

Hamstring was about to caution her against him as well.

"Those boys were never nothing but trouble for their poor mama. Why, they didn't even come around her until after she married Mike, and when she died, Mike couldn't get rid of them. He helped them get into the saw-mill business, but those two didn't appreciate anything. They always felt like Mike owed them a living. Sim ain't so bad. He's just trifling, but Jud—Jud has his eye on Tamarack. He thinks the ranch ought to belong to him. Him and Sim and Sim's wife Lena moved right in before Mike was cold in the ground." Hamstring chuckled. "When ole Jud sees you, that butt-kissing grin of his is going to be wiped clean off his face."

"I'm sure Mike must have mentioned having relatives back East."

"Oh, he did. Couldn't get him to shut up about you folks. But nobody ever thought any of his family would come out here. And Jud sure as heck didn't think anybody would show up to take the ranch away from him."

Araby was quick to protest. "But I didn't come here to lay claim to Mike's land or his money."

"You take what's coming to you, gal. Mike would have wanted it that way."

Hamstring cracked the whip across the horses' backsides, and the two chestnuts trotted faster through the stand of cottonwoods.

Araby sat back against the buckboard and enjoyed the ride, taking in all of the scenery and trying to remember every tree and flower so she could accurately describe it all later in her journal. Except for Hamstring's off-key humming and the plodding of horses' hooves over the hard-packed dirt, the only other sound was the gentle lapping of the Saint Joe as it broke over rocks and cascaded into little falls.

"Won't be long now," said Hamstring as he stuffed another wad of tobacco into his mouth. "I can smell Mattie's gingerbread cakes a-baking."

"Mattie who?"

"Don't know her last name, but she's the housekeeper at the ranch."

Araby frowned. "What happened to Mrs. Watkins?"

The Watkinses had been with her uncle for as long as she could remember. Slim had been the ranch foreman and Mrs. Slim, as Mike called her even though she would have made four of her husband, kept house and cooked for him.

Hamstring spit out some of his chew. "They wuz the first to go when Jud took over."

"But my uncle depended on Slim. Many times, I've heard Mike say he couldn't run Tamarack without Slim."

"You ain't telling me nothing I don't already know. That idiot, Burley Wilkerson, Jud put in Slim's place doesn't know his ass—whoops, pardon me m'am—his backside from a hole in the ground." Hamstring shook his head. "Course none of the boys will tell Judd that. It'd be their jobs if they did. Now me, I been fixing those cow-pokers' grub almost as long as you been in the world, and I don't intend to lose my job, so I just keep my mouth shut and don't complain to no-body. Why, I ain't never called any place but Tamarack home, and I'm too old to move on now."

"If I have anything to do with it, Tamarack will be your home for a long time coming," she assured him.

"Hamstring, do you think we can stop by Uncle Mike's grave?" she asked, a little farther along.

She was about to explain that she wanted to tell her uncle she had finally come to his beloved Tamarack, but the words choked in her throat.

"Ain't no grave around here, m'am."

"But Mike wanted to be buried on Tamarack land."

"I know, but the Cords couldn't get him down off the mountain. So they said. After that rattler bit him—"

"Rattler. What rattler?"

"Why, that's how your uncle died. Didn't nobody tell you?"

Araby shook her head. "Mr. Ford just wrote that Mike had been killed in a hunting accident. I just assumed that . . . I don't know what I assumed, but no mention was made of any snake."

"Well, that's how Mike died." Hamstring's voice grew hoarse. "They buried him up on the peak."

At that moment the horses broke into a gallop.

"They know they're almost home," said Hamstring, straining to hold back the reins.

Araby gave a sad sigh. It wouldn't be long now. Perhaps at Tamarack she could at last make peace with Mike and with herself.

The road narrowed through the pine forest for which the ranch had been named. Perched on a hill and all but hidden by the tamaracks was a sprawling, two-story house built from logs and shakes and split cedar.

Once atop the hill, Araby turned around and gazed behind her. The view the house commanded of the valley and the river was just as awe-inspiring as Mike had said. As far as the eye could see and then some was Tamarack land. If only Mike were there to show it to her!

Tramp was the first one out when Hamstring pulled the team alongside the front porch.

"I'll just help you get situated," Hamstring told Araby as he helped her down, "then I'll go around back and unload."

A man's angry voice blared out from inside the open door. "How many times do I have to tell you, Hamstring, I don't want any damn flour sacks cluttering up the front porch. Go round to the back where you're supposed to go."

"That's your step-cousin, Jud. Pleasant fellow, ain't he?" Hamstring winked and called out, "Yes, siree, Mr. Cord. I intend to do just that as soon as I get your company unloaded."

"Company? What company? I ain't expecting no company."

"Come on out, and see who I brung in from town." Hamstring rubbed his hands in anticipation. "I can't wait to see the look on his face when he finds out who you are," he said softly.

Araby was not at all prepared for the man who stepped out onto the porch. Cousin Jud was not exactly what she had expected, especially after all the warnings she had received about him. He looked to be about Jake's age—late twenties, early thirties, maybe—but where Jake Montana was an uncut stone, Jud was polished and refined. He was handsome, too handsome. His face was flawless. There wasn't an actor in New York who wouldn't trade his soul to have such good looks. His hair was dark and slicked back, and his moustache was neatly trimmed. When he smiled, his whole face smiled. His teeth all but sparkled.

Jud came out buttoning his vest and rolling down the sleeves of his white shirt. "Good afternoon, m'am. To what do I owe the honor of your visit?"

Tramp stayed close to her side. A low growl rumbled in his throat when Jud reached out to shake her hand.

"Hello, Mr. Cord. I'm Araby Stone-Leigh. I'm—"

Hamstring didn't give her a chance to continue. "This here's Mike Stone's niece. She's come all the way from New York."

Jud's smile faded, then came back even friendlier.

Araby quickly noted that Jud could turn his charm off and on at whim.

"My dear Araby. At last we meet. Mike spoke of you so often. Welcome to Tamarack. Come in. Come in and meet the rest of the family. Hamstring will see to your trunks."

Hamstring made a face when Jud's back was turned, then replaced it with a smile when his boss looked at him again.

Araby tried to keep her giggle to herself. "Thanks for everything," she told the ranch's cook. "Maybe later, if you have time, you can show me around."

Hamstring grew several inches. "Nothing would please me more, m'am. I'll be down at the cook shack."

With a final wave, Araby walked into the

house. Her shoes clicked loudly over the split-log floor. The hand on her shoulder was annoying, and at the first opportunity she stepped on ahead to get rid of it.

Pine bookcases filled with row after row of thick black volumes lined two of the walls, and on the third hung a huge Indian tapestry of birds in flight, their wings spread to gigantic spans. Rugs with similar designs were scattered over the floor and across the backs of gold brocade settees and wing-back chairs. Bowls and pottery bearing Indian designs were arranged atop sideboards that had been fashioned from pine.

The room looked like Mike. The scent of his cigar still lingered there. She half expected to see his imposing frame come bounding down the stairs at any minute.

A man and woman stood in front of the granite slab fireplace along the far wall of the huge room. Araby assumed the couple had to be Sim and Lena Cord. From the hostile glares they were giving each other, it was apparent that she had just interupted a family squabble.

"Sim. Lena. Look who's here. Mike's niece, Araby. She's come all the way from New York," Jud announced.

"Hello, Sim. Hello, Lena. I'm pleased to meet you," returned Araby cheerfully, even though the looks she was getting were less than friendly.

Araby studied both Cords. They were easily recognizable as brothers. The family resemblance was quite strong. Sim was a disheveled version of his brother, although his features were delicate and more defined. Araby had a feeling Sim paled in disposition as well as good looks in comparison to his older brother.

Sim shrugged his shoulders, then mumbled a quick hello and excused himself.

"He hasn't been feeling very well," Jud explained.

Araby nodded. Poor health wasn't the reason he stumbled and weaved past her. Anybody could see he was drunk.

Hands on hips and shoulders thrust back in proud defiance, Lena eyed her curiously.

Araby held her stare. So that was Lena. For some reason she had expected more of a woman and less of a girl. Maybe it was the calico skirt and white ruffled blouse that made her look so young, or the ribbon and bow that kept her chestnut locks off her neck, but Lena looked no older than seventeen or eighteen.

Lena said nothing, and neither did Araby. Their gazes held. Araby was just as curious about Sim's wife as Lena was about her. Was she really seeing Jake on the sly? Araby wondered. Why did the vision of those two locked in a steamy embrace make her want to claw out those pale blue eyes? After one look at Sim, it wasn't surprising that Lena would seek the arms of another man, but what could Jake see in her? Granted, she was pretty, but in a girlish way. Why would Jake settle for a mere girl when he could have his pick of women?

"So you're the actress, huh?" remarked Lena finally while circling Araby and examining every detail of her appearance. "To hear Mike tell it, you were some great beauty. Then, Mike always was prone to exaggerate."

Araby gritted her teeth. Lena Cord had a tongue that would slice wire.

"You're not quite what I expected, either, so I

guess we're even.''

Araby flashed Lena her most charming smile. Lena's face might be scrubbed clean, but there was no youthful innocence to her features. Up close, she looked hard and unyielding, like a woman of much experience.

''Lena, honey, why don't you run up and check on Sim?''

''Whatever you say, big brother.''

Had Araby just imagined it or had Lena's pout become even more pronounced when she breezed by her brother-in-law?

Jud picked up a bell from the sideboard and rang it. A tall, slim woman with graying hair pulled back in a severe bun appeared from the kitchen.

''We'll be dining out on the veranda, Mattie, so set the table up out there.''

After a silent appraisal of Araby, the woman nodded and disappeared back into the kitchen.

''My uncle spoke often of a Mrs. Watkins,'' Araby remarked innocently. ''Is she still here?''

Jud led her out onto the porch and seated her at a table that had been covered with a red-and-white checkered cloth. ''Mrs. Watkins? No, I'm afraid not. Her husband, Slim, took a job at Cross Fork. Shame. They were both mighty fine people. The salt of the earth.''

Araby was none too pleased when Jud scooted the chair closest to her even closer, then sat down. To her relief, Tramp wiggled in between them.

After Mattie had brought a platter of fried chicken and biscuits with bowls of potatoes and green beans, and filled their glasses with lemonade, Jud gave her a curt dismissal. When he turned to Araby, he was all smiles.

Araby heard very little of whatever it was he was telling her. The view from the veranda was breathtaking, just as Mike had promised. The river, the mountains, the valley—all of nature's wonders seemed even more spectacular from the perch atop the hill. There was a reason Mike called Idaho God's country, and now she knew what it was. No wonder Mike had given up city living. Only a fool would trade such peaceful surroundings for crowded streets and New York worries.

Jud pointed to her plate. "If you'd prefer something else, I'll have Mattie—"

Araby was quick to assure him everything was delicious, that she really was hungry, but that she was just too excited to eat.

"I just can't get over this spectacular view. Why, I could just sit for hours staring at those mountains."

"You'd be quick to change your mind when the first snow fell," Jud said. "Why, sometimes it snows in August, and it's the middle of June before we get dug out."

"It gets cold where I come from, too, Mr. Cord."

"Cold? Ha! We're talking blizzards with thirty-foot snow drifts." Jud put down his fork and turned to face her head on. His dark gaze left not one of her features untouched. "And no more of this Mr. Cord business. It's Jud. After all, we are family." He leaned still closer and rolled the tip of his moustache between his thumb and forefinger. "You know Mike wanted me to go to New

York with him this year. I have a feeling he wanted us cousins to get better acquainted. Something tells me he had a little matchmaking in mind."

Araby bit off a piece of her biscuit to avoid Jud's scrutinizing eyes. Uncle Mike would have never wanted her to meet Jud. There were plenty of Jud Cords in New York. Jake Montana, now—that was the kind of man Mike had in mind for her!

While waiting for Mattie to clear the table and serve the hot apple cobbler that Jud promised would melt right in her mouth, Araby took charge of the conversation. She told him all about her trip west and went into great detail describing the different places and people she had encountered, solely to divert the conversation from his compliments. She had heard them all before, but she had to admit that Jud's attempt at sincerity was better than most.

At the mention of Jake Montana, Jud's features became twisted. His eyes all but flashed fire. "Why, that no good son of a—did he try anything with you? If he did, by God, I'll break every bone in his body."

Jud's sudden outburst had caught her off-guard, and it took her a moment to come to Jake's defense.

"Mr. Montana was quite the gentleman, I assure you."

"A gentleman? Ha! I've never heard him called that before." The tension was slow to drain from Jud's face. "You know there are those who believe Montana was the one who robbed the train. I know I do. So does my good friend, Sheriff Otter."

Araby was about to defend her outlaw friend, to point out that the only money taken was that of Mr. Sullivan, who himself had stolen it in the first place. But common sense cautioned her to keep such protests to herself. Jake certainly needed no champion for his cause, especially when so ardent a defender as herself might do more harm than good.

Instead, she took a small bite of the cobbler and remarked off-handedly, "Oh, I don't think so. Had there been any similarities between the train robber and Mr. Montana, I would have noticed right off."

Jud stabbed at his cobbler. "Believe me, Horace Otter would like nothing better than to lock Jake Montana in jail and throw away the key."

"The only reason the Sheriff has it out for Jake," said Lena as she walked up behind them, "is that Jake did what a whole townful of lawmen couldn't do when he brought in Billy Westin."

Araby felt the last bite of cobbler stick in her throat. It seemed that Jake already had one out-spoken champion enlisted in his cause.

Lena pulled up a chair and sat down despite her brother-in-law's scowls.

"Billy Westin gunned down a whole family in cold blood over in Lewiston," Lena explained to Araby. "A ma, a pa, and six little young'uns. Jake was the only man in the whole territory who was able to track him down and bring him in."

Jud's smile was strained. "There are those in town who consider Montana a hero, my sister-in-law included. They seem to forget all those folks he killed when he was a gunslinger."

Lena was undaunted by Jud's scalding glares.

"He wasn't a gunslinger. He was a bounty hunter, and he didn't kill innocent people, either. Just those with a price on their heads."

"Sounds to me like you been spending too much time out at Cross Fork," Jud told her with a smile that was anything but friendly.

Lena shrugged her shoulders. "I don't see that it's anybody's business where I spend my time."

"We'll discuss this later," said Jud calmly. "Right now, if you'll excuse me, I'd like to be alone with Araby."

Araby did not miss the poison-arrow stares that passed from one to the other.

"Will you be staying here long?" Lena asked Araby, ignoring her brother-in-law. "Or will you be going back to New York as soon as the will's read?"

Jud's hand closed tight around Lena's arm. "Don't you think you're getting a trifle personal, little sister-in-law? Araby's only just arrived. She hasn't had time to unpack, much less pack up again."

"Just wondering." Lena's smile was forced as she shook free of Jud's hold. "You leave any bruises, and I'll be forced to tell my husband where I got them." She took her time pushing back from the table. "Speaking of Sim, I'd best go check on him. Jud, could I have a word with you, please."

"Excuse me, Araby, I'll be right back."

"Take your time," Araby told him.

"I've got to see you, Jud," she heard Lena tell her brother-in-law as they went back inside together. "What you're doing to me is mean and cruel and I can't—"

"Shut up," Jud whispered loudly.

Araby strained to hear more, but the voices had become mumbled and distant.

A few minutes later, Jud returned and sat back down beside her.

"Another family crisis resolved," he said cheerfully. "You'll have to excuse Lena. She's hard-headed and spoiled. Her mama and daddy couldn't control her, and my brother gave up trying. But that's no reason to trouble you with my problems." Jud leaned his chair back against the wall. "Speaking of Mike's will, the lawyer, Wallace Ford, is away for a while. I don't know when he'll be back."

"That's fine. I'm in no hurry," Araby told him. "I'll be staying for a month or so anyway."

"Oh, I see." His smile was quick to return. "Tell me, what's a sophisticated city girl like you going to do out here for a whole month except get bored right out of her pretty little head? We don't have any of those luxuries you're used to back East."

"Oh, I'm sure I'll find something to occupy my time, and as far as luxuries are concerned, the simpler my life is, the better."

"I see." Jud curled the end of his moustache. "Now about Mike's will . . ."

"Yes, what about it?" It was obvious that Jud was completely blind to the fact that she was rapidly losing patience. The will. That's where the conversation had been heading all along, she decided, looking him straight in the eye.

"Let's not beat around the bush, Araby."

"No, let's not."

"The way I figure it, Mike left Tamarack to you. Now that's only fitting, seeing how you two were blood kin and all. Mind you, Sim and me loved him like a father. Too bad he didn't come along until we were both grown."

Araby wished he would get to the point. The way he kept twisting the tip of his moustache was very annoying.

"Anyway, to make a long story short, I'd like to buy the ranch from you. Now, there'll be a lot of folks coming out here to make you the same offer, but I'd just like you to keep in mind that I did speak first, and any offer they make I'll be glad to match." He looked at her long and hard. "If you decide to sell, I believe Mike would want you to sell it to me in order to keep Tamarack in the family."

"I don't make a habit of second-guessing the dead, Jud, but I will give careful consideration to your offer if the time comes."

When she saw him reaching for her arm, she stood up quickly. "Thank you for a most delightful meal, but I must excuse myself. I'm still a little weary from my journey."

"Of course, of course. How rude of me to keep you at the table so long."

When he blocked her exit, she had no choice but to let him take her arm.

"Now about Wallace Ford," he said as he walked her inside. "I don't suppose he said anything about the will when he notified you about Mike's death, did he?"

"I was more concerned over my uncle's death than his will," Araby replied, her words as sharp as she'd intended them to be.

"Of course. I certainly didn't mean to imply that you weren't."

Before she could stop him, he leaned over and kissed her cheek. "It's been a very trying time for all of us."

"Perhaps Mattie can direct me to my room?"

Jud laughed. "Why, you can take any room you like. Me and Sim and Lena, why we'll be moving out whenever you want us to. We only moved in because we didn't want any squatters staking a claim."

He edged closer. "Of course, if you want us to stay, we'll be happy to oblige."

Araby stepped away. She was certain it was no accident that his offer was accompanied by a brush of his arm across her breast. "I'm sure I can manage on my own, thank you."

"You think you might be wanting some company after you get settled in?"

Araby didn't even bother to smile. He didn't give up! "Another time, perhaps. I've been looking forward to doing a little riding . . . alone."

"You just tell Burley Wilkerson—that's the foreman—which horse to saddle up for you."

Jud stood at the bottom of the stairs grinning from ear to ear.

Araby couldn't believe him! Her rudeness had not fazed him in the least.

"Say, maybe this evening after supper you'd like to go on a buggy ride. You'd be surprised at how many stars we got in Idaho."

"Oh, I'm sure I would." But it wouldn't be the stars that would surprise her, she decided, starting up the stairs. "Another time, maybe. Not tonight."

"Your wish is my command, dear lady," he

called after her.

"Thank you, Jud," she replied with no enthusiasm and without looking back down.

Araby could feel his eyes boring right through her skirt as she climbed the stairs. She hadn't quite figured Jud out yet, but she had a feeling he could be charming one minute and dangerous the next. She had a feeling, too, that it would be in her best interest to have no more contact with him than absolutely necessary.

"Jud, I want to see you now. Do you hear me?"

Araby ducked into the first open room. Just what was it that Lena thought so important? she wondered.

She peeped around the corner of the door just as Jud grabbed hold of his sister-in-law, twisted her arm behind her back, and dragged her out of sight in spite of her shrill protests that he was hurting her.

"I had Hamstring take your trunks to the room at the end of the hall."

Araby whirled around. "Oh, Mattie. You gave me quite a start." She managed a weak smile. "Thank you for seeing to my things."

The stern face showed no hint of friendliness. "You here to stay?"

"For a while."

"It's none of my business, Miss Stone-Leigh, but . . ."

The front door slammed with a loud bang. Mattie changed her mind about whatever it was she had been about to say and finished, "You need anything, you call me."

Araby called to her dog and started down the

hall. She hadn't even unpacked yet, and already people were asking her when she was leaving. She had a feeling she was one guest who was un-invited *and* unwanted.

6

Araby felt at home the moment she stepped into the room at the end of the hall. It was small, but cozy, with a brass bed, washstand, wardrobe and rocking chair all jammed inside. Had she been given her choice of rooms, that was the one she would have chosen. The way the ceiling sloped down to the floor on one wall made the room look tiny, but on the opposite wall there was a large windowed door that opened out onto a little porch and a spectacular view of the mountains.

By late afternoon, her trunks had been unpacked and taken away to be stored. The events of the past few days, as well as Hamstring's descriptions, the wagon ride from town, and her own impressions of Tamarack had been recorded in her journal. A few of the details she thought it best to omit, especially Jake's connection with the train robber and her thoughts regarding the Cords, just in case Mattie decided to nose around in her belongings.

After donning her black leather riding boots and a loose-fitting skirt and blouse, Araby sneaked down the stairs and out the back door to avoid Jud, whose voice she heard on the front porch.

She found Hamstring standing outside the bunk house at a worktable set up under the trees. He was up to his elbows in a huge bowl of dough.

"Roll up them fancy sleeves, and I'll show you how to make biscuits," he offered when he saw her.

"Maybe some other time. I'm not much of a cook."

"Now how on earth do you ever expect to get yourself a husband if you don't know how to make bread?"

"What makes you think I'm in the market for a husband?"

"The woman that ain't, ain't been born yet."

Araby laughed. There was no point in arguing with him. She had a feeling that the only person who got the last word around Hamstring was Hamstring.

The cook rolled the dough out on the table. "You just mark my word, young lady, the day's going to come when you'll come sashaying down here with your apron on just begging me to teach you everything I know about biscuit making."

She wondered if Jake Montana liked biscuits. If he did, then perhaps . . .

"Ah ha! See there? You're smiling right now." Hamstring shook a floury finger in her face. "You got somebody in mind already, don't you?"

Araby tried to keep from chuckling. "The

only thing I got on my mind right now is saddling up one of the horses and going for a ride. By the way, where's Cross Fork from here?''

''I knew! I knew it!'' The little man jumped up and down. ''That Jake Montana can go through a whole mountain of biscuits in one sitting.''

''Don't be silly. I didn't say anything about Jake Montana.'' She helped herself to one of the hot biscuits from the tray he just brought out of the cook shack.

While she sat there, Hamstring told her all about the workings of the ranch and pointed out the cowboys to her, calling them by name— Eugene, Oddie, Cauley, Avery, Bobby, Bo, Sam, Cory, and Luke. He didn't mince any words when it came to describing the spring round-up he'd been on last month.

''No siree, m'am, you never seen such a commotion as we have when the herd's separated. The calves get branded and castrated in an uproar of ropes cracking, cows bellowing, sweat dripping, and blood spurting with the dust and manure.''

He started cutting up vegetables for the cowboys' beef stew. ''The drive, now that was always Mike's favorite time. He wouldn't hear of any of them professional trail drivers. Said him and Jake and the rest of the boys could handle any stampede just as well, if not better, than they could. And you know something? He was right.''

Hamstring stopped to wipe his eye with his apron. ''These damn onions get me every time.''

Araby nodded. ''Me, too.'' She knew as well as he that neither his nor her own tears could be blamed on the onions. ''I miss him, too, Hamstring."

Hamstring sniffed a few times, then blew his nose on his apron. "Sometimes I get the feeling he ain't really gone. He's just away for a while. I like to think he's still up in the mountains hunting, and he'll come dragging in one evening all worn out like he used to do." He gave her a rough hug. "Hey, you know something? I sure am glad you're here."

"You know something, Hamstring? I'm glad I'm here, too."

"Maybe later, after you've gone for your ride, me and you can go cut a few poles and go down to the river. Those trout have really been jumping lately."

Araby knew that Hamstring and Mike used to go fishing every evening before supper in the summertime. "I'd like that."

"Good. Those ole cowpokes can have their stew. Me and you'll fry us up some of those golly-whoppers!"

"My mouth's watering already." Her good mood was quick to return. "I think I'll go on down to the barn and see if there's an old plug I can go out hacking on."

"You just ask for Rowdy," Hamstring told her. "That's the young fellow in charge of the barn. He don't say much, but he's a good boy and a hard worker. Tell him to saddle up old Sally for you. She's a sweet thing. Won't give you a bit of trouble."

"Old Sally. Right. I'll remember that." She took a couple of carrots from the vegetable pile. "See you later."

"Sure thing, honey. Oh, by the way. You follow the river upstream, and you'll end up right at Cross Fork. Reckon you better stuff a few biscuits in your saddle bag?''

Laughing, Araby shook her fist at him and headed down to the barn with Tramp close at her heels.

Once inside the barn, Araby took a deep, satisfied breath. Most people found barn smells revolting, but not she! To her, the smell of leather, horseflesh and fresh hay was invigorating.

The stalls had all been mucked out and spread with clean straw. A pail of water and a fresh bucket of oats stood inside each one.

There were only three horses left in the barn. The others were out working, she decided. All three were mares—a bay, a little white one that looked like she had a lot of Arabian in her, and a chestnut with four white stockings.

Araby visited each one, patted their noses, and gave out the carrots as she tried to make up her mind.

The bay looked half asleep. That had to be old Sally. She liked her horses a little more spirited than that. The Arabian had bit burns around the corners of her mouth, no doubt caused by a rider with heavy hands, so she couldn't in all good conscience take that one out. The chestnut was by far the fittest of the three. From experience, Araby knew that chestnut mares with white stockings as a general rule were high-strung to the point of being half crazy. Mike had written her about a little chestnut troublemaker he was trying to break, and that might well be the one.

''Howdy, m'am.''

Araby turned around smiling, expecting to find the nice stableboy Hamstring had told her about. What she found was a big, hefty cowboy with slicked-back black hair that was in bad need of a washing. She disliked him instantly. His smile—no, his leer—made her skin crawl.

''The name's Burley, m'am. What can I do for you?''

So that was Burley Wilkerson. She had expected about as much.

''Hello, Mr. Wilkerson. I'm—''

''I know who you are.'' A yellow-toothed smile flashed over his face. ''You're Miss Araby Stone-Leigh, Mike Stone's niece. Word spreads real fast around these parts.''

He walked slowly towards her, thumbs hooked under his belt, studying every inch of her and making no secret about it.

''I never did think I'd like working for a woman, but now, I believe I've done gone and changed my mind. Anything you want me to do, I'd be most obliged to be of service, m'am. Anything at all. Don't be shy about asking.''

''Thank you, Mr. Wilkerson.''

Araby took extra caution to make sure there was not one trace of pleasantness in her tone. There was no misreading the unspoken meaning in his remark. Everything about Tamarack's new foreman made her uncomfortable, but he'd be the last to know it. He was a bully. She could tell that just from looking at him.

He edged closer, his lips all but smacking. His stares were bold and frank, as if they could see right through to her bare flesh.

''A woman out here all alone can get mighty lonely on cold winter nights.''

Araby refused to be bullied. ''I believe you are forgetting just who it is you are speaking to,

Mr. Wilkerson. In the future, I suggest you remember.''

Burley stopped in his tracks. His head dropped down. ''Beggin' your pardon, m'am. I didn't mean no disrespect. I never did learn to keep my mouth shut when it should be.''

''I'm looking for Rowdy. Have you seen him?''

''Oh, yes, m'am. I sent him to fetch the blacksmith. You want a horse saddled? I can do it for you. I'd be happy to.''

''Thank you, but I can saddle it myself.''

Burley grinned. ''I'm really sorry, m'am, but we don't keep none of them sidesaddles on the ranch. Wouldn't do us much good.''

''Then I suppose I'll just have to make do with what you do have,'' she said coolly.

''Yes, m'am. The tack room's at the back. You just pick out whatever saddle you want.''

Burley reached up to stroke the chestnut's neck, and the horse jerked back. ''Easy, girl. Nobody's going to harm you.''

Araby watched Burley closely. She had a feeling he was putting on a show of kindness for her benefit. He was probably even more of a bully when it came to animals.

''She's a little skittish around strangers,'' explained Burley when the horse kicked out at him. ''But you get her under saddle, and she's a real fine mount. We call her Darling 'cause she's such a sweet thing.''

A little skittish, thought Araby as she stood back and studied the mare. Ha! Only crazy horses rolled back their eyes so the whites showed.

''You say her name's Darling?''

Burley nodded.

Araby was sure it was no coincidence that he failed to mention that the mare's full name was Devil's Darling. She knew all about the little chestnut mare. That was the horse Mike had been trying to school—or as he put it, trying to teach some manners to. Mike had a theory about that horse, and now was as good a time as any to test it.

Araby took the halter from the stall gate. "Here. Let me."

"I'll go get you a saddle."

Whispering soft words, Araby led the horse out of the stall. She knew Burley was standing off to the side waiting and probably hoping for the mare to trample her.

"Good girl. That's a good girl," she praised the horse as she led her outside and tied her up at the post.

Burley busied himself outside as she gave the chestnut a quick brushing and picked her hooves, all the while watching her and snickering to himself.

"Now if you'd rather wait, Miss Stone-Leigh, some of the boys will be coming in shortly. Their horses will be all tired out if you want to take one of them."

"I thought you said she's a good mount."

She knew exactly what he was pulling on her. He was covering himself in case the horse ran away with her or did worse.

"Oh, she is. She is," he hurriedly assured her. "It's just that—well, she hasn't been ridden in a few days, and I wouldn't want her to get uppity with you."

"No, I suppose not." Araby threw the saddle over the mare's back and cinched the girth tight.

"Especially after that glowing recommendation you gave her."

"Now, I'm not trying to tell you how to ride, m'am," Burley said, "but I've found if you hold the reins too tight, horses tend to get a little contrary. They'd much rather you give them their head."

"I'll remember that."

And do just the opposite, Araby decided. With a horse like Devil's Darling, the first thing you had to do was let them know right from the start just who was the boss. You didn't have to be mean and beat them into submission. Just be firm. All the instruction Mike had given her in horsemanship had not fallen on deaf ears.

After getting the bit into the horse's mouth, Araby took her riding gloves out of her pocket and put them on. She had a feeling she was going to need those if she didn't want blistered hands.

A young, blond fellow was leading a cow pony back to the barn. He looked from Araby to Burley and back to Araby again. The expression on his face was one of sheer panic.

"Uh—m'am? If'n I w-was you, I'd get me another—"

"Rowdy!" Burley shouted. "I sent you for the blacksmith two hours ago. Where is he?"

"Couldn't come," stammered the boy. "C-can't git here . . . till in the . . . morning."

"Then you better go soak that pony's legs," Burley growled. "I want him ready to cut cows tomorrow."

"Yeah, B-Burley . . . sure thing."

One of the cowboys Hamstring had pointed out to her earlier called out to Burley.

"Do it now, Rowdy," shouted the foreman as

he strode over to the gate to talk to Oddie. "Not tomorrow."

Rowdy waited until Burley's back was turned before leading the cow pony past Araby.

"Meaning no d-disrespect, m'am," Rowdy stuttered, "but you d-don't want to ride that horse. She ain't called Devil's Darling . . . for nothing. Tell Burley . . . you want me to git you another horse."

Araby felt sorry for the poor boy. It was clear from the nervous way he kept looking in Burley's direction that he was frightened to death of the foreman.

"Shh. It's okay, Rowdy. Don't worry about me. I know what I'm doing."

"You keep . . . those reins tight . . . even if you think she's choking 'cause . . . if'n you d-don't, she'll take off for sure."

"You want to have your job come sundown, boy?" shouted Burley.

Araby was quick to his defense. "It's my fault for detaining him. I was asking him how to get to Cross Fork."

Burley motioned Rowdy into the barn, then walked back over to where she was standing. "You don't want to go nowhere near Cross Fork, m'am."

"Oh, and why not?"

Burley tugged at the stubble of his chin. "Well, you see, m'am, it's like this. We been having a little trouble with the fellow that owns that place ever since your uncle passed on. Hard telling what they might do to you to get even."

"Get even for what?"

"No sense troubling you with the workings of the ranch, m'am. I can take care of everything.

That's what Mr. Cord hired me for." He stepped to within arm's length. "Why don't I give you a leg up?"

"No, thanks. I can manage."

Before Burley could get a hand on her, she lifted her left foot into the stirrup and threw her right leg over the saddle.

A group of cowboys had gathered at the corral gate, but she didn't look twice in their direction. It was obvious they were expecting a show, and she was to be the main attraction. She wouldn't put it past Burley and his cronies to be placing bets on how long she'd stay on. True, a few of their faces looked horrified, but she had no time now to assure them she knew what she was doing.

Araby picked up the reins and took a firm hold on the horse's mouth.

Devil's Darling stood there like a perfect darling, not one muscle flinching. Mike had said she was the perfect mount—as long as she was standing still. But as soon as a rider asked her to move, something snapped inside the horse's head and she just went beserk.

Araby took a deep breath. She knew what to do when the horse bolted out of control. She only hoped it worked!

"Remember what I said about keeping a loose rein," Burley reminded her.

"And give her her head. I won't forget."

Araby chuckled to herself. Burley certainly wasn't wasting any time getting out of Devil's Darling's way.

"It's okay, girl." She gave the horse another pat. "It's just you and me now. We'll show those cowboys a thing or two. Walk on."

In answer to the slight nudge on her side, Devil's Darling took a few jerky steps forward. A second nudge and she threw back her head, nearly hitting her rider in the chest. A third nudge, less gentle, and she walked on, her stride short and uneven.

Araby glanced up at her audience on her way out the gate. No one was talking. All eyes were on her. They were all watching and waiting for Devil's Darling to do whatever it was that had made her so famous.

A few steps outside the gate, the mare stopped dead in her tracks. For a moment, she stood there quietly. Then all at once, she starting snorting and pawing at the ground with her front hooves while her hind quarters twisted from one side to the other.

"Easy, girl. Easy. No reason to be afraid of me. I'm not going to hurt you."

She held tight to the reins while trying to gentle the mare with soothing words. Sitting astride that horse was like being on a powder keg about to explode.

"That's a girl," she cooed softly. "You and I are going to be great friends."

She gave her another nudge with her leg.

The horse reluctantly walked on.

Araby gave one last glance behind her. The cowboys were still waiting for her to get bucked off. She couldn't resist a smile and a wave. She'd show them. They'd think twice the next time they tried to get the best of her.

One or two of them applauded.

With reins still tight in her hands, she headed the mare out to the road she and Hamstring had traveled earlier.

She waited until she was out of the cowboys' sight before relaxing her hold. The time had come to see if Devil's Darling deserved her reputation. If so, now was as good a time as any to try out Mike's theory about breaking horses.

Suddenly, without warning, the horse bolted, charging off down the road in a frenzied gallop.

Determined not to be unseated, Araby kept her balance and remained erect in the saddle.

The horse slowed down only long enough to throw in a few bucks and a rear. Failing to get her rider off that way, however, she shot on ahead even faster.

Never had Araby been taken for such a ride! The trees sped past them, and the ground seemed to be jumping right up at her as the mare's hooves pounded it.

It seemed they had gone for miles and miles before Devil's Darling finally began to tire. Her mane and coat were drenched with sweat, and froth dripped from her mouth. The earth-shattering gallop slowed almost to a rocking-horse canter.

Araby took a deep breath. She was just as exhausted as the horse, but Devil Darling's schooling session had only just begun.

"You want to run, girl? Let's run!"

Her heels dug deep into the horse's sides.

The horse hesitated, but only for a moment. Then, once again, after another buck, she lunged forward, kicking out her heels.

Every time the mare showed signs of slowing, Araby kicked harder. Little by little, she could feel the untamed mass of horseflesh beneath her begin to respond to her commands. A tweak on the rein, and Devil's Darling would slow down. A squeeze on the right rein, and she would turn in that direction.

"Whoa," Araby instructed softly.

The horse came to a square halt. Her breathing was labored. She sounded as if she were about to collapse.

Still, the lesson was not over.

Araby pulled back on the reins and squeezed at the horse's sides.

Devil's Darling backed up in response.

Then, Araby let the reins go slack.

The mare stood quietly in place.

She picked up the rein and gave the horse a nudge with her foot.

The horse slowly walked on.

Only after the exercise was successfully repeated a dozen times did she allow Devil's Darling to rest.

Araby slid off the horse and led her down to the river, cooing soft words of praise all the way.

"A little more work, and you'll be the best riding horse for miles around," Araby told her pupil while patting her.

After drinking her fill, Devil's Darling laid her head across Araby's shoulder and nickered softly.

Araby hugged her back. "You and I are going to get along fine, sweet pea. Just fine."

The sun was setting by the time Araby made it back to the barn. A child's pony couldn't have behaved better than Devil's Darling on the ride home. Still, she could not help but be a little disappointed. She had arrived at Cross Fork only to find out that Jake wasn't there and wasn't expected until much later. She'd left a message with one of the ranchhands that she had come to see him. From the disapproving looks she received, Araby could tell that Western men just didn't think it proper for ladies to come calling on men.

One of the cowboys at Tamarack saw her coming back through the gate and disappeared into the bunk house. It didn't take long for them all to gather outside the barn. They all looked surprised, Burley more than the rest.

She was tired and hungry, and all she wanted was a long soak in a tub full of very hot water, but not one of those cowboys would know just how worn out she was!

Rowdy came out to meet her. "You okay, m-m'am?"

Araby nodded and said loud enough for the others to hear, "I'm fine, but I don't know about Darling. I don't think she's used to being ridden so hard."

It was all she could do to keep a straight face as she rode the horse through the middle of the group.

"Lovely evening, isn't it?"

A couple of the men smiled back at her; a few shook their heads in disbelief and grinned. The rest of them just stared. Uncle Mike had told her that the respect of a cowboy had to be earned, and she had a feeling she had done just that.

"Reckon we better wait till tomorrow to go fishing," said Hamstring when he came running out to see her.

Smiling, she nodded. "That's a good idea."

After she had dismounted, a few of the men came over to her and told her how sorry they were about Mike's death, then offered to untack Devil's Darling and bed the horse down.

Araby knew that was their way of trying to make up for letting Burley get by with his mean trick. She thanked them, but declined their offer. After all, the horse had served her well, and it seemed only right that she return the favor with a good currying.

There wasn't a sign of Jud or Sim or Lena when she finally returned to the house. A single plate was set at the big oak table.

Mattie appeared just as she was about to go upstairs. "Mr. Cord said to tell you him and his brother and Lena had to go into town, and they're sorry you'll be having supper alone."

Araby nodded. Her legs ached so that she could hardly climb the stairs.

Mattie followed her up. "I figured you might be wanting a bath when you got in, so I had one of the fellows take the tub up to your room. I put some of Miz Lena's fancy smelling powders in it. You don't tell her now."

Araby shook her head. "Thank you."

"And supper will be on the table whenever you're ready. You just let me know."

Araby thanked the housekeeper again, closed the door and bolted it, then began taking off her clothes and dropping them along the way to the tub.

Sighing contentedly, she stepped into the tub and sank up to her neck in perfumed suds. She might well stay there all night!

A little while later, Araby opened her eyes and glanced around the room. No wonder there was a draft. The door out onto the porch was ajar. Odd! She could have sworn it was closed tight when she walked in.

She started to get out and shut the door, but

something made her sink deeper. Somebody was in the room with her.

"Mattie, is that you?"

She knew it wasn't the housekeeper even before she asked.

Curses! Tramp was still with Hamstring, and the little pistol she sometimes wore strapped to her leg was out of reach.

Araby swallowed hard. If that bastard Burley Wilkerson had sneaked up to her room . . .

A shadow stepped out from behind the dressing screen.

" 'Evening, Araby."

7

Jake Montana! His was one voice she'd have no trouble recognizing.

" 'Evening, Jake.''

It was hard to keep her voice steady, especially as the temperature of the water had just shot up a hundred degrees. Thank goodness the room was all but dark. She didn't need a lantern to know Jake's eyes were straining through the dimness.

She heard him swallow hard.

"Won't you sit down? I'll be out in a moment."

"Oh, uh—take your time."

Araby sank lower into the suds. "I came out to Cross Fork earlier to see you," she said, pretending the conversation was no different from any other. "One of your men told me you weren't around." She tried to clear the lump from her throat. "Were you out rounding up more strays?"

"It's the rustlers we were after this time."

"Oh, I see."

She watched as his hat went from one hand to the other and waited for him to say something to explain his unusual entry into her room, but he said nothing. The only sounds to be heard were those of water splashing and her own unsteady breathing.

"I reckon you won't be needing those riding lessons after all."

Araby smiled. His cowboy friends must have told him she had been on the notorious chestnut mare. Too bad. Those lessons would have been the perfect opportunity to spend time with him. "One can never know too much about horses," she managed.

She could sense he was uncomfortable, even though slipping through the window had been his idea, but she kept on talking. She told him about the reception she had received from the Cords. If only she could have seen his face clearly when Lena's name was mentioned! Were they indeed lovers as they were rumored to be?

She could tell from his grunts that Jud Cord was not a person he held in very high esteem, and when she said something about Burley, Jake came right out of the rocking chair.

"Why, that good-for-nothing saddle tramp! If he doesn't show you the respect due you, I'll see to it he don't look cross-eyed at nobody again."

"Oh, I think I took care of Mr. Wilkerson perfectly well on my own." The ribbing he had taken from the rest of the men when Devil's Darling came plodding back to the barn like an old hag was well worth any trouble he had caused her.

Something Mike had said came to mind just at

that moment. All cowboys liked to fancy themselves as Lancelots out to rescue a damsel in
distress. If a gal's interested in one, she's got to let
him be her knight in shining armor, Mike had
told her, whether she needs one or not.

"What I mean is," she continued hurriedly,
"Burley realized real fast just who he was dealing
with. I don't think he'll bother me again."

"Well, if he does, you just let me know."

"I appreciate that, Jake."

Araby splashed at the water to let him know
she was about to emerge from her bath. If she
stayed in much longer her skin would be as
wrinkled as a prune. Besides, continuing their
chat in such a manner really was absurd—unless of
course they were both in the tub, and since it
would be too embarrassing to make such a sug-
gestion even in jest, she really had no other alternative.

"Could you hand me a towel, please? There's
one on the bed."

Jake tripped over the bed post when he went
to retrieve it. Careful to keep his eyes straight
ahead the other way, he backed up to the tub
holding out the towel behind him.

Araby stepped out and dried off quickly. "My
robe, please. It's hanging on the wardrobe."

Once again, he stumbled his way across the
tiny room and handed her what she'd requested
without turning around.

Quickly, she slipped her arms through the
satin sleeves and belted the sash tight around her
waist.

Jake remained with his back turned.

Araby felt her way to the bedside table and lit
the candle inside the lamp. "There. That's

better."

She waited a moment for Jake to take the cue to turn around, but when he did not, she assured him it was safe to do so.

Jake turned around slowly. Downcast eyes started at her bare feet and began a lazy climb to her face.

Araby could have sworn she heard a muffled "damn" escape from his tightly closed mouth.

"Anybody ever told you you're the prettiest woman that ever walked the face of this earth?"

She shook her head. Jake wasn't the first to give her so grand a compliment, but he was the first to make such a remark without expecting some sort of favor in return.

"Well, I'm telling you now. You truly are."

"Thank you." Her words were barely a whisper.

They stood there for the longest time, she beside the bed and he next to the tub, just staring at each other, neither speaking, neither moving an inch for fear the spell of the moment would be broken. How could the emotions running rampant inside her be explained? Never before had she wanted to fling herself at any man and let whatever might happen just happen!

It took her a moment before she started thinking straight again. As Mike was so fond of telling her, she had taken leave of her senses. Just what was coming over her? What was it about Jake Montana that made her want to throw caution to the wind?

Jake's face broke out into a big grin. "I reckon you're wondering why I came in through the window instead of by way of the front door like most folks."

"The thought did cross my mind," she admitted.

His smile was contagious. Obviously Shakespeare's heroes weren't the only ones who made spectacular entrances. Jake could no doubt teach all the Romeos of the world a thing or two!

"Jud would have me shot for trespassing if he caught me here."

Araby nodded. There was no love lost between those two. By coming there to see her, Jake had risked his life. Dare she hope that meant she had come to mean as much to him as he did to her?

She sat down on the edge of the bed.

Jake pulled up the rocking chair.

Their legs all but touched.

"Did I tell you Mike helped me buy my first spread?"

"You told me he helped you get into the cattle business." She had a feeling he was searching for something impersonal to talk about. If so, that meant he had come there for no reason other than to see her. That made her feel very happy, and the fact that he had gone about it in such an unorthodox way made it all the more romantic.

"I told you I used to be a bounty hunter, didn't I?"

Once more, she nodded.

"If it hadn't been for Mike, I'd have been ten foot under by now. He helped me buy Cross Fork, too. 'Course I paid him back every cent, even though he kept insisting I put my money back in the ranch."

Araby looked up in surprise. Where had she gotten the idea he only worked at Cross Fork?

"All the cattlemen in the valley are locking

horns with Jud. Did you know he's blaming everything on you?''

She was so busy watching the candlelight reflected in his eyes that it took a moment for what Jake just said to sink in.

''Blaming what on me? I've only just arrived.''

''Yeah, well, nobody puts much stock in what Jud Cord says anyway. That is, nobody except for a few of his friends. Unfortunately the Sheriff is among that select group.''

Her curiosity was piqued. For a moment, Jake's powerfully broad shoulders were forgotten. ''Exactly what is Jud blaming me for?''

''Reckon I'd best start at the beginning.''

Araby nodded, encouraging him to go on. She could listen to that slow, exaggerated drawl of his all night.

''You see, the best crossing there is to get the cattle over the river to pasture in the spring and back again in the fall is through Tamarack land. Now Mike, he told all the ranchers years ago they were welcome to cut on to his land whenever they had to, and none of them ever abused his generosity or took advantage of it.''

It took a moment for Araby to be able to concentrate more on what was being said than who was saying it.

''Anyway, to make a long story short, Jud's already put out the word that if the ranchers want to bring their herds back through this year, they got to pay, and pay dearly, too.'' Jake rocked slowly back and forth. ''If they don't pay, they either have to bring their cattle back through by way of Devil's Kitchen, and risk having them break their legs going over boulders and their necks when they fall from the cliffs, or bring them back through the marsh. Now, the marsh is a sure death trap for the cattle. If they mire up in the muck and can't get out, they'll kick and die from exhaustion. If the mud don't get them, the wild parsnips will.''

She knew from Mike that wild parsnips were poisonous to the cows.

''The ranchers around here are caught between a rock and a hard place. If they do pay the price Jud's demanding, they're not going to break even, even if all the cattle make it to market. If they don't pay, they'll lose a lot of their herd anyway.''

Araby could well understand their dilemma. ''Damned if they do, and damned if they don't.''

''Reckon that's as good a way to put it as any.'' Jake stopped rocking. ''Now that you're here, Jud's telling everybody that you were the one who came up with that idea, and that he's just carrying out orders.''

''Do they believe him?''

Jake gave a half smile. ''Naw. They know who's behind it.''

Could it be that was the only reason he had come calling? she wondered. Surely not. After all, what he had just told her could have waited until the next day or the day after. None of the ranchers would be bringing their cattle back down for another month or so. Maybe Jake just thought he needed an excuse to come calling at such an hour and under such unusual circumstances.

Still, that wasn't what was most important at the moment. What Jud was trying to do was tantamount to extortion, and he had no right, no right at all, to take advantage of Mike's death for his own gain. That in itself was unforgiveable. And for him to lay the blame on her, that was inexcusable. She had a mind to tell him just that!

"You tell the ranchers for me, Jake, to just ignore Jud. Mike's been letting them use that crossing for twenty years. I'm not about to go against my uncle's wishes."

"Well now, that's real nice of you, and I'm sure all the ranchers will appreciate it, but . . ."

Araby knew the point he was trying to make. "I don't care what Jud's told you or anybody else. He doesn't run Tamarack, I do. That is, I will in twenty-nine days."

She took the letter from Wallace Ford out from the back of her journal, where she had put it for safe-keeping, and handed it to Jake to read.

Jake leaned closer to the light.

His nearness made her shiver. Every time he let out a sigh, her heart pounded even more loudly.

Jake folded the letter and handed it back to her. "Jud's been bragging that Mike left Tamarack to him. I knew he was lying. Mike didn't have much use for either of those boys. Never did. He just tried to help them because he felt he owed something to their poor mother." He chuckled to himself. "I knew he'd see to it that the Cords didn't get their hands on any part of Tamarack. Why do you reckon Mike wanted to make sure you stayed here for a month, though?"

Araby had already figured out the answer to that, but she was certainly not going to tell him that had been her uncle's way of making certain the two of them got acquainted.

"Oh, I suppose it was because he'd been

hounding me to take a rest from my acting and just enjoy life for a while. I'd been promising him for a long time that I would come out here to see him, but there was always some reason I'd put it off until the next year." She paused and took a deep breath. "Next year won't be coming for Mike. I didn't come out here to get what I can get, and I'm not staying the month because the will says I have to. I'm doing it because I owe it to Mike."

"Whatever your reason, I'm glad you came," Jake said quietly. "Real glad."

He started to reach for her hand, then pulled his back.

They sat staring at each other without speaking.

Araby wondered if he had any idea at all just how much she wanted to lose her fingers in his thick, dark waves. Surely he could sense her yearning to smooth away the signs of the sun and the wind from his face. He had to know just how badly she wanted to touch him, to hold him close, just for a moment . . . only for a moment. Didn't he?

"Yeah, I sure am glad you came here." Jake cleared his throat before going on. "Your showing up sure played hell with Jud's plans to take over the ranch. He knew Mike had kinfolks back East, but he didn't think any of them would come out here. He'll try to buy Tamarack from you. I'd be surprised if he hasn't already made you an offer. What you do with the ranch is your business, but if you do decide to sell, I'd appreciate you giving me first chance. I wouldn't cheat you. I'd give you fair dollar."

Araby kept her head lowered. If her eyes met

his, he would surely see just how disappointed she was. For one brief, glorious moment, she had allowed herself the luxury of thinking that she herself was the reason he was so glad she had come to Tamarack. He'd just told her differently. How foolish for her to have thought otherwise!

Somehow, she managed to keep her voice from betraying her true feelings. "I can certainly understand your concern. After what Jud's tried to do about the crossing, his owning Tamarack could be disastrous for the entire valley. To be honest with you, I'm not quite sure what I'm going to do. It's impractical to think I can keep it and run it myself, but I'm not sure I want to sell it, either. This land meant so much to my uncle. Why, selling it would be like selling his dreams. Tamarack's all that's left of Mike."

"Mike would be real proud to hear you say that." Once again he reached for her hand, and once again he pulled back. "Mike did love this land, that's for sure. And I have an idea he wanted you to love the land the way he did, and that was why he wanted you here for a month."

"I'm sure that had a lot to do with it," Araby agreed.

Just what would Jake's reaction be if she told him the ranch wasn't all Mike had in mind for her to fall in love with?

His tone grew solemn once more. "You be careful of Jud. He's one smooth talker. Quite a lady's man, too, and I understand he's used to getting his way."

"His way with the ladies or with business deals?" she couldn't resist asking.

Jake didn't crack a smile. "Both. And he's just as dangerous either way."

"You have my word that if I decide to sell Tamarack, I'll give you first chance." She wondered if he would go now that he had gotten what he'd come after.

"I appreciate that, Araby. Really, I do." He rubbed his palms over his trousers, then held out his hand.

For a moment she forgot that a handshake was necessary to seal the deal. He hadn't wanted to hold her hand after all.

She offered him her hand, and he gave it a firm shake. His hand was rough with callouses, a working man's hand. She hated to let it go.

"It's getting dark. I'd best be going," he said for the third time.

Araby could only nod. It was dark when he arrived, so what was the hurry?

"There aren't any gopher holes out here?"

She caught her breath. She couldn't believe she had asked that!

"I came over on foot."

"Of course. I don't suppose you could very well tie Buck up out front, could you?"

Her hand stayed locked in his long after the deal had been sealed. Just who it was doing the holding she wasn't quite sure. Was he pulling her to him, or was she going there of her own accord?

Her whole body went weak. What was the matter with her? Her inner strength had always been a source of personal pride. How could it fail her now, when she needed it the most? Surely she was not on her way to becoming one of those ridiculous females whose resolve crumbled at the first sign of trouble.

She waited for Jake to make a move after he stood up, but his feet stayed in place. If he were in any hurry to leave, he was certainly making no headway toward the balcony.

Araby knew she shouldn't ask the question that had been eating at her for the last little while. If she did, he would surely cut loose and run. But she had to. She had to take the risk. She'd not have a moment's peace until she knew the answer.

"Is Tamarack the only reason you came here tonight?"

Jake said nothing. Not once did he blink as his gaze searched her face.

Araby could hear his heart racing. Or was that hers?

Finally, he spoke, his words soft but firm. "What do you think?"

His breath fanned her cheeks, making them burn even hotter.

She shook her head and mumbled, almost inaudibly, "I honestly don't know."

"There's only one reason I came here, Araby, and I promise you that reason ain't Tamarack. I came to see you. I admit that. To tell you the truth, I've had nothing else but you on my mind since last night—and the night before that."

"Oh, Jake."

Before she had a chance to tell him that he had been on her mind, too, and for just as long, he had taken hold of her shoulders with both hands, pulled her to him, and stopped her words with his lips.

His arms wrapped themselves so tight around her she could hardly draw a breath, but at that moment, being able to breathe was the least of her concerns.

His kisses were long and hard and filled with

desperation. One no sooner ended than the next began.

Jake let out a groan and took a step back. "If I don't get out of here soon, I won't be going at all."

Last night she had let him get away. Tonight, she wasn't going to make the same mistake. The problem was just how was she going to tell him that. After all, she'd spent so much time saying no, she wasn't quite sure how to go about saying yes. Maybe she'd better just say it!

"Don't go."

"You want me to stay?" He seemed unsure, not of himself but of her.

"I want you to stay."

"What about come morning?"

Araby had a feeling she'd want him to stay forever come morning. She couldn't tell him that, though. If she did, it would probably scare him off.

"Come morning, we'll go downstairs and have breakfast with Jud if you like."

Jake laughed. "I can see you've got your uncle's sense of humor."

Araby waited, wondering. Had she made a fatal mistake by speaking her feelings?

Finally, Jake lifted her hands to his lips and kissed each finger, his eyes not straying for an instant from hers. Then, ever so gently, he pushed her back and kept her at arm's distance for what seemed to be hours.

She knew what he was doing, and that endeared him to her all the more. He was giving her time to reconsider and back down if she wanted.

Her gaze held his. The desire she saw reflected inside his eyes mirrored her own. She wanted him and was not ashamed to let him know it.

"Are you sure, Araby?"

"I thought you cowboys took what you wanted and asked permission later," she teased him.

"Ladies aren't like strays. We can't rope 'em, wrestle 'em, and brand 'em." Finally, he smiled. "Though it might work out better if we could."

Araby laughed softly.

His expression was quick to change, and his voice took on an uncharacteristic seriousness. "Now I don't know how we cowboys measure up to those fancy dans back East, but I'll tell you this much. We don't go after something unless we really want it, and once we decide that, we'll not stop at anything until we get it."

If he only knew! It wasn't until she met him that she had met a real, honest-to-goodness man.

"And am I what you want, Jake?"

He nodded. "Ever since Mike showed me your picture three—no four—years back, I knew right then that no other woman could ever hold a candle to you."

"My picture?" She pushed him away. "Then you knew all the time who I was?"

"Guilty as charged, m'am."

"Then why did you . . . ?"

She stopped before she stuck her foot in her mouth. If he had known all along, then why had he pretended to think she was a mail-order bride on the train? Had he meant what he said about not being in the market for a wife?

"Why did I what?"

"Never mind."

The granite-hard chest pressing into her made

her forget just what it was she had been wondering. No matter. There'd be time later for chatting . . . much later.

Jake untied her sash and watched her robe open over her hips and legs. The pink folds of satin parted to reveal soft ivory curves and rises beneath.

Blister-toughened hands eased inside, gently caressing her roundness. Then, becoming bolder, eager fingers began a delicious voyage into territories never before explored.

Her heart pounded, stopped, then pounded again even louder and harder. Her knees were as wobbly as a newborn foal's. It took every bit of strength she could muster to wrap her arms around him and hold on tight.

His lips were all consuming, and she returned his kisses with an intensity that matched his own. One groan after another tumbled from her lips. How much longer she could endure the fire raging inside her, she was not certain, but if it were not soon brought under control, the entire room would become an inferno!

Tentatively at first, Jake's touch became sure and confident in its quest to discover and explore. He was clearly no stranger to the female anatomy, for he knew all the secret little spots that gave so much pleasure.

Araby could tell there had been other women, but who or how many had come before her mattered little. What was important now was that there'd never be anyone else again! They were his past. She was his present and his future.

Jake eased her robe off her shoulders, and it fell the rest of the way down to the floor. Then he stepped out of her embrace and solemnly took in

169

the lush beauty just revealed to him.

Araby wanted to ask if what he saw pleased him, but she could tell from the way his eyes hung on to every detail just what that answer would be.

Once again his arms came around her, but this time they neither caressed nor explored. Instead, they lifted her off the Indian rug and ever so gently laid her down in the middle of the patchwork quilt on the bed.

His gaze content to feast on her and nothing else, Jake took off his holster and placed the gun within easy reach on the bedside table. His boots hit the floor with a dull thud, and his trousers followed close behind. When he started to unbutton his shirt, Araby pushed away his hands and began doing it herself, her fingers itching to stroke the strong cords of flesh straining against the light blue cotton.

His head dropped back with a moan, and his chest began to rise and fall in rhythm with his labored sighs.

The more intense his breathing, the bolder her hands became as she began her own exploration. Never before had she dreamed of taking such liberties with any man, even if she were wed to him.

Jake leaned down to blow out the light.

Araby reached out to stop him. She wanted to see him, see all of him, as well as each expression crossing his face.

With one long kiss after another, Jake eased her back down. His hard, lean form hovered above her, reveling once again in the sight that had been presented to him.

Desire flooded her whole being. Roaming

hands swept over her, sending delicious little shivers up and down her length. Eager breasts rose to his touch. A flick of a finger was all it took to bring their pink tips to crested peaks. Slowly his hands moved downward, one on each side, teasing, tickling, promising. One slid down her stomach, the other caressed the swell of her hips. And where his hands went his lips came not far behind.

There was no part of her that did not quiver from his touch. She was helpless to control her own reactions. He orchestrated her every movement. No longer did she belong solely to herself.

A hunger such as she had never known before took possession of her. One word pounded over and over inside her head. Jake . . . Jake . . . Jake. Silent pleas begged him to take what she was only too happy to give him. She belonged to him. She was his and had been long before they ever met.

At long last, he eased down onto her and covered her with his powerful frame. His chest was crushing, just as she had dreamed it would, but its weight was welcome.

She needed no guidance. Her movements flowed naturally from her. Her legs entwined themselves around his, pulling him still closer.

Something hard and warm parted her thighs, and she opened herself up to him, beckoning him inside.

Araby gasped in sweet, sweet agony. What little pain there was proved to be short-lived. At last they were as one. His body melted into hers, and the whole world was filled with him and him alone.

Jake began moving inside her, slowly at first, then more and more intensely.

A little uncertain at first, she rose to meet his thrusts, then relaxed and waited for the next, when her back would arch higher, encouraging him to go deeper. She wanted to give as much pleasure as she was receiving, and any doubts that she was were quickly dispelled by his muffled moans.

Then, just as she was losing herself in the intensity of his strokes, sensations she was at a loss to explain suddenly erupted, sending her into a wondrous frenzy. Her fingers dug deep into his back while her legs clung tighter and tighter. She could not contain her little squeals of delight.

Strange tremors shook her insides. The explosions wracking through her touched off more fiery bursts and shattered her world into a thousand, a million, tiny pieces.

Her eyes closed with a smile. Surely no experience with love could ever be sweeter.

The same smile that had closed her lids opened them again a while later. The candle had all but burned down to the wick. For a moment, she thought she had been dreaming, but the strong leg thrown across hers assured her no dream could be as satisfying as that reality she had just experienced.

Jake was no apparition. He was there in the flesh. He, too, had succumbed to a love-sated fatigue. His mouth bore the same contented smile as her own.

In his sleep, he reached out to her, and she snuggled down in his embrace. If only that night could go on forever.

8

" **G** ood morning, Araby. Slept well?"
Jud was waiting in the dining room
when she went down for breakfast the next
morning.

"Very well, thank you."

Araby paused for a closer inspection of an
Indian bowl atop the sideboard. It was hard to
keep from being all smiles. Actually she had
never spent a better evening, even if she had
gotten only a few hours' sleep—and that after her
late-night visitor had left her room the same way
he entered. How many times during the course of
that glorious night had she poked herself just to
make sure it was no blissful dream she had
experienced? A hundred times if once!

Jake Montana. Just thinking his name was
enough to lift her off the ground. She dared not
dwell too long on what had happened during
those delicious hours lest she be sent spinning
right into the heavens. Paradise! That was what

she had found in his arms. If she lived to be a hundred, she'd never again know such joy. What lessons she had learned! What a teacher she had!

If she had one regret, it was that the script for her next play had been left on the table beside the bed. Jake had noticed it in the wee hours of morning as he had strapped on his gun and grumbled something under his breath about New York. After last night, she didn't even know where New York was. Nor did she care. Jake knew, and she could tell from his tense frown that he cared, too.

After she had taken her seat, Araby looked up to see Mattie's querying face staring down at her. Whatever the question, if indeed there had been one, she'd not heard. Even if she had, she couldn't possibly comprehend. Her mind was miles away—at Cross Fork in fact.

The look on Jud's face was similar to the housekeeper's. "What do you want for breakfast?"

"Oh, anything. Anything will be fine."

"Bring Miss Stone-Leigh what I'm having." Then in a kinder voice, he said to Araby, "You seem somewhat preoccupied this morning. Is there something on your mind?"

Araby shook out her napkin and spread it over her lap. Actually, it wasn't something, but someone. Of course, she couldn't very well tell Jud that, or anyone else for that matter. For five years she'd been on stage, and all that time she had fought off amorous advances and overtures from men she knew and some she didn't know. Two days in Idaho and it was a completely different scenario. All her life she'd been waiting for a man like Jake, and she hadn't even known it.

Jud touched her hand.

She drew back instantly.

"Is something troubling you, Araby? I'd be glad to help if I knew what's wrong."

"Actually, Jud, there is something bothering me." Now was as good a time as any to set him straight. She just had to go about it very carefully.

"When I was in Castle Rock, I overheard some of the ranchers talking, and what they said very much concerned me."

"Go on."

"From what I could gather, they were all upset over some charge that was going to be levied on them for bringing their cattle back across the river over Tamarack land." She very quickly decided it would not be in her best interest to offend Jud. Perhaps she'd best give him a way out. "Of course, I'm sure there must be some mistake. Uncle Mike would never expect money from his neighbors in return for a favor."

The angry creases that marred his good looks vanished as quickly as they appeared. "It seems there has been some sort of misunderstanding. I'll see to it that everything's cleared up."

Araby smiled. She had no doubt about the source of such a misunderstanding. Still, confronting Jud would serve no purpose.

Mattie served platters of ham and eggs, and they began their breakfast in silence.

Midway through the meal, there was a loud knock at the door, then the sound of boots stomping across the floor.

"Gotta talk to you, Boss."

Jud shot his eyes from Burley to Araby, then back to the foreman again.

Burley took off his hat. "Oh, 'morning, m'am.

Sorry to disturb you."

"Good morning, Mr. Wilkerson. Is something wrong?"

Jud spoke up quickly. "I'm sure whatever it is can wait until we've finished breakfast."

Araby could sense that, whatever the problem, they did not want to discuss it in front of her. "Oh, no, please. I insist. Anything that concerns Tamarack concerns me."

Burley waited for Jud's nod before going on. "It's Montana, Mr. Cord. I saw him snooping around before daylight. Before I could get my gun, he was gone."

Araby held her breath. She could feel her face going paler. Jake really would have been shot for trespassing!

"A gun?" Jud chuckled. "Really, Burley, there's no need for violence. Just ask him what he's doing here, and if he's lost something, help him find it. It's as simple as that."

Araby could see Jud's indifference was just a show for her benefit. At the mention of Jake's name, his whole face had contorted in anger.

"But boss, that's not. . . ." When Burley saw Jud motion in Araby's direction, he did not finish. Instead, he nodded. "Sure, boss. Whatever you say."

"Just a minute, Mr. Wilkerson," Araby called out when the foreman turned to leave.

"Yes, m'am?"

It wasn't easy keeping her temper under control. "In the future, I suggest you refrain from shooting anyone until you speak to me first. Is that understood?"

Burley looked to Jud.

Jud nodded.

"Yes, m'am. I understand."

After Burley left, Jud didn't give her a chance to remark on what had just happened. "I'm sure you'll be wanting to visit Mike's grave and pay your last respects. I'd be happy to take you up to Butte's Peak whenever you're ready."

Araby stopped chewing. "Butte's Peak?"

"That's where we were hunting when Mike got bit by the rattler," Jud explained.

Araby had long ago cõmmitted the contents of Mike's letter to memory. "That's odd."

"What do you mean?"

"Mike wrote to me that he was going hunting on Freezeout Mountain."

"He changed his mind at the last minute. You know how Mike was."

Araby said nothing. She knew exactly how her uncle was, and if Jud knew him half as well as he claimed, he'd know, too, that once Mike's mind was made up nothing could change it.

Jud snapped his fingers. "Of course. I remember now. Mike wanted to go up Butte's Peak after a grizzly one of the miners spotted up there. From what I heard, that big ole bear was the granddaddy of them all. Stood as tall as three good-sized men one on top of the other. Or so I heard."

He laughed. " 'Course we didn't see anything that even resembled that monster. Guess he must have heard we'd come looking for him and made tracks the other way."

Araby found little amusement in Jud's efforts to be funny. It bothered her that Mike had gone to Butte's Peak. She supposed he really could have changed his mind, but that was so unlike him. It bothered her, too, that Jud was trying just a little too hard to convince her.

"Guess you heard there's a big dance in town Saturday night. Not only is it the Fourth of July but rumor is, Idaho is about to become a state." Jud leaned closer. His dimples danced on his chin. "I'd like very much to take you."

"Thank you, but someone's already asked me."

Araby had a feeling Jud didn't want to take her to the dance nearly as much as he wanted to change the subject.

"Montana?" he asked.

She nodded.

Jud didn't seem particularly disappointed. "If I told you to be careful of him, you'd think I was jealous. And I am. A little. You watch out for him anyway. Where ladies are concerned, he's got some reputation." He gave her a big wink. "Hey, you'll save me a dance, won't you?"

Araby forced a smile. "Of course."

Just then, she caught a glimpse of Lena tiptoeing past the door with her boots in hand. Jud saw her, too, but said nothing.

Araby called out for Lena to join them, but the invitation was ignored.

Jud pushed back from the table. "I better get going. I'm late enough as it is. Anything I can do for you in town?"

She assured him there was not. "Oh, just one thing before you go." She met his stare and held on. "About Jake. As far as I'm concerned, he can come and go on Tamarack land as he pleases. I'd appreciate it if you'd remind Burley of that."

Jud's smile stayed put. "Of course, Araby. Whatever you say. You have a good day now, you hear."

Araby poured herself another cup of coffee. There. That hadn't been so bad. After all, she did own Tamarack, or she would very soon. It was time someone stood up to Jud Cord, and that someone might as well be her.

She watched out the window as Lena rode off on a buckskin. A few minutes later, Jud took off in the same direction on a palomino.

She gazed longingly in the direction of Cross Fork. She wouldn't see Jake until noon. That was four whole hours away. It might as well be forty.

" 'Fess up, Araby. Hamstring made these biscuits, didn't he?"

All afternoon, as they languished in the shade of a willow tree by the river's edge, Jake had taken such delight in teasing her.

"And just what makes you so certain I didn't make them myself, Mister Know-It-All?"

Araby sat on the grass hugging her knees close to her chest. Picnics in the park would never be the same again, not after today. The repast was simple—fried chicken, buttermilk biscuits, and apple popovers—but it tasted so much more delicious than caviar and smoked salmon. Buck and Darling grazed nearby. Tramp was busy chasing butterflies. What an absolutely perfect afternoon! If only the day could last forever!

Araby smiled. She remembered having said the very same thing about last night.

Jake tickled her nose with a blade of grass. "The way I figure it, those of the gentler persuasion fall into two categories—gals who can cook and gals who don't have to. And you are definitely one of the ones who don't have to."

"Silly me. And I thought I was in a class all by

myself.''

"You are. Why, you could have any fellow you wanted without ever going near the pots and pans.''

"Suppose it's you I want?''

Her eyes searched deep into his. It wasn't her nature to be so bold, not usually. However, during the past twenty-four hours she'd found herself doing and saying a lot of things that weren't necessarily true to form.

"You got me, Araby. You know that. You got me for just as long as you want me.''

She could tell from the way his voice dropped at the end of his remark that the script he'd seen on the table still bothered him. Should she tell him that, at that very moment, she didn't care if she never set foot on the stage again? No. If she did, he'd probably think she was just leading him on.

Jake chewed off the end of the blade of grass and spat it over his shoulder. "You know, the only trouble with having an actress for a lady friend is that a fellow never knows when she's play-acting and when she's not.''

Araby threw her shoe at him. It hit right where she had aimed between his legs.

"Ouch!''

"Last night was no performance, Jake Montana, if that's what you're thinking.''

"Reckon you're mad at me now, huh?''

Araby pushed him back. "You bet I am.''

She wasn't mad, not really. She supposed she could understand why he might think that. How was he to know for sure she wasn't some bored rich girl out for fun and frolic to pass time?

"Couldn't you tell . . . I mean, didn't you

know that I'd never . . . ?''

"Been with a man before?" He nodded. "I know that, and I'm honored that you thought enough of me to let me be the one. It's just that . . ."

"It's just what?" She moved closer to him. "Tell me. Tell me what it is that bothers you."

It took several stops, starts, and sputters before Jake attempted an answer.

"Damn it, Araby, I've had my share of women. I'd be a liar to say I hadn't, but . . ."

Araby waited for him to continue. She certainly hadn't expected him to have led a monk's life. Without names and faces, those women meant nothing to her. One thought was a little troubling, however. Had Lena been one of them?

Jake threw a pebble into the river and watched it skip along the surface. "What I'm trying to say is . . . Ah, hell, I don't know myself what I'm trying to say. I guess I just don't like the idea that you're here today and gone tomorrow."

Araby reached up and touched his cheek. Light fingers traced a broken line down to his chin. "How can you be so certain I'll be gone tomorrow when I don't know for certain myself?"

"Are you saying you might not go back to New York?"

"The thought has crossed my mind."

Only just at that moment. But she didn't tell him that.

Araby listened while Jake expounded on the many merits and virtues of living in Idaho—towering mountains, lush valleys, rolling meadows, unspoiled plains, wide open spaces. She'd heard it all many times before from Mike.

There was no denying any of those attractions.
What Jake did not realize, however, was that a
desert would be paradise if she could share it with
him.

She touched her cheek to his. She wanted to
tell him that, but it would be better if she didn't.
At least, not yet. It wouldn't be fair to lead Jake
on, or herself for that matter. Like it or not, she
had her career to consider. It had taken years of
study and more years of hard work to get where
she was today. Could she so easily give that up?

At that moment, yes.

"To tell you the truth, Jake, I don't know
what I'll end up doing, and it just wouldn't be fair
for me to pretend I do. I guess it'll just take time
for me to sort my life out."

Jake seemed satisfied with what she'd just
said. Falling back down onto the grass, he pulled
her down with him. "Maybe I better help sort
you out."

"I think that's a wonderful idea."

Araby wound her arms right around his neck.
She may have dreamed of going out West and
falling in love, but never in a million years would
she have expected it really to happen. Jake was
everything she wanted in a man. He was everything a man should be. He was good and kind and
honest, not to mention the fact that he was the
handsomest man she'd ever laid eyes on. She'd
found everything a woman could want in him.
Having found it, how could she ever give it up?

Slowly, he took the pins from her hair. "I
hope you don't think I'm trying to influence you
one way or another."

"Mmmmm. I'll try to remain objective."

That was much easier said than done. By the

second kiss, she knew for certain she would agree to anything . . . everything.

"You know something, Miss Araby Stone-Leigh? I do believe you are even more beautiful in the sunlight than by candlelight."

He kissed open each of her blouse buttons, then nipped at the eyelet straps underneath until the camisole slipped off her shoulders.

"Maybe I'd better reserve final judgment until tonight."

"Whatever you say."

Araby studied his face carefully. Not one detail would she ever forget.

With a sigh of pleasure, she closed her eyes and enjoyed the love bites nipping over her neck. Her heart seemed to rush to every bit of flesh he caressed. Excitement lurched inside her long before he slid her skirt down her legs and threw it into the bushes behind them. Only he could satisfy the tremendous aching deep inside her.

Deciding he wasn't getting out of his clothes nearly fast enough, she reached for his silver belt buckle. "Here. Let me help."

Fiery hot hands showed no mercy. They tormented her with each stroke, teasing and caressing those same hidden spots that had eagerly awakened to his touch the night before.

Soon, very soon, she would once again be sent soaring beyond passion's highest pinnacle. Of that she was confident. Jake alone possessed the magic that would set free the burning sweetness imprisoned within her.

Sheltering her softness with his strength, Jake poised himself over her.

Unlike last night, she needed no help matching her body's responses to his. Desire charged across her in a burning rampage. Her back arched naturally, and she rose to meet him, each movement more in control than the last. Little bursts of hysteria ebbed and flowed inside her, leaving her powerless to control them.

Their breathing came together, then parted again in mumbles and moans.

Araby laid back and smiled. So that was what all her experienced friends ranted and raved about. They had been right, absolutely right. This was ecstasy—spine-tingling, awe inspiring ecstacy!

"Jake?"

He made a sleepy noise.

"Jake, are you awake?"

Tickling fingers ran down his spine and back up again.

"I am now, darling."

Should she tell him or not? Surely he had already figured it out for himself.

No, better not. The moment was special. It would be lost forever, never again to be recaptured, if he didn't feel what she was feeling.

"Never mind."

She tightened her hold around his back. She didn't want to lose him. There was nothing she wouldn't do to keep him—nothing at all.

He kissed her cheek and yawned. "I love you, too, Araby."

Rolling over onto his side, he took her with him.

A moment later, he was snoring.

Nestled close against his firm hips, Araby spent the next few minutes content just to watch him take in one breath and let out another. He belonged to her, and she belonged to him. He had told her he loved her. That declaration would bind them together forever.

"Oh, I do love you, Jake Montana," she whispered into his chest. "No matter what, I'll never love anyone but you."

She closed her eyes, and soon she, too, fell victim to the numbed sleep of satisfied lovers.

When they awoke, the sun had drifted farther west.

"What do you know about Uncle Mike's death?" Araby asked as she began to dress.

Frowning, Jake tucked his shirt into his denim work trousers. "Just what Jud told me. They were all up on Butte's Peak tracking some big grizzly. Mike sat down on a log to shake a rock out of his boot, and a rattler came out from under the log and bit him. Jud said he cut open the wound and tried to suck out the venom, but the poison went straight to Mike's heart."

The frown that had set into Jake's features became even more pronounced.

"Do you believe it, Jake?"

"What do you mean?"

"Do you think he was telling the truth?"

Jake let out a long breath. "I'd feel a whole lot better if I could have seen those fang marks for myself."

Araby nodded. So would she. While talking to Jud earlier, she had felt something just wasn't quite right about the circumstances surrounding Mike's death. Now, after what Jake just said, she realized she wasn't the only one who was suspicious. There was a lot more to her uncle's accident than Jud had let on. One way or another, she was going to get to the bottom of it.

She decided to carry her suspicions one step

further.

"Do you think the Cords killed him?"

His jaw tensed. "That thought has crossed my mind."

"Did you talk to the Sheriff about it?"

Jake laughed, but his laugh was not one of amusement. "Jud and Horace Otter are as thick as thieves. If murder was suspected in Mike's death, you can just bet who the prime suspect would be. And it would not be Jud Cord!"

Araby looked at him in dismay. "Surely you can't mean the Sheriff would . . ."

"Believe me, nobody shows up Otter without paying for it."

"But surely there's someone else. Someone in a position higher than the Sheriff."

"I have thought about going to the Marshal, but I need proof before I start accusing anybody. I can't expect him to arrest a man just because I have a gut feeling." Jake kicked at the ground. "Not only do I not have proof, trouble is, I don't even know where to go to look for it."

"Between us, we'll find that proof." Anger flared in her eyes. "If the Cords killed Mike, I want them to pay. And I want them to pay with their lives."

Jake slid a protective arm around her waist and drew her to him. "They'll pay, all right. You have my word on that."

Araby was reluctant to withdraw from the haven of his embrace, but at that moment, there was something more important to think about. "Doesn't it strike you odd that they buried Mike up on Butte's Peak instead of bringing him home to Tamarack?" she asked Jake.

"Jud had an answer for that, too. According

to him, they tried bringing him back for a proper funeral, but the vultures . . . they wouldn't . . ."

Tears swelled in her eyes. He didn't have to finish. The picture was vivid in her mind.

"How far away is Butte's Peak?"

Jake kissed away the tears. "It's a good day's ride there and back. Why?"

"Because I have a feeling that's where we should start looking for that proof."

"You mean Mike's grave?"

Araby nodded.

"We don't know if there is a grave. Jud says he buried him, but we don't know for sure. If he was lowdown enough to kill him, you can bet he wasn't going to bother with laying him to rest. I wouldn't put it past him just to leave him where he dropped."

"But there is a grave," she assured him. "I know that for a fact because Jud offered to take me there. I think I ought to take him up on that offer, don't you?"

It took Jake a while to answer.

Arm in arm, they strolled along the river's edge.

Araby knew what was worrying him. She didn't like the idea of being alone with Jud any more than Jake did, especially so far away from Tamarack. But if she didn't go, they'd never know the location of the grave, and without the grave, their search for evidence would be over before they even got started. However, convincing Jake of that would not be easy.

Jake listened to what she had to say before he started shaking his head.

"I don't want you to be alone with him. Jud Cord is dangerous. There's no telling what he might do."

Araby raised her skirt to remind Jake she was not without protection. That little pistol stayed strapped to her leg at all times.

"Do you think I wear this just to be in fashion?"

Jake did not smile.

"Believe it or not, cowboy, a lady does not have to go West to find trouble. We have our share of it in New York."

Jake kept shaking his head.

He was not easily swayed, not even when she took aim, fired and hit a knot on a log that was floating down the river.

"Jake, Jud is not going to hurt me. He wants me to sell Tamarack to him, so he's going to be on his best behavior."

She hoped what she said was true.

Jake held tight to her shoulders with both hands. "Don't try and second guess a murderer, Araby. If you do, you'll wind up digging your own grave."

"But, Jake—"

"There's no buts about it! If he wanted Tamarack bad enough to gun down Mike in cold blood, just what makes you think he's going to show you any more mercy?"

She could't argue with him on that point. She had had that same thought herself. Still, it was worth the risk!

"Unless Jud takes me to the spot where Mike's buried, we'll never know for sure just what did happen."

Araby did not elaborate on what the next step would be after the grave had been located. They both knew what would have to be done then, but some things were better left unsaid. The grave itself would prove nothing. What was inside would.

She waited until they were riding toward home before she broached the subject once more.

"My mind's made up, Araby. Not even you can change it."

"But we stand to gain so much!"

His frown stayed put. "That does not make the risk to your life any less."

"But I want to take the risk!"

"I suppose you're going to tell me next that you're going up to Butte's Peak with Jud whether I like it or not."

For a change, Araby kept quiet. She had hoped it wouldn't come to that. But she was going no matter what Jake said!

"Damn! You are as hard-headed as a mule, woman!"

The start of a grin pulled at his mouth.

"Mike warned me I'd have trouble with that stubborn streak of yours!"

Her eyes danced with delight. "Oh, he did, did he?"

"Yes, he did."

"So what are you going to do about it, Montana? Turn me over your knee?"

"If I thought it would work, I would, but it would probably just make you meaner." Jake brought his horse to a halt in front of her. "I'm going up to Butte's Peak with you and Jud."

"But Jud won't . . ."

"Jud won't know I'm anywhere around."

It took her a few moments to understand. When she did, she returned Jake's smile. Of course. Jake used to track men for a living. He knew how to follow his quarry without their knowing he was there. That just might work.

The horses walked on.

"That way, if Jud does have any ideas about getting rid of you, I'll be close enough to—"

"To what? Come to my rescue?" she teased him.

"No, to help you drag the body back after you shoot him with that fancy little gun of yours."

Buck stopped suddenly. No matter how hard Jake kicked him, he refused to go on.

Even Tramp was acting peculiar. One moment he had been running on ahead, and the next he was frozen in place.

Without warning, Devil's Darling kicked out, then started dancing where she stood. Her front quarters swung in opposite directions from her back end.

Araby stayed in the saddle. She took up so much of the rein that the mare's head was bent down to her chest.

She started to ask Jake what was happening, but one look at him told her the question would fall on deaf ears. There could be but one reason for the mesmerized expression on his face. And not even she could compete with it for Jake's attention!

The black stallion and his herd of wild horses were somewhere nearby. Buck and Darling had caught wind of them. So had Tramp.

Araby listened. She heard nothing out of the ordinary.

Jake turned his horse around and faced the river again.

Devil's Darling whirled around before Araby could stop her.

The hills rumbled. She could have sworn it was thunder, but there was not a cloud in the sky.

The spell was broken when the rumbling ceased.

"You want him, don't you, Jake?"

"That I do. But I'm a patient man. I can wait just as long as need be."

She wondered if the same applied where women were concerned. Maybe some time she'd ask him.

"Race you to the gate, cowboy."

Devil's Darling lunged ahead.

Both horses and both riders were nearly out of breath by the time they reached Tamarack's gate. The race had been too close to call. The horses had run neck and neck the entire distance.

It was just as well there wasn't a clear-cut winner, Araby decided, catching her breath. Jake wouldn't take too kindly to being beaten by a woman, much less an Easterner!

She invited him up to the house for a drink and assured him that after her earlier conversation with Jud and Burley, no one would shoot him for trespassing—at least not while she was with him.

"Are you sure I can't entice you?" she teased when he declined her offer.

"You, lady, could entice me to do just about anything." He leaned over and kissed her. "However, I do have a ranch to run, and seeing as how I've been out gallavanting with a beautiful woman all day, I'd best be getting back."

Her fingers danced up his leather leggings. "You'll be sorry."

"I already am." He took hold of her hand and put it back on her saddle. "What about tonight?

191

Want to keep a lonely cowboy company?''

Araby blew him a kiss. He didn't have to ask twice. ''I'll leave the window open.''

9

Hamstring came up to the barn to meet her when he saw her coming. "I see them biscuits did the trick. You're grinning from ear to ear, gal. What'd I tell you?"

"You were absolutely right! I'll be around for my first biscuit-making lesson tomorrow." Araby hopped down from her horse and undid the girth. She was in such a good mood that not even Burley could spoil it!

"Where's Rowdy?"

Hamstring held the saddle while she took off the bridle and fastened the halter over Devil's Darling's head. "He's out back soaking one of the cutting pony's legs that's got all swoled up."

Araby led Devil's Darling into the barn and into her stall. "How about Burley?"

"Him and Jud took off somewhere. Hard telling where." Hamstring poked her in the side. "You sure got old Burley's goat yesterday. Them cowboys are still ribbing him about that. Why, you know he was laying odds how long you'd stay on that cayuse's back before she bucked you off?"

Araby laughed. "I figured as much."

"And the look on his face when Devil's Darling came dragging back in—Lordy mercy me!" Hamstring couldn't stop grinning. "Why, if I'd a dropped dead right then, I'd a gone to my maker with a smile on my face."

Araby gave the mare some hay, then started brushing her chestnut coat.

"You going to the dance Saturday night?" she asked Hamstring.

"Wild horses couldn't keep me away." He danced a jig. "I may be getting long in the tooth, but all my parts work just fine."

Rowdy led in a lame horse. "Howdy, f-folks."

"Good afternoon, Rowdy. Hamstring and I were just talking about the big dance. You're going, aren't you?"

Rowdy led the cow pony into the stall beside Devil's Darling. "Naw, I never wuz much f-for dancing. Never did . . . did learn how."

"That's no reason to miss out on all the fun." Araby closed the stall door behind her, and when Rowdy came out of the next one, she was waiting for him. "Come on. I'll show you how."

The young cowboy turned every shade of red. "I . . . I'm not real light on m-my feet, m'am."

"Nonsense." She lifted her arms. "Come on. Give it a try."

"You better do as she says," Hamstring piped up. "Or else you might find yourself looking for another job."

"Don't you pay him any attention, Rowdy." Before he could back away, Araby took hold of his arms. "Now you just put this hand around my waist. That's right. Now take my hand in yours. See? That's not so bad now, is it?"

"If . . . if you say so."

"You're doing just fine." Araby shot a wink and a warning glance over his shoulder to Hamstring.

The cowboys' cook started humming a lively tune.

"Something a little slower, Hamstring."

"Yes, m'am." He obliged with a waltz.

"Perfect. Now, you just look at my feet, Rowdy, and follow my steps. One, two, three. One, two, three. Follow. One, two, three—good. Not so fast. One, two—ouch."

Rowdy jumped back. "Sorry, m'am, but I t-told you . . . I'm pretty hopeless."

"That was my fault, not yours." She guided his hands into place once more and hummed along with Hamstring. "One, two, three . . . One, two, three . . . That's wonderful. Perfect. Look at this, Hamstring. He's a natural."

When the tune finished, Araby clapped while Rowdy blushed and shuffled in place.

"Come Saturday night, you will be in great demand by the ladies of Castle Rock," she assured her pupil.

"Gals ain't . . . well, they ain't n-never had much use for me."

Hamstring elbowed his ribs. "That's because you don't pay them any attention. You got to smile and chat about the weather and tell them how pretty they look. Ain't that right, Miss Araby?"

"You listen to Hamstring. He knows how to court a lady." Suddenly, she had an idea. Why hadn't she thought of it before? Those two could be perfect for each other. "You know something, Rowdy. I think I know just the girl for you. She's pretty and sweet and very, very nice. Just a little shy, though."

Rowdy's eyes went bluer. "You do? She is? Why, I . . . don't mind her being shy. I'm a little t-timid myself. What's her name?"

"Mandy."

He repeated the name slowly. "Mandy. That's a real pretty name, ain't it?" His smile faded. "She won't like me. Not when there's lots of . . . lots of cowboys."

"But you're just the kind of cowboy she's been waiting to meet."

Rowdy grew even taller. "You think so? Really?"

"I know so," she assured him.

"Well, maybe t-tomorrow, if you . . . if you got the time . . . we can have another dancing lesson?"

"I think that's a splendid idea, don't you, Hamstring?"

"Mandy. You know, I reckon that's just about the prettiest name I ever did hear. Mandy." Rowdy kept repeating the name as he went on about his chores.

"I think the boy's in love," Hamstring chuckled, giving Araby a playful poke. "Must be that time of year, heh?"

"I wouldn't know."

Araby walked away, trying to keep a straight face. Maybe it was that time of year!

"Come on, Tramp."

Whistling the same tune Hamstring had been humming, Araby lifted her skirt and ran up to the house throwing in a kick or two every few strides.

Never had she thought such happiness possible—but it was, and Jake Montana was the reason for it!

She started up to her room, then turned around and went back down. She might as well find Jud and let him know that she'd decided to take him up on his very kind offer to escort her to Butte's Peak.

Jud was nowhere to be found. She did find Sim, though. He was in the parlor stretched out on the settee. One hand held a glass; the other held his head.

She very nearly tiptoed out and left him in his drunken stupor, then changed her mind. After all, Sim had been with her uncle when he died, too. Without his brother to prompt him, Sim might even let something slip.

"Oh, hello, Sim. I didn't see you in here. Something wrong? Not feeling well? May I get you something?"

The younger Cord grunted in response.

"You don't mind some company, do you?" She sat down in the chair nearest the settee. The smell of whiskey hanging in the air was potent enough to intoxicate a sailor!

Sim gave another grunt, then rolled over and burrowed his face in the Indian tapestry that was draped over the settee.

"I had a very pleasant chat with your brother this morning. Such a nice man. I hope we all can become friends, considering we are practically family."

Sim lifted up his head long enough to take another drink, then buried it again.

Araby put on her friendliest face and chatted away, only to be ignored.

"I feel that in times like these, times when

we're all grieving a loved one, we should all stick together just like a real family. Don't you think so, Sim?''

Sim rolled over. ''Stick together . . . that's what Jud says.'' His words were slurred and barely coherent. ''Yes, siree. Stick together. Jud knows all about that. Jud knows all about everything. Just ask him. He'll be glad to tell you how smart he is.''

Araby had a feeling he wasn't particularly fond of his big brother.

Hands folded demurely atop her lap, she continued. ''Mike was such a wonderful man. He'll certainly be missed, won't he? It's a shame. Truly it is. You know, he wrote me about you and Jud all the time. They're mighty fine young men, he used to say. His only regret was that you two were already grown-up when he met you. Mike always wanted sons. I guess you and Jud were the ones he never had.''

She hoped Mike would forgive her lies!

Sim gulped down the rest of his whiskey, then somehow managed to right himself and stumble to the sideboard to pour himself another.

''He was very excited about the hunting trip with you and your brother. Seems to me, though, he wrote something about going to Freezeout Mountain.''

''Changed his mind. You know Mike.'' Sim slumped back down on the settee.

''At least in the end, he was happy doing what he loved best and with people he loved. And who loved him.''

She tried to get him to look at her, but Sim focused on everything else but her.

''How awful to have watched him die,

knowing there was nothing you could do."

Sim swilled the whiskey and stared down at the glass. "Rattlesnake. Bit him when he set down. Shaking out a rock in his boot. Jud cut open the bite. Too late. Poison. Right to his heart. Dead in no time."

Araby frowned. He didn't need his brother to prompt him. Sim had memorized his lines so well he could deliver them even when he was drunk. Curses!

She tried another approach. "How sad that Mike couldn't be laid to rest in the ground he so loved!"

Sim's words were as lifeless as the look on his face. "Leave him there. Had to. Couldn't bring him back. Vultures picking at the bones."

Araby cringed. Had they left Mike's body to rot where it had fallen, that was exactly what would have happened. The vultures would have picked the bones clean!

"Couldn't bring him home. Couldn't. Buzzards everywhere."

Araby shaded her eyes. If Sim weren't so drunk, he'd see the hate raging inside her.

It took her a moment before she could continue.

You'll have your revenge, she silently swore to her dead uncle. I'll see to that myself. They'll pay. They'll pay.

"What a comfort you and Jud must have been for Uncle Mike in the end."

She was gritting her teeth so, the words could hardly get out past them.

"The end. Couldn't stay. Couldn't watch. Sick to my stomach. Jud made me. I didn't want to. Said I had to or he'd tell."

Araby leaned closer. "Jud made you do what? What did your brother make you do? What was he going to tell?"

Sim just sat there shaking his head.

It took all the self-restraint she possessed to keep from accusing him of murdering her uncle. He was about to break. She could sense it. But if she were wrong, if he did not give in to the pressure and confess, then her advantage would be lost.

No, she'd wait. She could afford to be patient. Sooner or later, she'd find out the truth, and when she did, the Cords would not escape her wrath!

Araby studied Sim closely for his next reaction.

"Jud has offered to take me up to Butte's Peak to see Mike's grave. I think Mike would appreciate it if we all went up there together to pay our respects. Don't you, Sim?"

Sim's face paled even grayer. "No. Not going back. Never. Jud can't make me. Won't let him. Not this time."

Araby heard the front door slam.

"Shhh. It's all right, Sim. Nobody's going to make you do anything. There. That's it. Have another drink."

Jud was all smiles when he walked into the parlor. "Well, would you look here! I'm so glad to see you two getting acquainted." He stopped behind the settee. "I bet my little brother's just been talking your ear off."

Araby could tell from Sim's wince that the squeeze Jud was giving his shoulder was not a friendly one.

"Sim isn't feeling very well," she said quickly. "I walked past and saw him doubled over, so I came in to see what I could do for him."

Jud walked around the settee and sat down beside his brother. "That was very kind of you to be concerned, Araby. Wasn't it, Sim?"

Sim nodded.

She noticed that he didn't look Jud in the eye either. Not that she blamed him. Jud's face might be all smiles, but his eyes were full of hate—hate for her and his brother both, she suspected.

Araby heard the front door close again.

A moment later, Lena walked by. Jud called out to her.

"Oh, Lena. There you are. I was just about to come look for you. Sim's not feeling too good. Can you help him to his room?"

"Sure, Jud. Whatever you say."

Araby wondered where Lena had been. Her clothes were wrinkled and her hair in disarray. Wherever she had been had caused a definite change for the better in her disposition. She did what her brother-in-law asked without objection, said a few kind words to her husband when she helped him to his feet, and even gave her a smile and a pleasant nod on her way out of the room with Sim.

Jud threw up his hands. "My poor brother. He's drinking himself to death just like our daddy did. You'd think he would have learned his lesson by now."

Jud stared at her so long and so hard that she began to think perhaps he had heard more of her conversation with Sim than he had let on.

"I don't mind telling you, Araby, knowing you'd be here when I got back made me run my horse a lot harder. Why, my dear, are you blushing?"

Dark lashes swept down over her cheeks. Her face was hot, but the crimson splayed across it most definitely was not been caused by embarrassment over some silly remark. She was mad, damned mad. What a cocky bastard! He had murdered her uncle to acquire Tamarack, and now he thought all he had to do was seduce her and the ranch would be his. Accusations were not all she wanted to hurl in his face!

Jud rambled on about some deal he had just pulled off in town. No doubt his business acumen was intended to impress her!

Araby listened and gave an occasional nod while he applauded his own shrewdness. She may have left the stage for a while, but her acting skills were still being tested. Dealing with the likes of Jud and his brother without giving away her true motives would be by far her most challenging role yet.

"I hope I'm not boring you, Araby, but the reason I'm going into such great detail about my business dealings is so you will understand that I am quite substantial. I've made numerous investments that have paid off handsomely."

Jud walked over to the sideboard and poured himself a drink. "I'm not wealthy yet, but I certainly intend to be. It won't be long now before I can offer a lady like you all those fine things she's used to having, and a few others besides."

Araby did not raise her eyes. That was definitely not the topic of conversation she was expecting. The sale of Tamarack, yes, but not something so personal as his romantic designs on her. Just what kind of an idiot did he take her for?

"What I'm feeling for you, my dear, I've never felt before with any other woman. I know we've only just met, but certain things in life are destined, and I believe fate has brought us together.''

His smile could have charmed a snake, but his eyes stayed cold, dangerously cold.

''Now, I have enjoyed the company of many ladies, I will admit, though none of them could hold a candle to you, my dear. I'm not adverse to settling down with one woman. The reason I haven't done so before now is that the right one just hadn't happened along—that is, until yesterday.''

It took all the self-control she could muster to keep from telling him what a low-down, no-good son of a bitch he was! Instead, she kept her words to herself and her eyes on the floor.

''I'm not perfect. I'll be the first to tell you that, but my vices are few. I like my whiskey as well as the next man, but I do know when to stop. I gamble, but only when I know I'll win. Occasionally, I get a little hot under the collar, but I don't get violent. I guess what I'm trying to say is that I think I'm falling in love with you. I hope you'll look kindly on me.''

Araby stiffened. He wasn't above telling her Mike himself would have given his blessing to such a union.

''Goodness, Jud. I don't know what to say.'' She chose her words carefully. ''You flatter me. Truly you do. Under different circumstances . . . what I mean is, I came here to mourn my uncle. I don't think . . . ''

''Hush, hush, my dear.'' He patted her hand. ''I understand perfectly what it is you're trying to say, and that makes me admire you all the more.''

She lowered her eyes once more. Perhaps that

was as good a time as any to make plans for their visit to Butte's Peak.

"It was very kind of you to offer to take me to my uncle's grave, Jud. I do appreciate that. I feel a visit there may help me come to terms with his death."

"A wise decision, my dear. We'll go to Butte's Peak—say, next Monday, if that's agreeable with you."

Araby kept her frown to herself. Monday was five whole days away. She had hoped they could go sooner than that. She had a feeling Jud was giving himself ample time to go and dig the grave. If that were the case, then there was no guarantee he was even taking her to the place where Mike's accident had occurred. Still, that was a chance she had to take.

"Whatever day suits you is fine with me. I know you're a very busy man."

He twirled the tip of his moustache. "But never too busy to be of service to you, my dear Araby."

"You're very kind, Jud. Thank you." She nearly choked on her words.

"It's the least I can do for you and for Mike."

Araby rose quickly. She couldn't bear to be in the same room with him another minute. The man was despicable!

"You're not leaving, are you?"

She ignored his outstretched hand. "I'm afraid I haven't completely recouperated yet from my long journey."

"Yes, of course. A nap would do you good. Perhaps later you'll permit me to accompany you on a stroll."

Araby nodded. That was the last thing she

wanted to do. Unfortunately, she had very little choice in the matter. Until she found out what she needed to know, Jud must never suspect he had lost the upper hand.

Almost as soon as she opened the door to her room, Araby noticed her journal was not opened and on the bed where she had left it. Instead, it had been closed and placed neatly on the bedside table right beside the script for her new play.

She picked up the leather volume and flipped through it. Perhaps Mattie had moved it when she came in to tidy up.

The last letter Mike had written to her fell out.

Araby reached down to pick it up, then stood at the window looking out and fanning herself with the letter.

It was no coincidence that the journal was not where she had left it. Nor was it a coincidence that the letter had been returned to its envelope. She distinctly remembered having used the letter to mark one page of her journal, and the envelope to mark her place on another page. Thank heavens she had followed her instincts and not written anything incriminating about Jake or confided in her diary her suspicions regarding the Cords.

Someone had been snooping in her room. She doubted that Mattie was the culprit. Mattie couldn't read. Just that morning she had asked Araby to read some descriptions and prices of cloth from the Montgomery Ward Catalog aloud for her. No doubt Jud was the one who had decided to make her personal affairs his business.

A sly smile stole across her lips.

The next time her uninvited guest came

calling, she'd make certain there was something a little more exciting than a description of the Saint Joe for him to read!

The evening had passed quickly. After a "nap," during which she never closed her eyes, but instead stared up at the ceiling daydreaming about Jake, Araby had gone fishing with Hamstring. While he fried up their catch down by the river, she listened to many of the same stories she had heard over and over again from Mike. Not that she minded the repetition. The stories made her feel closer to Mike. It was still hard to accept the fact that he was dead and she'd never see him again. Hamstring's was the best idea by far. Mike wasn't dead. He was just on a long hunting trip.

As much as she would have liked to, she had no excuse to bow out of the stroll with Jud. Ironically, it was Lena who came to her rescue. They had run into her on their way out of the house. To Jud's obvious chagrin, his sister-in-law had invited herself along and had not permitted the two of them to spend one moment alone together. Araby could have hugged Sim's wife for doing her such a favor!

When she finally was able to retire to her room and settle into bed wearing her dressing gown and nothing else, Araby found that sleep would not come easily. It might be hours before Jake slipped in through the window, but the thought of his doing so excited her so much that she couldn't even close her eyes. All she could do was lie there and wait and imagine their lovers' reunion.

The heat of the day had cooled quickly as soon as the sun went down, and now the valley was showered in moonlight. Soft whinnies could be heard coming from the barn. Someone was playing a harmonica. Its soft hum drifted with the breeze. A few of the cowboys were still gathered around the campfire outside the bunk house. Araby listened to their faint laughter. Soon, they'd be bedding down for the night. It would still be dark when they began their day all over again.

Araby hugged her pillow tight and stared at the script on the bedside table. It was a good play. She'd read it on the long train ride to Idaho. It was more than a good play. It was a masterpiece. The playwright was truly brilliant. The female lead would be a challenging role indeed. Every actress she knew would do just about anything to be cast in so versatile a part. Yet, the director had offered the choice role to her. She hadn't even had to read for it. If she wanted the part, it was hers. That one portrayal could insure her place among the theater greats. But where had all her enthusiasm gone? Not once since arriving at Tamarack had she been tempted to turn a single page.

New York! That's where her enthusiasm had gone. Back there, that bundle of pages had been more precious than all of the jewels in her trinket box. But here, it was just taking up space.

New York! It was a whole other world away, a fantasy land where life revolved around one party after another, and whether or not one received the coveted invitations to the most prestigious parties was one's most pressing worry. Being privy to the latest gossip, mingling with the rich and prominent, being seen in all the right places with the right people—those had not long ago headed her list of priorities. Now, such concerns seemed ridiculously silly and trite. She hadn't been living. She had only been going through the motions. Just how long could she have endured so purposeless an existence?

It was well after midnight before the window opened and Jake tiptoed in, carrying his boots.

"You still awake?" he whispered when he leaned down to kiss her.

"I was listening for gunshots."

"Don't you worry none about that," he told her as he started to undress. "Burley Wilkerson couldn't hit the broad side of a barn if he was standing a foot away."

Araby laughed with him, but she failed to share his humor. Burley would do whatever Jud wanted, even if it meant putting a bullet in a man's back.

Jake slipped into bed and under the covers.

"Jud's agreed to take me to Butte's Peak on Monday," she told him while they snuggled close.

"Why Monday?"

"I don't know. Maybe he wants to give himself plenty of time to get the grave dug."

Jake finished the thought for her. "And destroy any incriminating evidence that's still lying around."

"We'll get him. Won't we, Jake?"

"You bet we'll get him, honey. By the time we get through with him, Jud Cord will wish he never heard the name Tamarack."

A kiss, which had been intended only to sooth and console, became filled with passion and desire moments later.

Jake untied the ribbons closing her gown. "You don't need this to keep you warm. Not when I'm around."

Araby lay back and enjoyed his hands running wild over her body. When he was around, she didn't need anything but him. When he wasn't around, she needed him even more.

Mumbling her name over and over, Jake pulled her bare, luscious curves into his hard flesh. His touch was rough with raw possession.

"I've been waiting for this all day, sugar."

He held her so tight she thought for sure her breath would give out.

"All the time I was working at Cross Forks, I couldn't get you out of my mind."

"Mmmm. Tell me more."

Playful teeth nipped at his neck while adventuresome fingers began their exploration of rock-hard contours and ridges.

Araby could tell from his heavy-breathing silence that her boldness did not intimidate him. She became even more brazen.

Wicked hands danced over his chest, kneading the smooth cords of muscles.

"Do you like this?"

Somehow he managed a nod.

"How about this?"

His belly tensed when she kissed it.

Teasing lips blazed a hot trail down the inside of his thighs. "And this?"

Hands digging deep into her backside, Jake answered by rolling her over and pinning her so snugly beneath him that she could not move. His tongue played the same cruel tricks on her. Like her, he showed no mercy.

Her own yearning had left her powerless to move. She wanted to touch him, to direct him, to guide him to such joys as he had never known before, but she was powerless to do more than lie there, willing victim of the all-consuming need that fired them both.

Every part of her responded instantly to the daring intimacies of his caresses. Her surrender was a much welcomed relief.

His love flowed inside her, taking her to still higher peaks of ecstasy. A sweet, delicious agony throbbed inside her, robbing her of all sense and reason. Fame and fortune? They no longer mattered. New York could have its elegant high life. She'd gladly give up the world for her cowboy and not think twice about it. Having been schooled in the art of love by him, she could never settle for anyone other than the master.

Hours later, they lay exhausted in each other's arms.

"Do you know what I wish, Jake?" she whispered. "I wish right now never had to end."

He sprinkled kisses through her hair. "You better be careful what you wish for. It might just come true."

Araby hugged him close. If only it would!

The next time she awakened, the bed was empty, and Jake was standing at the window staring out.

She called out his name, and he motioned her over.

Dancing in the moonlight, legs prancing and tail high and proud, was that big, black stallion, the leader of the wild horses.

"Oh, Jake, he truly is beautiful."

"He's magnificent. He's not afraid of anything or anyone."

There was no mistaking the pride or the longing in Jake's voice.

"Look how close he's come to the house. It's

like he's challenging every cowboy around to come after him.''

The stallion reared high and reached for the stars. Then with a loud snort, he took off running with invisible demons in pursuit.

Jake kept staring out the window long after the horse had disappeared into the night.

''He's come looking for mares. If there's one in season, he'll be back.''

Araby patted the empty place beside her. Smiling to herself, she watched as he made his way back to the bed. His mind may have been on wild horses a moment ago, but as soon as he was caught in her web of arousal once again, such thoughts would flee just as swiftly as the stallion had.

Bodies joined, souls merged together, they became as one, and the fire that lay quietly smouldering grew into raging flames once more.

10

Araby stood on the front porch taking in the panorama surrounding her. In only a few short days, she had come to love that great land just as her uncle had loved it. In all her travels, she'd never come across a place where the scenery was so breath-taking, the air so pure and the water so blue. Tamarack truly was a bit of heaven come to earth! She loved it there, and like her uncle, she could not envision herself ever leaving. Only a fool would trade the enchantment of untamed beauty for sidewalks and city blocks.

It would be dark soon. Already the valley was falling under the spell of the evening. The hills and meadows would soon be lulled to sleep by the gentle lapping of the Saint Joe. Flickering lights were already dancing on the peaks of the Coeur d'Alene mountain range that stood sentry over all of Tamarack's domain. Sounds of the night invaded the solitude of dusk—a cow's bellow for its lost calf, the sharp bark of a coyote in the hills, the sweet music of frogs swarming in the meadow sloughs, the splash of trout jumping. These were sounds she had come to recognize and to expect each night about that time.

Araby breathed in that sweet air and smiled to herself. How pleasant the evening was! It was just cool enough for the lace mantilla draped over her shoulders. Of course, once Jake arrived to take her to the dance, there'd be no need for a wrap—not when his strong, protective arms would do the job just fine.

For the first time since her arrival at Tamarack she was alone. Mattie had gone up into the hills to visit a friend who was married to a prospector. Jud and Sim and Lena had removed the last of their belongings that afternoon. Much to their surprise, Wallace Ford had come calling the day before and brought with him Mike's Last Will and Testament. The Cord brothers had not been mentioned in the will at all, which enraged Jud, but he had hidden it well. Tamarack and all its possessions had been bequeathed to her. That came as no surprise to Araby. Nor was she surprised to learn of the thirty-day provision.

Jud's excuse for moving off the ranch had nothing to do with the fact that he had no right there. Instead, he told her he was doing so in order that he could come courting her without compromising her reputation and starting unseemly gossip. Burley had packed up his bags and left, too, which had been fine by her, since it saved the trouble of firing him. The fellow who had been Slim Watkins' right-hand man—a bald, quiet fellow named Curley—took over as boss.

How lucky could she be! She'd gotten rid of Jud and Burley both in the same day. Burley wouldn't be back. Unfortunately, Jud was not gone for good.

It was obvious where Jud had gotten the idea that after a respectable mourning period for her uncle, she would be receptive to his romantic overtures. Ever since she had discovered that someone was very interested in her private thoughts and personal reflections, she had filled her journal with glowing praises of Jud's fine attributes. She had confided in her diary that even though Jake tried to convince her that Mike would have wanted the ranch sold to him, her intention was to sell it to Jud because he would pay the most money. Jake had gotten a big kick out of the journal entry that compared him to Jud. Jud, she had written, was a "worldly, handsome, sophisticated gentleman who knows how to woo a lady." Jake, on the other hand, was "a crude cowboy, pig-headed, and insensitive to a lady's emotional needs."

Jake arrived on time, and from the look on his face when he halted the team of horses in front of the porch, Araby knew she had accomplished what she had set out to do. He was truly dazzled!

"What's the matter, cowboy? Cat got your tongue?" she teased him while he stood staring at her with his mouth open.

Jake motioned for her to turn around so that he could view her from all angles.

She was only too happy to oblige.

If ever she had looked desirable and beautiful, then tonight was most definitely such a night! Her gown, a dusty rose silk, had been designed by one of New York's leading fashion designers for her last role as an heiress. The style was simple but smart, with a low dipping neck and nipped-in waist that flattered her hour-glass shape all the more. Monsieur Pierre would no doubt be throwing one fit after another if he knew his prize creation were being worn to a Saturday-night dance in an Idaho cow-town.

As the wagon bumped along the road along the river back to Castle Rock, Jake was unusually quiet. Something was obviously bothering him, and that bothered her.

She took hold of his arm. "You know, Montana, I just cannot figure you out. Here you are on your way to the big dance with a girl you know can refuse you nothing, and you haven't even tried to kiss her. Now what do you make of that?"

"I think I'm a damned fool!"

His laugh was without its usual heartiness, and his kiss lacked the fire that usually burned her lips.

"How was that?"

"If I were your grandmother, that kiss would have been most appropriate."

"I'll try to do better."

Araby waited, but he did nothing but crack the whip across the horses' backsides and stare straight ahead.

"You really do look beautiful," he told her a little while later. " 'Course, you'd look that way in an old sack. I kinda feel sorry for all those fellows you left pining away back East."

She tightened her hold on his arm. So that was it! The life she had left behind in New York had been on his mind quite a lot of late. Would she never get it through that thick skull of his that those fellows he kept referring to meant absolutely nothing to her?

"It's you I love, Jake."

"Oh, I know you do, darling. And I love you, too. It's just that—well, I don't think we should go on fooling ourselves." A sad longing came into his voice. "Now, I know you said you want to stay here at Tamarack, and I believe you do. But the time'll come when you're going to start missing all those things you left behind, and when you do, you'll start hating Tamarack and me and everything else keeping you in Idaho."

Araby laid her head on his shoulder. He was wrong, but she could talk until she was blue in the face and not convince him of it. She belonged with him. He knew she belonged with him, too. He just wouldn't admit it. How many more times would they have this same discussion before he realized she didn't need all those fancy trappings to be happy?

"You just wait, Jake Montana. Twenty years from now, when you're trying to figure out a way to get rid of me, I'll remind you of this little chat, and you'll have to eat your words!"

He stopped the wagon. "Just promise me something. When you get ready to go, just go. Don't stay here because you feel you owe anybody anything."

"That's never going to happen, but if it'll make you feel better, I promise to just pack up and go without so much as a good-bye. Satisfied?"

Araby snuggled close beside him. Of course, if he were to marry her, he'd never have to worry about her going anywhere. The problem was getting him to realize that, and solving the problem would definitely require her undivided attention, so the sooner she started working on it, the better.

"You know, Jake, we really don't have to go into town at all."

Mischievious fingers showed no mercy as they darted down his chest and in and out between buttons.

"All that noise . . . all those people . . . why, I wouldn't mind at all going somewhere quiet and cozy where we could be alone," she told him. "Just the two of us."

"Sounds a little dull to me."

Araby was relieved. Thank goodness his sense of humor was returning.

"I don't think it would be dull at all, Jake. We could go some place and . . . and talk."

"Talk? Now that sounds like a good idea. What about?"

"Whatever you want to talk about." She ran her hand down the inside of his leg. She could tell he didn't want to talk any more than she did. "Unless there's something else you'd rather do?"

"No, can't think of anything," he said in his slow drawl. "Can you?"

Her hand got bolder. "Are you sure you can't?"

"I'm sure."

Araby balled up her fist and hit him in the stomach. "Maybe this will help you think of something."

Jake doubled over laughing. "You're fun to tease."

"You might tease, but I don't."

Hot, willing lips trailed kisses down his neck while devilish fingers slipped behind his gold belt buckle.

"What about it, cowboy? Want to have a little fun with a city gal?"

"You don't have to ask this old cowpoke twice."

Jake headed the wagon into a stand of trees, where low-hanging willow branches would shade them from the moon's glow.

Jake jumped down into the wagon bed and spread out the blanket. "I brought this along just in case you got chilly on the way home."

Araby grinned. She had a feeling he had anticipated moments such as these just as eagerly as she. Did his stomach plunge to his feet every time he thought of making love to her? she wondered as he lifted her down. Hers did!

They undressed in silence. The only sounds to be heard for miles around were the horses patiently munching on clumps of river grass and willow withes, and the splash of water against the rocks.

They came together in a heated rush of tangled limbs, sweet groans and hurried caresses. His need was great, but no greater than her own. She told him so with urgent kisses and frenzied jerks and shoves. There would be time later for hours of lazing in each other's embrace, reveling in the delights of sharing and exploring, but now was not that time. Playing lovers' games would only send them raging out of control. Already, they were beyond the point of desperation. Their hunger had to be satisfied now!

She could not hold back her cries of fulfill- ment when he finally took hold of her hips and plunged himself inside her.

Fingers clawing, arms and legs flailing, they sought relief from the explosive pressure mounting inside them.

And when it was over, when they had soared

together to uncharted heights, then floated back to earth, Araby knew that had there been any doubt before, there was none now. If two people had ever been made for each other, surely she and Jake were those two. Still, she had her work cut out for her to convince him that a city girl could be happy in the western wilds just as long as she had a cowboy to keep her company.

She would have been content to stay by the river the rest of the night and sleep in the wagon, or to return to Tamarack and lock themselves in the little room at the end of the hall, but Jake would not hear of it. He wanted to go to the dance and show her off, and that was fine by her. As long as they were together, she didn't care where they were.

A little while later, Jake pulled the wagon alongside all the others.

"Say, have I told you just how beautiful you look tonight?"

Jake swung her down from the buckboard, but he didn't let go of her, not right away. Instead, he pulled her even closer and pressed her tightly against him while his hands stole a few more quick caresses.

Araby nuzzled his cheek. It hadn't taken long for the excitement to start building again.

"Yes, you have, but tell me again so I don't forget."

He was quick to oblige her request.

She threw her arms around his neck and nibbled at his ear.

"You'd better watch that, lady, or I'm liable to rope you, throw you down and brand you."

"I'll not put up a struggle." Her lips feasted on his. "That I promise you."

His narrow hips pressed deeper into her.

She could not resist letting her wandering hands linger below his belt buckle. He was so strong, so virile. If he wanted to take her right there in the alley between the livery stable and the harness shop, she'd not object. The effect that man had on her was sinful—wonderfully sinful!

Jake gave her a gentle tug in the direction of the activity ahead. "You done wore me out, woman. The least you can do is give me a minute to catch my breath."

She counted with each step she took. "Fifty-nine seconds, fifty-eight seconds, fifty-seven seconds . . ."

Laughing, they strolled towards the town center arm in arm. She didn't need a looking glass to know the after-glow of love still burned bright on her cheeks. Surely she could not speak to anyone without giving herself away. The moment she uttered her first word, everyone would know just what she and Jake had been up to.

She laughed to herself. Shameless hussy . . . jezebel . . . wanton woman. That's what she was! All of them! Gone forever was the prim and proper ingenue who once thought a show of intimacy was a kiss on the cheek. Taking her place was a woman—a woman with unbridled passion, a woman who wanted to give love as desperately as she wanted to receive it. Who cared if everyone they met guessed the reason for their delay? They'd only be green with envy. Let them.

Castle Rock had come alive with excitement at the time when most of its residents would normally be tucked in bed. Young and old alike were dosey-doeing in the streets to the music of fiddlers and banjo pickers. Children ran helter skelter playing Happy Is The Miller Boy and Run Sheep Run. Sunday-go-to-meeting clothes—or funeral duds, as Jake referred to his navy blue suit—had come out of wardrobes for the night. Men like Jake, who felt more at home in chaps and denim, jerked at stiff, starched collars and yanked at their string ties. Confident and aggressive on the range, they all looked a little uncomfortable and ill at ease out of their surroundings.

It was these men's women who gave Araby the most cause to wonder. Since arriving in Castle Rock, she had met quite a few of the ranchers, miners, and loggers, but their mates had been noticeably absent. From the way the men talked about their wives and women in general, it seemed that females were ranked just below livestock in regard to worth.

Araby studied every woman she passed closely. Their faces were drawn and haggard, their expressions so sad. Even all dressed up in their best gingham and ruffles, they looked despondent and depressed. They seemed to have no reason to be festive, so they didn't even bother going through the motions. The Fourth of July was just another day as far as they were concerned.

Mike had called the settlers' wives the backbone of the West, for these women had braved much suffering and disaster after disaster to follow without question husbands who were driven by some great need to carve their futures in a vast new land. Strong bodies and brave hearts out to achieve the impossible against all odds—that was how Mike had described these women. She wondered if she could be so strong!

Jake seemed to know what she was thinking each time she smiled at one of the women and said a kind word.

"They might not look it, but some of them are a lot younger than you."

Hand in hand they mingled with the crowd in the street.

"Wives at thirteen, mamas at fourteen, old women before they're twenty . . . by the time they're thirty—well most of them don't make it that far," he said quietly. "It's a hard life for a woman out here. A hard life."

Araby knew what he had on his mind.

"If a woman loves her man, she'll go through hell and back for him."

"Take a good look at them, Araby. That's just where they've been."

The double oak doors of the Ruby Rose were flung open, and people were milling about inside. The chaises and settees had been moved out of the salon and the fancy carpets from the Far East had been rolled up and stored under the stairs. Felix was tending bar while the girls flitted and flirted around the room.

Everyone knew Jake and greeted him with back slaps and bear hugs. If his rancher friends had any doubts when he introduced them to Araby, those misgivings were quickly dispelled when folks learned she was Mike Stone's niece. She could tell right away that her uncle had been well liked and much respected. All of them were eager to offer their condolences and share with her a funny story or fond memory they had of him. She'd always been proud of Mike, but never any more so than tonight. Mike's old friends were quick to warm to her and just as quick to point out to Jake that he'd be a damned fool to let her get away. For that, she could have kissed every one of them!

Belle was the first of her old friends who spotted her. Red curls bouncing, she ran over to greet her.

"Oh, Araby—Araby honey, you would never in a hundred years believe what has happened to me!" she exclaimed, nearly squashing her with those fleshy, pink-chiffon arms. "My Charlie turned out to be rich, and I do mean rich! That shack he was taking me to, it ain't no shack at all, honey. It's as fine as any of them mansions on Rich Street in Chicago. Why some woman ain't snared him before now I'll never know. Their loss is my gain!"

Araby couldn't get a word in edgewise. When she finally did manage to start a sentence, Belle grabbed hold of her once more.

"You knew all about it, didn't you? Why, you sly fox. That cowboy friend of yours told you, didn't he?" Belle laughed. "I can tell you knew. Those big eyes of yours don't tell lies."

Araby confessed. "I knew, and I am so happy for you. I would love to have seen your face when you got home to the shack."

"I damn near had a heart attack." Belle fanned herself furiously with her handkerchief. "Whew! That Charlie, he's some man. He'd put to shame all the others I've known. Why, when it comes to knowing how to treat a woman, he's forgot more than all of them high-falootin' gents put together ever knew!"

Araby squeezed her friend's hand. Her smile grew still larger. The horseshoe-nail wedding band was still there, but on the finger with it was a band of emeralds, diamonds, and rubies.

"Oh, Belle, I am so glad you're happy. I don't know anyone who deserves it more than you."

Tears filled her eyes. "Happy?" she sniffed. "Why, I'm done past happy. I'm thrilled! I'm ecstatic! Every day I wake up with my sweet Charlie beside me I think I've done died and gone to heaven."

Belle gave her nose a loud blow. "Enough of that sentimental mush. How have you been keeping?" She nodded to Jake, who had been pulled away by one of his ranch hands. "From the way you two was hanging on to each other for dear life, I'd say you were keeping just fine. Smart gal. I'd latch on to him if I was you. There's too many floozies in the world who'd love to sink their claws in him."

Araby gave a quiet smile. She wondered if her friend suspected that latching on to him was exactly what she had done on their way to the dance. From the knowing look on Belle's meticulously powdered and rouged face, she had probably guessed. After all, where the ways of the world were concerned, Belle was an old hand! She could tell, too, that Belle was just itching for her to admit to a romance, but there were some things that were better left secret.

"How are Lucinda and the other girls?" Araby asked, deliberately changing the subject. "Were they as lucky as you finding a good husband?"

Belle rolled back her eyes. "You know, I did my best with those gals. Tried to give them a little culture and expose them to the better things in life—and for what, I ask you? Nothing. Why, no sooner had they been spoken for by three of the finest bachelors in Idaho than they took off for California. Lucinda got some fool notion in her head that she wanted to start up a real fine house like what Ruby's got here.''

She gave a thoughtful nod. '' 'Course I can see her point. The way she figures it, if they stayed here and married those fellows, they'd still be earning their keep on their backs and doing a lot of other back-breaking chores besides. One way you keep your money, and the other you don't even earn any.'' She let out a sigh. ''Oh, well. I did my best by those girls. Couldn't have done any better by them had they really been my nieces. I wish them well. Lordy knows they're going to need all the good luck and well wishing they can get.''

Jake came up behind Araby and slipped an arm around her waist. ''You two ladies were talking a mile a minute.'' He gave her a chaste peck on the cheek. ''Somebody's ears must have been burning up a storm the way you were going on. Who you been talking about?''

Araby sank deeper into his hold. How she loved having that strong, manly arm wrapped around her. In his embrace she felt so secure, so protected!

''We were just talking about Charlie and how happy Belle is in her little shack.''

''How's that old codger treating you?'' he asked Belle.

Belle fluttered her long lashes. ''I have no complaints. Charlie don't, either. I see to that.'' She looked from Jake to Araby and back to Jake again. ''How have you been keeping, Jake?''

He tightened his hold around Araby's waist.

"I don't have any complaints, either."

His breath was hot in her ear. Araby wondered if he had on his mind what she had on hers.

"My throat's a little parched," he said. "I believe I'll go see what Felix can do about it. You ladies like a glass of punch?"

Araby nodded. "Thanks, I could use something cold."

Jake winked.

Belle scanned the crowd. "My Charlie just went after another sarsaparilla. He'll be back just as soon as he's through chewing the fat, as he says, with his old buddies."

With one lady on each arm, Jake led them over to a quiet corner of the salon where they could chat without having to yell over the crowd, then excused himself and headed for the bar.

Araby waited until he was out of earshot before asking about Lucius. Jake had a jealous streak, and nothing could be gained from arousing it.

"Lucius left yesterday, headed for Clarkia. Me and Charlie had him out to the house for dinner Thursday night. Did I tell you I'm learning to cook? Well, I am. Charlie says I'm doing real good, too. You'll have to come out and sample my beef stew. Charlie says it'll put hairs on your chest."

Belle giggled like a schoolgirl. "Anyway, back to Lucius. He'd heard there'd been a big gold strike down there, and he wanted to be sitting at the tables ready to take their money when the miners got to town. I'll miss him. He was as fine a man as you'd ever want to meet. He thought the world of you. Why, with just a little bit of gentle persuasion, I bet you could have talked him into settling down and trading in his deck of cards for a hoe."

Araby shook her finger at Belle. "You know as well as I do that Lucius and I were just friends, nothing more. So you just keep those winks to yourself. Besides, no woman can change a man from what he is, and there's no point in wasting time trying."

"How about that cowboy of yours?"

Dimples dancing across her cheeks, Araby watched as Jake maneuvered through the crowd balancing three cups of punch.

"Jake's perfect," she said proudly. "I wouldn't change one thing about him even if I could."

"That sounds like marrying talk to me," Belle teased her.

Araby waved aside her remark.

Actually, what Belle had said was not as silly as she had made it out to be. There was nothing silly about marrying Jake. As a matter of fact, that was pretty serious business. For someone like Araby, who'd never been interested in settling down and raising a family—perish the thought, she used to tell her relatives and friends when they even hinted at such nonsense—the prospect of doing so now was very inviting indeed! Mike had done a fine job handpicking the man she should marry. Jake Montana had been made to order. But how could she convince him that he'd never find a more suitable match than her?

Jake handed her a cup of punch, then gave one to Belle along with a kiss on the cheek. "That's from your beloved. He's wheeling and dealing some big mining proposition with a fellow from Lewiston and said to tell you he'd be along directly."

"That's my Charlie. No matter how important his business, he's always got time for me." Her little finger crooked, Belle sipped her punch. "I'm practicing being a lady. I want Charlie to be proud of me!"

Araby kissed the heavily rouged cheek. "You don't have to practice. You are a lady."

Charlie grabbed hold of his bride from behind and swung her around into his arms. "Come on, honeybunch. What say me and you show these folks how a couple of newlyweds can shake their legs."

"Whatever you say, dumpling. You're the boss." She pinched his cheek. "Isn't he just the sweetest thing you ever did see?"

Before Araby had a chance to respond, Charlie had whirled his bride away and was clearing off the dance floor.

"How 'bout you, Araby?" Jake asked as he smiled a kiss at her. "I'll try not to step on your feet this time."

Araby held tight to his arm. It wouldn't matter if he did!

Three fiddlers, a harmonica player, and a pair of banjo pickers had gathered in the center of the salon. Lee Roy Jacobs, a red-faced homesteader with a big mouth and a big belly to match, stood up on a turned-over washtub and yelled for the men to grab hold of their ladies.

Araby and Jake joined the big square-dance circle that was forming around the band.

"I don't know what to do. I've never square danced before," she told him.

"Don't worry. Lee Roy calls out the moves."

"Grab your partners, gather round!" Lee Roy's booming, sing song voice called out. "Take hands now. Everybody circle right. Come on friends, on your feet be light. To the left now, folks. John, don't be a poke. Take those gals and whirl them around. Not too close or you'll be settling down."

By the time Lee Roy had told the men to swing their partners one last time, Araby was ready to collapse in Jake's arms.

"You don't mind if I sit the next one out, do you?" She leaned against him, fanning herself with a handkerchief. "I'm not used to that kind of dancing."

"You city gals never could keep up with us cowpokes."

Someone waved to her from across the room.

It took her a moment to realize that the girl peering out from behind the salon draperies was Mandy. In less than a week, her young friend had been transformed from a gangling girl to a budding young woman. She could see Ruby's hand in the change and was delighted. Ruby and Mandy both stood to gain considerably from their association with each other.

Grinning from ear to ear, Mandy crossed the room.

Araby noticed right away that her steps were not nearly as short and timid as they used to be. She noticed, too, there was no more shoulder slumping and drooping her head so she wouldn't have to look anyone in the eye.

Araby gave her a hug and made a big fuss over how pretty she looked in yellow and how lovely her hair looked up in curls.

Mandy's face lit up more with each compliment, and when Jake teased her about lending her his bullwhip to fight off the fellows, she positively glowed.

Araby couldn't resist giving her another hug. "You're happy, aren't you? You're really happy?"

"Oh, yes. I really am. Ruby is wonderful. She's been just like a mama to me. She had a lot of pretty dresses made for me and bought me two new pairs of shoes and a purse to match each one. Why, she won't even let me lift a hand around here. All she says she wants me to do is just be her friend. I think that's real nice of her, don't you?"

Araby nodded. Mike had been right. Ruby was a very special lady.

"And do you know something else? Ruby's teaching me to read and write and do numbers. We've even had one or two French lessons. *Bonjour*. That means good day. *O Rever*. That's goodbye." Mandy giggled with excitement. "And she's teaching me to be a proper lady, too. We've been working a lot on my, my elo . . . elo . . ."

"Elocution."

"That's it. Elocution. That means to—oh heck, you know what that means, don't you? Anyway, Ruby tells me I can be anything I want to be, and you know something, Araby? I'm going to make something out of my life!"

"That's wonderful, Mandy. You can be whatever you want to be."

Jake agreed.

"How is Ruby?" Araby glanced around the room. "I keep looking for her, but I haven't seen her."

Mandy shook her head. "You won't see her.

She's not coming down. Something's bothering her real bad, and she won't come out of her apartment.''

"She isn't sick, is she?" Araby asked with concern.

"No, not unless you call a broken heart being sick," Mandy replied. "She keeps talking about some fellow she wished she'd married, but says it's too late now 'cause he's done gone and left her. I told her she ought to go after him, but she said she couldn't, 'cause he's dead. I think that's real sad, don't you?"

Mandy's frown was quick to disappear. "Oh, I know what, Araby! Why don't you go upstairs and see her? I bet you could get her to come down and join in the fun. She likes you a whole lot. She told me so. She said you reminded her of somebody she used to know."

Jake agreed with Mandy. "Sure sounds like a good idea to me. It's not going to do Ruby any good at all sitting up there moping by herself."

Araby hesitated. It sounded like a good idea, but it might not be. Grief was a very personal emotion, and people dealt with it in different ways.

"I'm not sure whether it's a good idea or not. If Ruby's that miserable, she might not want any company."

It took little persuasion to get her to change her mind. As Jake pointed out, if she really did remind Ruby of Mike, then maybe she'd find some comfort in having his niece there.

"Maybe I should go. I suppose if she doesn't want the company, the worst she can do is tell me to leave."

Mandy was shocked. "Oh, no, she'd never

tell you to leave! Not Ruby. She's too much of a lady to do that."

Araby smiled. Ruby really was a lady—in every sense of the word.

Jake turned to Mandy and held out his arm. "I'd be real honored, m'am, if you'd give me the pleasure of this dance."

"Oh, no, I, I couldn't possibly," she stammered. "I mean, dancing is the one lesson I'm not doing good in at all."

"All the more reason for you to practice."

Jake led her away under protest. He threw Araby a wink over his shoulder.

At that moment, she had never loved him more!

11

After a quick exchange of pleasantries with Felix and Mae, Araby started up the stairs. Halfway up, she paused and looked back down at the crowd below. Jake was swinging Mandy around and around. Belle looked up and waved, and Araby waved back.

Her smile faded. Jud was standing alone in the corner, his eyes on hers. She could feel her face crimson under the intensity of his stare. He nodded, then with a smile, touched the brim of his hat. Araby managed a wave before she turned and continued up the stairs.

Something made her look back down at him when she reached the top step. He was no longer standing alone. Lena had joined him. Sim was nowhere nearby. From the looks of it, their conversation was far more serious than casual chit-chat. Jud was shaking his finger in her face, and Lena was standing on tiptoe and shaking hers right back.

Araby was curious. Theirs was no family squabble. Still, she kept on walking down the hall before they spotted her.

She knocked softly on the door to the lavishly furnished suite.

"Ruby? It's me, Araby. May I come in?"

She heard a long sigh, then a pause, then the sound of slippered feet scuffing across the floor.

Ruby opened the door just wide enough to let her in. "How kind of you to drop by, my dear," she said, forcing a smile as she tightened the sash of her dressing gown. "Do come in and sit down, and I'll pour us a cup of tea."

"I can only stay a moment. I didn't want to leave without saying hello."

Araby sat down on the mahogany and red-velvet chaise and pretended not to notice when Ruby poured whiskey into her own cup instead of tea.

Poor Ruby looked like a walking corpse. Her eyes were red and puffy and set far back into her head. Her hair was tangled and matted, and her face drawn and pale without its powders and rouges.

Ruby smoothed back a few strands of hair, then gave up and let them fall back across her forehead. With teacup in hand, she settled back into bed and leaned against the plumped-up pillows.

"I look a fright, I know."

Ruby held the cup with both hands. When she raised it to her mouth to take a sip, her hands shook.

"Most days I cope rather well. Others . . . well, other days there's just no reason for getting out of bed. I suppose I could lie to you and tell you I'm just feeling poorly, but what's the point? I miss Mike so much, and ever since I learned of his death, I've been dying myself a little every day. If I'm lucky, maybe I'll be gone, too, come winter."

"Ruby, don't you dare talk like that! You know Mike would have a fit if he heard you saying such things."

Araby moved to the edge of the bed and took hold of Ruby's hand to steady it. "Mike's gone, Ruby. We can't bring him back no matter how many tears we shed. I don't think he'd want us to grieve for him the rest of our lives. Mike was the kind of man who'd want those he loved and those who loved him to remember all the good times they had with him. He'd want them to remember him the way he used to be."

Ruby's face brightened for a moment as she told Araby how Mike used to come stomping up the stairs and pick her up and spin her around in his arms the moment she came to the door.

"Oh, Araby. I still can't believe he's dead." She buried her head in a pillow and sobbed.

Araby said nothing. It was far better to let Ruby cry. She'd be there if later she wanted to talk, or if she just needed a strong hand to hold. She couldn't believe Mike was dead, either. Ever since Hamstring told her about his way of dealing with Mike's death, she, too, had thought of him in that way. The only trouble was that Mike wouldn't come back down the mountain from hunting, not this year, or the next, or the one after, either.

Araby gave the shaking shoulders a comforting hug and let Ruby go on crying and rambling on and on about changing the past. If she had it to do over again, she said, she would have accepted Mike's marriage proposal and to hell with anybody who didn't like it!

Araby very nearly revealed her suspicions to Ruby regarding Mike's death, but at the last minute decided against it. She trusted Ruby to keep such news to herself, but the poor woman was in such a shaky emotional state that there was no telling how she might react to the startling revelation that Mike's death had not been accidental.

"Oh, Araby," Ruby sniffed. "If I had it to do all over again, I would have married that uncle of yours and gone to live at Tamarack and not give a damn about what anybody else thought," she said for the tenth time. "He tried I don't know how many times to marry me. I kept refusing him. I guess he just got fed up with me saying no, so that's why he married that other woman. But that didn't change anything. I still loved him, and he still loved me. What a fool I was! If only I had it all to do again. Oh, Mike, you were always right. We deserved happiness as much as anybody."

Ruby collapsed into Araby's arms.

It took a long time for her to compose herself.

"At least I have my memories," she said at last, her voice quiet but strong. She held tight to her handkerchief. "I'm bloody lucky to have those! Most people aren't left with that much."

She took a cigarette from a gold box on the bedside table, stuck it into a tiny pearl-encrusted holder, and lit it. "If only we could go back in time and live our lives differently. But we can't." She drew hard on her cigarette, then blew the smoke out slowly. "I guess that's what they mean about hell being right here on earth."

A few minutes later, a smiling Ruby gave Araby a gentle shove. "Now you get yourself back downstairs and have a wonderful time. I'll be along just as soon as I make myself a little more presentable," she promised.

Ruby walked her to the door, but waited a moment before opening it.

"Don't you make the same mistake I did, young lady. The love of a good man is the most important part of life, and don't you let anyone convince you otherwise. Fame and fortune don't mean a thing. Take it from somebody who found out the hard way."

Araby clasped Ruby's tiny hands between her own. "I had to come all the way to Idaho to learn that, and believe me, that is one lesson I shall never forget."

"There's a lot of talk going around town about you and Jake Montana." The sparkle had returned to Ruby's kitten-gray eyes. "Mike would be so happy. He just knew you two would hit it off. I don't know how many times he said to me that if he ever got you two together, there'd be more sparks flying than firecrackers popping on the Fourth of July."

Firecrackers popping on the Fourth of July! That was exactly how it was when the two of them got together. Araby couldn't have described it better herself, she decided on her way back downstairs.

She was pleased to see Jake still whirling Mandy around the dance floor and even more pleased that her young friend looked as if she were having the time of her life. She scanned the room looking for one cowboy in particular, then headed toward him when she spotted him.

Rowdy was leaning against the wall—holding up the wall, as Mike would say—while Hamstring stood beside him clapping his hands, stomping his feet, and giving his invisible dance partner a turn or two around that side of the room.

When Rowdy saw her coming, he shook his head and gave her a shy grin. "I . . . I don't reckon I'd b-better," he said when she held out her arms.

Hamstring nudged him and teased him about losing his job if he didn't do what the boss wanted.

"I'd be terribly disappointed if you didn't dance at least one dance with me, Rowdy, especially after all those lessons."

"Go on, son," Hamstring encouraged him. "Didn't your pa ever tell you not to never say no to a lady, 'specially when she's a pretty as Miss Araby?"

Rowdy reluctantly stepped forward.

"You're next," she called out to Hamstring as she took hold of one of Rowdy's hands and positioned the other around her waist.

"Yippeeio!" Hamstring leaped off the floor. "You won't have to ask me twice. My daddy didn't raise no fool."

Rowdy counted the steps under his breath as Araby maneuvered him in the direction of Mandy and Jake.

"That's it. You're doing very well," she kept assuring him. "That's wonderful. One, two, three . . . one, two, three. Good. Having a good time, Rowdy?"

"Yes, m'am."

Araby smiled. The poor boy was miserable, but that was all about to change. He might not be enjoying himself now, but he would be very shortly.

When the dance ended, and Lee Roy insisted the crowd give him and the boys a little break, Araby made certain she and Rowdy were standing right beside Jake and Mandy.

When Rowdy caught sight of Mandy, and when her eyes came to rest on him, Araby could tell that at that moment her two young friends were the only people in the room.

Jake noticed it, too, and gave her a wink.

Araby introduced one to the other, but she doubted either of them heard a word she said.

"Hey, there. My name's Rowdy."

"My name's Mandy."

Rowdy repeated her name softly. "That's a real pretty name. I believe it's just the prettiest name I ever did hear."

"Really?" Mandy blushed. "It sounds real pretty when you say it . . . Rowdy."

Rowdy flicked back a blond strand that kept falling over his eye. "I reckon a fellow would have to stand in line to get a dance with a pretty lady like yourself."

"There ain't no line, but if there wuz, I'd let you jump up ahead of ever'body else."

Rowdy stood taller. "You would?"

"I would."

Rowdy reached out and timidly took Mandy by the hand. "I'd be real honored if you'd dance the next dance with me."

"You would? Why—why yes. I believe I'd like that, too."

They walked slowly away, their eyes focused only on each other.

"And afterwards, maybe if we get tired, we can

get us a cup of that punch and take a stroll through town," Araby heard Rowdy suggest.

She wondered if he realized he wasn't stuttering.

"That sounds wonderful, Rowdy," Mandy told him, taking hold of his arm. "I'd enjoy that very much, too."

Jake slipped his arm around Araby's waist. "Matchmaking must run in your family."

Araby smiled. Apparently, Mike had made no secret of his desire to get the two of them together. It was apparent, too, that if Jake had any objections, he wouldn't keep slipping in through her bedroom window.

"What say me and you take another turn or two around the dance floor?"

"I think that's a splendid idea."

Jake folded her close into his arms, and she gave a long sigh. Whatever he wanted was just fine by her!

Later in the evening, when they had paused from the dancing long enough to cool down with another cup of punch, Araby motioned to Rowdy and Mandy. They were sitting on the stairs laughing, talking, and holding hands.

"Love at first sight," she said quietly.

"Even us rough and tough cowboys aren't immune to that malady."

Jake's warm breath caressed her hair.

Araby felt her heart skip one or two beats. Perhaps this would be the night he would ask her to be his wife.

"What do you say we head on back to Tamarack?" Jake's yawn was much exaggerated. "All of this celebrating has done gone and wore me out."

Araby smiled into his neck as he danced her toward he door. From the way his hands were taking liberties above her waist when no one was looking, she had a feeling sleep was not exactly what he had in mind.

The ride back home seemed to last forever.

Jake held the reins with one hand while his free arm kept a tight hold on her. When the wagon bumped past the willow bower where they'd made love earlier, they looked at each other and shared a long sigh.

Tramp came running down the road to meet them just inside Tamarack's gate. Without waiting for them to stop, the black, fuzzy dog jumped into the back of the wagon and nosed his way between them.

Outside the barn, Araby whistled for Darling. A loud whinny came from inside. While Jake unhitched the team, she went to visit her horse and gave her a hug. That little chestnut mare had become as fine a riding horse as anyone could want. She was polite and willing—a real lady!

Later, when Jake had turned his horses out to pasture for the night, they walked on up to the house arm in arm, with her head resting on his shoulder.

"You know, Jake, I never knew what real happiness was until I came here to Tamarack and to you."

"I hope that feeling lasts, darling. I hope it lasts for both our sakes."

There was a wistfulness in his tone. He had his doubts. She already knew that. What he didn't know was that she intended to spend the rest of her life dispelling them.

To convince him, she attacked his mouth

with a shameless hunger.

"It will last, Jake. You just wait and see. It will last forever and ever."

I'll make it last, she vowed silently.

Araby stepped inside her room and frowned. "That's odd. I know I blew out the candle when I left."

"Even if you didn't, it would have been burned down long before now." He looked behind the dressing screen, then stepped out onto the porch. "Maybe I'd better have a look around the rest of the house," he told her when he stepped back in.

"I don't think it would do any good. I'm sure whoever my late-night visitor was, he's long gone by now."

She opened the drawer to her bedside table. The journal was in its place, but then, whoever took the liberty to read it was always careful to put it right back where it came from.

She opened the diary to the entry marked July the third and handed it to Jake to read.

The longer he read, the bigger his smile became. "Pig-headed? Arrogant? Stuck on myself? Why, Miss Stone-Leigh, you do have the kindest things to say about me."

His hands resting on her hips, he pulled her close. "And that Jud Cord. I had no idea you held him in such high esteem. Why, the way you go on sweet-talking about him, I'm liable to get jealous."

Strong fingers dug into her flesh with promises of the joys to come.

"Going to double-cross me, huh? Go behind my back and sell Tamarack to Jud just because he'll give you more money? Why, I've got a mind to turn you over my knee and give you a good tanning."

Araby's laughter echoed throughout the room. She was about to dare him to make good on his threat when she caught the scent of a very distinct smell floating through her room. It was sweet, very sweet. Perfume, perhaps, but definitely not her own. She'd smelled it somewhere before.

"What's wrong?" asked Jake.

She breathed in another whiff. Where had she smelled it before? And on whom?

"Do you smell that?" she asked finally.

It took him a moment, then he nodded. "Smells good."

She watched him closely for a reaction, but there was none. She knew who smelled of gardenias, but he did not. Had they been involved in a love affair, surely he would have recognized who the smell belonged to.

"And to think, all this time I thought it was Jud snooping around in here."

"You're talking in circles, Araby."

"It's Lena," she explained. "Lena's the one who's been sneaking up here reading my journal and reporting back to Jud. He put her up to it."

"That sounds just like Jud Cord. I wouldn't put anything past him."

Jake sat down on the bed. Araby sat beside him.

"You know, that poor gal's always been crazy over him. He wouldn't marry her, so she up and married the next best thing—his brother."

Araby listened closely. Jake was just stating

the facts. There were no personal overtones what-soever in his voice.

"Did I tell you Lena's folks used to own Cross Fork? It like to have killed her when they sold the ranch and decided to move to Sacramento. She still rides out from time to time to visit the place. Guess she's homesick. Now that I think about it, she was out there yesterday—no, the day before. Poor thing. Can't help but feel sorry for her."

Jake pulled off his boots.

"Reckon that's how them rumors got started about me and her. Shoot. Jud probably started them himself so Sim wouldn't suspect he was being cuckolded by his own brother. Oh, well, other folks' problems aren't ours."

He lay back onto the bed and pulled Araby down with him.

"Me and you, we got enough to worry about on our own."

Her eyes searched deep into his. She could see the want flickering in the turquoise depths.

"I hope worrying isn't what you've got on your mind for tonight." She traced the outline of his lip with her finger. "I can think of one or two more exciting ways to wile away the hours."

"Can you now?" His tongue followed the path of her finger. "Tell me more."

"I'll do better than that, cowboy. I'll show you."

Her eyes not leaving his, she slid up his chest.

"Aren't you afraid of messing up that pretty party dress of yours?" he teased her.

She massaged his body with her own. "You talk too much, cowboy. You could have had it off me before now."

Without saying another word, he rolled her back over, and before she knew it, he had done just that.

12

Araby sat on a stump in the shade fanning herself with an old straw hat. It was not yet noon, and already the sun's rays were scorching. She and Jake had left Tamarack long before dawn, and having made the same journey yesterday with Jud, she knew it would be nearly dusk before they arrived back home again. Jake had made the trip with them. Luckily, however, Jud had not guessed they were being trailed.

Anxiously, Araby watched as Jake dug deeper and deeper into the rocky ground. Jake was about to confirm that strange sensation that had overcome her yesterday as she stood over the mound of rocks that had been marked by a crude cross. She couldn't explain that eerie feeling then, and she couldn't explain it now, but she knew that Mike was not in that grave.

Jake tossed up the shovel, then scrambled out of the hole. He wiped the sweat off his face, then turned up the water canteen and drank thirstily.

"We were right. Nothing down there but rocks and more rocks."

Araby stared across the way at Twin Sisters Peak. Jud had gone to a lot of trouble to dig an empty grave just so she'd have a place to come to pay her final respects. There was no doubt about it—none at all. Jud had killed Mike, not a rattlesnake, and he had left him to rot right where he'd died!

"What should we do now?" she wondered aloud. "Should we go to the Sheriff?"

Jake shook his head. "Wouldn't do any good. We can't prove anything. We'd have to have a body to do that."

"But an empty grave. Surely . . ."

"Jud would just admit to not giving Mike a proper burial. As far as the law is concerned, that's no crime."

Araby pressed on. "But what about the grave? That in itself is suspicious."

Jake agreed. "However, Jud would just tell Otter he came up and dug it or had one of his boys dig it just so you'd be spared the grief of knowing your uncle hadn't been given a decent funeral."

Try as hard as she might, she could not keep the horrible images of vultures sweeping down on her dead uncle from her mind.

Jake seemed to know the thoughts plaguing her and pulled her close.

"Mike will have his revenge. I'll see to that," he told her gently.

"We shall both see to that!" Her words were strong with conviction. "Jud and Sim will pay for what they did to my uncle. They'll pay with their lives, even if I have to put the bullets in them myself," she added with a bitter determination.

''They will pay!''

The ride back to Tamarack was long and hot and dusty. More than once they had to stop to let the horses drink from the cool stream and rest in whatever patch of shade they could find.

There was no laughter and very little talk along the way, only a grim silence. All Araby could think about was how horrible Mike's death must have been. Being struck by a rattler was terrifying enough, but looking down the barrel of a gun, just watching and waiting for the killer to pull the trigger, would surely be much worse. She could only pray that his death had been quick and painless. Maybe Jud had shot him in the back, without warning. After all, he wasn't man enough to face his victim. Nor would he have had the courage to draw against her uncle. If he had, Uncle Mike wouldn't have been the one who drew his last breath on Butte's Peak.

Butte's Peak! Of course! Why hadn't she thought of that sooner? She had only Jud's word that they had gone hunting on Butte's Peak. What good was the word of a murderer? Why, he and Sim had told everybody that's where Mike had died, and who could have disputed him? They hadn't gone hunting on Butte's Peak! Mike hadn't been murdered on Butte's Peak. She and Jake could have stayed on that peak a month, scouring every rock for evidence of foul play, and not have found a thing. Jud might be a coward, but he was no fool. Anyone who didn't believe him would have been led on a wild-goose chase. The answers they were looking for were miles and miles away in an entirely different direction.

''Mike didn't die on Butte's Peak.''

Araby's announcement broke the silence.

"I'll bet he never set foot here." She reminded Jake again of the last letter she had received from her uncle telling her of his plans to go hunting on Freezeout Mountain, his favorite spot to hunt. "Mike would not have changed his mind. Not at the last minute! Not any time!"

Jake rammed his fist hard into his thigh. "Damn it to hell! Jud made certain anybody who didn't believe his story about the rattler would be looking in the wrong place. I played right into his hands!"

"We both did, but no matter. We know where to look now—Freezeout Mountain. That's where we'll find the proof we need to guarantee that the Cords hang for what they did."

Jake did not share her enthusiasm. "It'll be like looking for a needle in a haystack." Seeing her disappointment, he was quick to add, "Of course, the best place to start looking is the spot where Mike always went to make camp. I can get us there with no trouble at all. It's just that . . ."

"It's just that what, Jake?"

"Well, honey, there's a lot of territory to cover up on Freezeout, and to tell you the truth, Jud isn't stupid enough to leave a lot of loose ends."

Araby reined Darling into a halt. "If there's one loose end, I'll find it. If I have to, I'll stay up there till this time next year looking for it."

Jake reached for her hand. "We both will. I'm in this, too, remember. I want Jud to pay just as much as you do. I just don't want you to . . ."

"You just don't want me to what?"

"I just don't want you to get your hopes up," he said.

"We will find what we are looking for on

Freezeout Mountain." She knew they would, and nobody was going to tell her any differently. Not Jake, not anyone! "Can we go up there tomorrow?"

Jake nudged his horse along. Araby did the same.

"We could," he answered after long deliberation. "But I don't think it's a good idea."

"You don't think it's a good idea?" she snapped back. "Then what do you suggest we do—I do?"

She immediately regretted her outburst. Jake was more than her lover. He was her friend, her best friend. He was the last person she should be short with.

"I'm sorry, Jake," she apologized. "I know it's no excuse, but I feel so helpless. It makes me so mad knowing that Jud is walking around healthy and happy while Mike is lying dead in some ditch." Tears stung her face. "It's not fair. It just is not fair at all! Forgive me?"

"Forgive you for what? For loving your uncle? For being determined to avenge his death? There's nothing to forgive, Araby, honey." He took the bandanna from around his neck and dabbed at her tears. "Now, if you'll just hear me out and let me finish what I was about to say . . ."

She grinned. "I promise."

"All right. The reason I don't think it's such a good idea for us to go to Freezeout Mountain tomorrow, or even the next day, is because I don't believe it's to our advantage to move too quickly. I think Saturday will be soon enough."

Her shoulders dropped. Saturday? But that was four whole days away.

She was about to tell Jake so when she caught

herself. He wouldn't have chosen that particular day if he didn't have a good reason for doing so.

"We'd never make it there and back in one day. It'll take two for sure, maybe even three, depending on what we find."

Araby nodded. She cautioned herself to be patient. She supposed Jake had his reasons for the delay.

"If you're gone from Tamarack overnight," he explained, "someone is bound to get suspicious. And suspicion is something we don't want to arouse, especially Jud's. Now I know Burley's long gone, but in case Jud still has somebody at the ranch reporting back to him—Mattie, let's say—then you need to come up with a good excuse for going away for a day or two."

Araby nodded. What he said made sense. She couldn't just up and go without Jud wondering just what she was up to. And she supposed, too, that if Jud did have a spy at Tamarack, it might well be Mattie. After all, he had hired her, so her loyalties would be with him, not with someone who was there for only a short time.

"I'll put out the word that I'm going to be spending a few days with Belle and Charlie."

"Good. Nobody would think there's anything unusual about that." He gave the brim of her straw hat a playful yank. "Don't worry. We'll get to the bottom of this. You have my word on that."

Araby smiled. Of course they would! She'd settle for nothing less than seeing Jud and Sim with nooses around their good-for-nothing necks! She'd make certain they were shown no more mercy than they had shown Uncle Mike!

Whether or not they found the proof they

needed to implicate Jud and his brother in Mike's death, Araby wondered if it wouldn't be a wise move to go over Sheriff Otter's head directly to the United States Marshal, and present the facts of the matter to him.

She was about to suggest this to Jake when Buck and Darling both stopped dead in their tracks at the same time. Her horse's sudden stop all but sent her catapulting over the mare's head.

Both horses threw back their heads and snorted at the sky.

Araby didn't have to ask what was going on. She knew. The wild horses were somewhere nearby.

She looked for them, but all she saw were the gigantic slabs of granite that formed the boundaries of Satan's Kitchen, the desolate wasteland they were about to cross. There, nothing green grew; not even scrub grass poked up from the rocks.

Jake lifted high out of the saddle, and with his hand shading his eyes from the sun reflecting off the rocks, he searched in every direction.

Araby listened. She knew they would hear the horses long before they saw them.

Soon, the sound of thundering hooves pounding the unyielding ground could be heard in the distance.

She waited, all the while watching and straining to hear. It was hard to tell just where the rumble was coming from, but it was becoming louder with every breath she drew.

"The creek we just stopped at a little ways back—that's where he's taking his herd," Jake announced confidently.

Without warning, he jerked his horse back

around. "Come on!"

Araby followed at a gallop. It was all she could do to keep at least one of the horse's hooves on the ground with each stride.

Jake led her through a cut between two great stone masses, then veered a hundred or so feet off the trail to a hill of boulders that must have been part of a large rockslide centuries ago.

He explained as they trotted to the back of the mound that if given his druthers, any horse, wild or tame, would stick to a trail that was already there instead of blazing another one.

"By the time the stallion picks up our scent, the rest of the herd will already have caught wind of the creek, and there's no stopping them when they're headed to water."

Jake swung down from the saddle.

Araby stayed astride her mount. She'd have far more control in the saddle than on the ground if Darling did go beserk when the wild horses stampeded past. She could sense Jake's excitement. The air was fevered with his anticipation. He wanted that stallion! He wanted him bad! Part of her wanted Jake to get him, too, but another part of him hoped and prayed that the black creature would continue eluding his would-be captors, Jake included.

A sound like summer thunder rumbled over the sky. The cloud of dust that had formed on the horizon moved closer. Soon, if they were lucky, they'd be so close to the horses when they came galloping past that they could reach out from behind the mound of boulders and touch them.

Everything happened so quickly! One moment the horses were out of view, and the next they were right up on them. Never before had she witnessed a more awesome sight than the charging band of mustangs with a cloud of dust billowing out behind them.

The ground shook so hard, that Araby thought the mound of boulders would come tumbling right down onto them as well as onto the horses.

She peered out from around the rocks to see more.

The stallion galloped ahead of his mares. His sleek ebony coat glistened in the sunlight. The big, black horse moved with the grace of a ballet dancer. Araby was certain that at any moment he would become airborne and soar right over them like a winged Pegasus.

Every now and then, the stallion would cut back behind his herd, then come charging up the middle nipping at the mare's back ends to goad them into a faster pace.

Magnificent! That was the only word she could think of to describe so noble a creature.

She wondered if he knew they were there and decided that he had probably been watching them ever since they left Tamarack.

Jake took his lasso from the saddle horn and handed Buck's reins to Araby.

She knew what was on his mind. The stallion had already passed so close to them that they could see the sweat beading his coal-black coat. If he ventured so close again, Jake would be ready for him.

Suddenly, the stallion reared straight up, right in the middle of his herd, and boxed with the sun. He let out a piercing neigh, then ran back to the mares behind him and bunched them all together. With flying manes and tails, the mares charged past.

Buck remained calm, but it was all Araby could do to stay in the saddle. If she were to allow the tiniest slack in the rein, she'd find herself flat on the ground and without a horse.

One of the mares lagged behind the others. At her side was a foal struggling to keep up.

Araby held her breath. She knew what would happen if the mother and baby did not speed up. The stallion would kick the foal to death so that the mare would not have any reason to tarry behind.

Just as the stallion went for the foal, the baby horse kicked out all four of his long legs and fled with his mother to the middle of the herd.

Araby breathed a sigh of relief for the foal as well as for the stallion when the magnificent black creature galloped past with no other horses behind him and well out of range of Jake's rope.

For no apparent reason, the stallion stopped abruptly, then turned around and pranced back to the mound of boulders. Every muscle in his great body rippled.

Araby couldn't believe what she was seeing. The horse was courting danger, and he not only seemed to know what he was doing, but he seemed to be enjoying it as well.

"You bastard. Teasing me, aren't you?" Jake's words were quiet and filled with respect. "You know my rope won't make it quite that far, don't you?"

Lariat at his side, Jake took a few steps closer.

The great beast did not flinch. He stood perfectly still, as though he were daring Jake to take just one more step.

They stood there, man and animal, a respectful distance apart, both knowing the battle was not yet over and each one wondering who the victor would be when it was.

The stallion went up on his hind legs once more.

Jake raised his arms to shield his face from the powerful hooves.

Instead of charging forward, the horse danced backwards. The sound he made was less a snort than a mocking laugh. Catch me if you can! Then, with his front legs still boxing with the sun, he turned on his back heels and fled to catch up with the others.

Jake walked back toward her, smiling.

What secret had the two of them shared? Araby wondered.

"Next time," he told her with a wink. "I can feel it. Next time, he'll be mine."

"Next time," echoed Araby in agreement. She wondered if Jake really did want that horse, or if it were the pursuit he most enjoyed.

"Found out what happened to the Spotters' bay," Jake told his foreman when they returned to Cross Fork. "She was picked up by that crazy stallion. So were the Beckers' two Arabians, and Buddy Giles' paints. Damn! Where are my manners? Slim Watkins, Araby Stone-Leigh. Mike Stone's niece. Slim used to be the foreman over at Tamarack," he told her.

Araby smiled and nodded. Slim was every bit as skinny as her uncle had described him. He really did look like a rail.

Slim tipped his hat. "Pleased to meet you, m'am. Your uncle was a mighty fine man. I'm truly grieved over what happened."

"I appreciate that," she told Slim. "He certainly thought the world of you."

"I'm proud to hear that, m'am. Real proud." Slim spit a stream of tobacco out behind him. "By the way, consider yourself lucky that Burley Wilkerson up and left. You got yourself a real good man in Curley Reece. He'll do you right."

Slim tipped his hat at Araby once again. "If you folks will excuse me, I got me some fences up on the north side that need mending." He started to walk away, but turned back after only a few steps. "Oh, Jake, some Indian came looking for you while you were gone. He wouldn't say what he wanted, and he didn't want to talk to nobody but you. Jake Montana. That's all he'd say. I asked him where he came from. He says, Jake Montana. Who sent him? Jake Montana. What did he want? Jake Montana."

Jake leaned over and gave Buck a pat. "Silver Bear must have sent one of his braves after a couple of those calves I promised him."

Jake turned to Araby and explained that he and Chief Silver Bear, the Coeur d'Alene Indian chief, were good friends who did favors for each other. He'd supply the chief's tribe with cows every now and then, and in return the braves would help round up strays.

"It don't pay to have an Indian as an enemy, that's for sure," Slim said. "But that wasn't no brave that was looking for you. One of the fellows said he looked more like one of them medicine men with all those pouches strapped around his waist. He didn't think he was no Coeur d'Alene neither. This Indian's head was as round as a white folk's."

"If his head was round, then he must be a Flat

Head. All the other tribes deform their babies' skulls at birth so the heads won't be round," Jake told Araby. "If it was a Flat Head, he's mighty far from home. I reckon he'll be back to see me if it was important."

"Friendly, I hope?" Araby asked after Slim had excused himself.

Jake was deep in thought. "What?"

"The Indians, are they friendly?"

"Oh, yes. They are. Of course they don't have much choice in the matter. Most of them have been confined to reservations. Damn shame, too. There's enough land for everybody to go on about their business."

The horses walked on through chest-high grass, and Araby thought about what Jake had just said. She'd heard her uncle make the very same remark time and again. The Indians had been coerced and beaten out of their land, then left to survive on land where even animals could not endure. The cruelties inflicted on them during the Indian Wars were deplorable. Glory-mongers like General Custer were made heroes. Mike had known Custer and despised him. According to him, the general could weep at a sentimental drama one night, and the next morning lead his troops in a slaughter of women and children who were alone in their village.

"Mike had a soft spot in his heart for the Coeur d'Alene Indians," Jake remarked as they cut up the road that would take them to his cabin. "He deeded them some of the best timberland in the territory so they wouldn't have to go to a reservation. The government agreed to let them live there just as long as they lived at peace with one another and with the folks around here. Chief

Silver Bear called your uncle the Great White Protector and made him a member of the Coeur d'Alene tribe.''

More tears clouded her eyes. She'd never known that of her uncle. Then again, he wasn't the kind of man who went around bragging about good deeds and expecting praise in return.

''You can imagine how furious Jud was when he found out what Mike had done,'' Jake went on. ''He'd had his eye on that property for a long time.''

Damn Jud! Damn him, damn him, Araby cursed. He was such a greedy bastard that he would stop at nothing to get what he wanted, even if it meant taking another life! He'd pay! If it were the last thing she ever did, she'd make him pay!

''When word got to Chief Silver Bear about Mike's death, he grieved for him just as he would for a member of his own family,'' Jake said quietly. ''Although he made no mention of it to me, I'm certain his heart was heavy with worry for his own people. Without Mike to protect them, the government could easily break the agreement and herd them to reservations far away from their beloved mountains.''

Araby braved a smile. Mike might be gone, but his good will and generosity would live on. She'd personally see to that.

''I'd like to get a message to Chief Silver Bear,'' she told Jake. ''And let him know that I intend to carry out my uncle's wishes. His people will not be forced to leave their homes by anyone, not if I have anything to do with it.''

Jake reached over and took hold of her hand. ''I'll get word to him that Mike Stone's niece

shares her uncle's concern and respect for the
Coeur d'Alene people."

Araby smiled a little more easily. As long as
the Coeur d'Alene remained on Tamarack land, a
part of her uncle would live on there through
them.

"There it is," Jake announced proudly.
"That's where I hang my hat—when I'm not
slipping into a lady's bedroom window, that is."

He pointed to a log cabin that was all but
hidden among towering pines. Its roof was gabled
and covered with split cedar shakes. A large
chimney made of river rock held up one side.

" 'Course it's nowhere near as grand as
what's over at Tamarack," he added quietly.

"What?" It took her a moment to realize what
he had just said. "Oh, I think it's lovely. It looks
so quaint and cozy. Just what I'd expect to find in
a fairy-tale setting."

From the shrug of his shoulders, she could
sense he had mistaken her reverie concerning her
dead uncle for disappointment in where he lived.
It would not be easy convincing him otherwise.
Perhaps he had anticipated such a reaction, and
that was the reason he had never brought her
there before.

He gave another indifferent shrug. "It's
home."

"That's more than I can say about the house
at Tamarack," she remarked while tying Darling
up at the porch railing.

"What do you mean?"

His downcast expression slowly faded as she
spoke. "Mike never had a home, not a real home.
Oh, sure, the house at Tamarack is grand and
beautiful, but it was never anything more than a

house. A home is where you live with your family, with people who love you. Mike spent most of his life there alone. The woman he loved refused to marry him because she was afraid her past would haunt them and destroy their feelings for each other. When he finally did marry, it wasn't out of love but because he was afraid of growing old alone.''

''Mike told you that?''

''He didn't have to. I could feel his pain every time I saw him. A loving family at Tamarack. That was one luxury he never had.''

''Mike wasn't a complainer, that's for sure. He may have been miserable, but he never let on.'' Jake shook his head. ''That Mike . . . he was a hell of a good man.''

Araby agreed. ''It's so unfair that he never really got a chance at happiness before he . . . before Jud killed him.''

''I'm sure Mike would be real happy right now if he could see you and me. Getting us together was all he ever talked about.''

Araby held him close. So he had known all along!

''How about you, Jake? Does it make you happy?''

''Everything you do makes me happy.''

He picked her up and swung her into his arms. ''Come on. I'll show you the rest of the house.''

Laughing, Araby held tight to his neck. ''Hey, you're not supposed to do this until . . .''

''Until what?''

She hesitated, but only for just a moment. ''Until nobody's looking.''

''I don't see nobody.'' With that, he gave her

a smacking loud kiss.

Araby let out a sigh of relief. Thank goodness he had been satisfied with her answer. It was a good thing she had caught herself before something silly slipped out that would make her look like an absolute idiot. Until we're married, she had been about to say. Why, Jake would have dropped her flat had she said that. Marriage was one subject he avoided like the plague, even when it involved someone else.

He turned the knob and kicked open the door with his knee.

Once inside, he kept her in his arms.

That was fine by her. She was in no hurry to be put down. That was the best place to view the cabin from.

The cabin was far neater than she had imagined for a man living alone. Everything was tidy and in its place. The split cedar boards making up the floor had been hewn smooth and swept clean. In one corner of the room sat a square-topped cook-stove with four holes. A cast-iron skillet rested on one of them, and on another was a big black bean pot. Next to the stove was an open-faced cupboard. Cups and plates all bearing the same blue willow design were arranged on its shelves. Hanging from round pegs driven into the wall were frying pans, a hot-cake griddle, and different sizes of pots and pans. A table with long, split-log benches lined one wall, and opposite it on the far side of the room was a huge fireplace made from the same river rock as the chimney outside. Nearby was a cedar bed-frame. The faded quilt on top was pulled tight and tucked under the mattress.

"Well?"

She could tell Jake was anxious for her opinion as he put her feet back down on the floor.

"I think it's wonderful. It's perfect. So cozy."

This was a place where she could definitely be happy. Of course, she'd be happy anywhere if she was with him.

"What's up there?" She pointed to the ladder-like steps along the wall beside the cupboard.

"Nothing much. Just some traps and a pelt or two."

She held out her hand. "Show me."

There were no furnishings in the loft, just a long pole that ran lengthwise across the room. Thrown across it were several bearskins, some socks, and three pairs of long underwear. Two hams and a leg of venison also dangled from the pole.

"Seeing as how it's just me, I don't need a lot of room." He ran his hand along the black fur. "Never know, though. One day this whole place up here might be filled with a bunch of screaming young'uns."

Araby smiled at the thought. A lot of little Jake Montanas! He'd make a wonderful father, but first he'd have to become a husband—preferably her husband—and that would be no easy task. Why, he wouldn't even look her in the eye when he talked about one day maybe having a family!

"You like kids?"

His question surprised her so much that she nearly tripped on one of the steps on her way back down.

"Very much." Actually, she'd never really been around children, but if she had been, she knew she would have liked them. Now, his children she would absolutely adore. "Being an only child myself, I look forward to having a large family . . . someday."

"You do?"

"Oh, yes." There was no need to tell him she'd only just that minute decided it.

Jake pulled her down onto the bed. "You know, I didn't figure you for the kind of gal who'd want to have a family."

"You figured wrong, cowboy. I do want a family."

Araby was about to tell him she'd be all too happy to give up her career as an actress, move into a cabin in the pines, and start having babies when a loud rap sounded at the front door.

Jake jumped straight up. "Yeah?"

"Me, boss."

He went to open the door, while Araby got up and turned her attention to a collection of wooden animal carvings on the mantel.

"Little Joe just told me we got a cow and two calves dead up on the east forty, boss. He thinks a wolf got to them."

"Damn, those traps we set ain't doing a lick of good!" Jake took his shotgun from the gun rack hanging just inside the door. "Guess we better go wolf hunting." He glanced back at Araby, then told Slim to saddle a fresh horse and wait for him at the barn.

"Do you have to go now?" She was disappointed and didn't try to hide it. Another few minutes of talking about families and babies, and he just might have proposed.

"Oh, you could talk me into staying, Miss Stone-Leigh. That's a fact. You got ways of persuasion that would drive a sane man crazy."

He allowed his hands to linger above her waist, but only for a moment. "You could talk me into staying very easily, but I don't think those mama cows would be too happy with me the next time that wolf came calling."

Araby backed away. "When you put it that way, I can't even kiss you good-bye in good conscience."

"Come here, you." He pulled her hips into his and kissed her. His kiss got longer and harder.

"The wolf," she reminded him. "I'll not have the blood of innocent calves on my hands."

They walked out onto the porch.

"You best be heading back to Tamarack while it's still light," he suggested. "I'll get one of the boys to ride with you."

She turned down his offer. "You forget I travel with my own protection," she said, patting the lower part of her leg where the pistol was strapped.

"In that case, I better watch it the next time I come up behind you and give you a big ole bear hug," he teased her. "Or I'm liable to find myself shot."

"You're liable to find yourself shot if you *don't* grab hold of me." She pushed him away when he tried to put his arm around her. "Go. The sooner you leave, the sooner you'll get back."

Jake untied the reins from the porch railing and looped them back over Darling's neck.

"Follow the path down to the smokehouse, then go right. It's a short cut to Tamarack. You'll get there in half the time it takes going along the river."

Araby blew him a kiss over her shoulder.

"Oh, and don't forget to leave the window

unlocked,'' he added, walking beside her.

Araby chuckled softly, then nudged her horse into a trot. How could she forget something that important?

13

A raby trotted her horse down the smokehouse
trail, then cut across Cross Fork pastureland
and headed home. It didn't take her long to get
her bearings once she was under way. Soon she'd
be passing Mission Point. If it weren't getting so
late, she'd cut across the creek and visit the
Mission of the Sacred Heart.

Mike had told her all about the mission. Its
history was rich and interesting. Built half a
century ago by Jesuit priests and the Indians they
were trying to convert, the mission was the first
Catholic undertaking in Idaho. It had served as a
neutral campsite for Indians as well as for
trappers from the Hudson Bay Company. Many
warring tribes, including the Coeur d'Alene, the
Nez Perce, the Spokane, and the Yakima, put
down weapons for the annual pow-wow and
came together there in friendship to conduct their
religious services. For ten days during that annual
gathering, the slopes surrounding the mission

were dotted with teepees from all the different tribes. Children and barking dogs swarmed over the grassy knolls while squaws congregated in the sun and warriors hunted, fished, and competed in games of skill and sport.

Araby stopped to take a quick look.

The mission was abandoned now and had been ever since the start of the Indian wars. The building was still standing and most of the rocks were still in place, but shrubs and trees were gradually overtaking it. Even deserted, it looked interesting. Perhaps tomorrow or the next day, she'd come back and explore.

Araby gave Darling a little kick, and the horse plodded on, but Araby halted again when she saw two horses tied up on the back side of the mission. Perhaps some weary travelers were making camp there that night. She stood up in her stirrups for a better look. One of the horses was a paint, the other a palomino. She had seen those same two horses together before—but where?

It took a moment for her to realize she'd seen the two taking off together, one behind the other, at Tamarack several days ago. Their riders weren't weary travelers.

Jud and Lena! What were they doing there—together? And why would their horses be hidden out back if their meeting there were innocent?

Araby was curious. Suppose it had been Jud, and not Jake, that Lena had been meeting all along?

Leaving Darling to graze, she waded through the creek, then cut across the field and plowed through grass that was nearly as tall as she was. She could hear voices, those of Jud and his brother's wife, but could not quite make out what they were saying.

Hardly daring to breathe for fear of being caught, Araby peeped in through one of the openings that had once been windows.

She was right! Jud and Lena were there. Jud was standing in the center of the room leaning against a wooden support column. Lena was pacing in front of him, head shaking and fists pounding her thighs.

A horse nickered.

Lena whirled around.

Araby dropped down to the ground.

"Come on, darling," she heard Jud tell his sister-in-law. "Don't be so skittish. There ain't nobody around here but you and me."

Araby stayed on the ground. From the heavy breathing and rustling of clothes coming from inside, she had the distinct impression that those two had not come there to discuss family business.

"Stop it, Jud. Just you stop it. If Sim was to find us here like this, he'd kill us both."

Jud's laugh sounded evil. "Sim ain't gonna find us, sugar. Even if he does, he's so drunk he wouldn't know what was going on. Besides, when did your conscience start bothering you? Hell, we done it in the same bed where Sim was passed out snoring, and I don't remember that bothering you much."

"I don't care, Jud. I don't like it one bit. Sim's getting suspicious. I know he is. If he don't know already, he will soon, and you won't be the one he takes it out on."

"Come on, baby, let ole Jud have a feel of those—"

"Stop it, Jud. I mean it."

"What's the matter, darling? You don't like what old Jud's got to give you anymore?"

There was a long silence.

Araby peered over the edge of the window.

Jud had Lena pinned against the post. Her skirt was up around her hips, and his knee was rammed between her legs. She would struggle against his groping hands, then give up, pound at his back some more, then surrender to his savage kisses and return them with a frenzied assault of her own.

Araby heard Jud laugh that evil laugh once more and describe to Lena in graphic detail just what he was going to do to her if she'd ask him real nice.

Head lowered, she started backing away. What Lena and Jud were doing there was their business. She didn't even want to know, much less stay there and watch them.

She heard Jud curse, then deliver a stinging blow across Lena's face.

"Damn you, bitch! What'd you bite me for? Look at that. You drew blood, you crazy bitch!"

"You know what that's for, you bastard," Lena spat right back. "You want to poke that thing in somebody, you go see that fancy actress of yours. You make her do all those things you make me do."

Araby stopped her retreat. Why was Lena dragging her into their sordid little affair?"

"Honey, you don't have to be made to do anything. You love it."

"You go straight to hell, Jud Cord. And let go of me. I'm getting out of here."

Araby ducked down behind the well just as Lena came running out of the mission.

Jud was right behind her, laughing and cursing. He grabbed hold of her arm and twisted it behind her back.

Araby held her breath. She was afraid to move. They were so close she could see the pain on Lena's face and the cruelty contorting Jud's.

Lena screamed. "Let go. You're hurting me."

"You love that, too, don't you, slut? You love it when I get rough. You beg for it, then, don't you?"

Araby watched in horror as Jud took a handful of hair and yanked it so hard that Lena's head was pulled back against her neck.

The louder Lena screamed, the louder Jud laughed.

"Tell me how you love it when I get that razor strap after you. You get down on your knees and beg me to stripe that ass, don't you? Don't you, bitch?"

"Yes, Jud, yes, yes, yes," Lena whispered through her tears.

Araby winced. She could almost feel Lena's pain. Jud was revolting. Lena was just as disgusting for letting him abuse her.

She curled up closer to the well house. If only she had left when she had the chance! Now there was no way she could get away without them seeing her! She wasn't sure just how much more of this perverted scene she could take!

"What was that, Lena, sugar? I didn't hear you."

Lena sniffed.

"You don't tell me right now, and you won't get a second chance, little sister-in-law. I'll leave you. You won't ever see me again. That drunk I have for a brother can have you."

"No! Don't go, Jud. Please," Lena begged. "You know I've got to have you. I can't live without you. No, don't push me away."

"Get off the ground. It's not my feet I like to have kissed."

"You're right, Jud. I love it when you take that strap and tan me. I love it. I love everything you do. You want me down on my knees. Look at me. I'm on my knees, Jud. I'm begging. Don't leave me. I'll kill myself if you do. I swear I will."

Araby could not believe what she was hearing. Lena was insane! She was crazier than Jud! Both of them needed to be locked away for their own protection.

Jud helped her up, then embraced her.

"It's all right, honey. I'm not going anywhere. When I do leave, I'm taking you with me. I love you, sweetheart. You know I love you. That's why I get a little rough with you from time to time. Shhh, don't cry, honey. I'm right here. I ain't gonna leave you."

"But what about Araby?" sobbed Lena. "What about you going back to New York?"

"Shhh. You don't have no cause to be jealous, sweet pea. No cause at all. I've just got to string her along a little while. Not long. Just long enough to get what I want—what I want for me and you, Lena. It'll be just us real soon. Sim's not long for this world."

So Sim was about to share Mike's fate. Jud obviously had no qualms about killing anyone, his brother included.

"But what about all those things she wrote in that diary of hers about you trying to court her? You just don't know how much I hurt when I read those things about you and her."

Lena sounded so pitiful Araby could almost feel sorry for her. So it had been her all along who'd been snooping in her belongings. She had thought as much! From the sound of it, Lena was more concerned about Jud's fidelity than about becoming a widow.

Jud chuckled. "Hell, darling, I can't help what Miss High and Mighty writes about me. Are you going to blame me because she wants me? She wants me real bad, too. You know, every time I'm in the same room with her, she's rubbing it up against me trying to get me to pleasure her a little bit."

Araby cringed. It was bad enough having no choice but to sit and listen to his filthy lies—but having to watch as well while he supplied the body motions made her blood run hot! Hanging was too good for Jud Cord. He needed to be tortured to a slow death.

"Stop it, Jud. You know I can't bear the thought of you bedding another woman."

"Just because she's got an itch don't mean I'm going to scratch it," Jud told her.

"But why do you even have to be nice to her? You said yourself she's nothing but trouble," Lena complained.

"I want that ranch, and if playing up to her means I'll get it, then I don't see as I have any choice in the matter. You do anything to mess that up and I swear I'll—"

"I won't mess it up, Jud. I promise."

Araby sat curled up in the rocking chair waiting for Jake to sneak in through the window. There was no point in going to bed. She wouldn't be able to sleep. She'd tried, and everytime she closed her eyes, that horrible scene at the mission came back to haunt her.

To add to that nightmare, Jud had been waiting for her when she reached home. He was all smiles, very charming, the perfect gentleman. It was all she could do to keep from being sick all over him and the bouquet of wild flowers he'd somehow found to pick for her. She told him no, offering no excuse, and went inside the house. When he tried to follow, she slammed the door in his face. Upstairs in her room, she bolted the lock, took the pistol from the holster around her leg, and pointed it at the door, ready to shoot if Jud tried to break in. As soon as she was certain he had left, she had Mattie draw her a scalding hot bath. The incident at the mission left her feeling dirty, but even if she scrubbed her skin raw, she knew she could never rid her mind of it.

When Jake arrived, Araby told him all about Lena and Jud's meeting. Certain details and descriptions had to be omitted. Even considering the intimacies they had shared, some of the facts were just too awkward and embarrassing to recount.

"You should have seen her cowering to him even after he hit her and made her do all kinds of awful things," she told him. "Jud has cast some kind of a sick spell over her. No matter how much abuse he subjected her to, Lena kept crawling back for more. Why, she all but begged him to abuse her. I don't know whether to pity that poor girl or despise her for being so weak. Where's her self respect?"

"That poor girl never really had a chance," Jake said sadly. "Her daddy used to beat her and her mama both. If Jud or her husband doesn't kill her first, I wouldn't be at all surprised if she didn't take a gun and blow out her own brains.''

Araby shivered. That wouldn't surprise her, either. ''If I were Lena, I'd take the gun to that bastard Jud's head,'' she exclaimed angrily. ''He doesn't deserve to go on living.''

''Now don't you go getting yourself all upset,'' he said quietly as he patted her arm. ''Jud will get what's coming to him. One way or another, he'll get his just reward.''

''I wish he would hurry up and get it. That's one funeral I will be delighted to attend.''

While Jake finished eating from the supper that she had prepared for him, she told him about all the promises Jud had made Lena, including the one to kill her husband.

''Too bad somebody can't warn Sim, but it wouldn't do any good,'' he remarked between bites. ''The way Sim sucks on that whiskey bottle, he'll probably save his brother the trouble of killing him.''

Araby was about to say that whatever Sim got he had coming for his part in Mike's murder, but changed her mind and kept her opinions to herself. Jud and Lena had ruined her afternoon. They weren't going to ruin her time with Jake that night. Why dwell on such unhappiness? They were all doomed—Lena, Jud and Sim—and whatever their fate, it was nothing less than they deserved.

''Hey, we're not going to spend the whole night talking about those crazy Cords, are we?'' Jake strained to get his boots off. '' 'Cause if we are, I think I'd better have another piece of that chocolate cake.''

''No, we are not going to spend the rest of the

night talking about them." Araby got up out of the rocking chair and began massaging Jake's shoulders. "But you can have another piece of cake anyway. As a matter of fact, you can have just about anything you want."

Jake pulled her around and sat her down on his lap. "Does that include you?"

"That includes me."

Jake pretended to give this serious thought, then decided, "I think I will have another piece of cake."

Araby punched him, then jumped up before he could retaliate.

"I'll fix you for that." Laughing, he lunged over the bed after her. "The time has come for you to be taught some manners, young lady."

"Are you threatening me, cowboy?" She stuck out her tongue.

He tried to grab her. She ducked under his arm.

"That ain't no threat. That's a promise."

"If I were you, I wouldn't make any promises I didn't intend keeping," she said, wiggling by just out of arm's reach.

"Oh, I keep my promises."

Suddenly there was nothing teasing about Jake's look—or his tone. It wasn't what he said but how he said it that made Araby wonder if he were implying that she did not keep promises.

"I keep my promises, too, Jake."

"I hope so, honey, 'cause a cowboy's heart can be broken, too."

The light from the candle flickered in his eyes, making the turquoise dance even more than usual.

Araby reached up and touched his face.

Solemn lines of concern that had not been there that afternoon were now etched into his brow. How was she ever going to make him believe that she would love him forever? She had promised him that. Promises were sacred. When he vowed his eternal love, she hadn't questioned him.

"I love you, Jake. I don't care what you say or what you do, I'll always love you, so you might as well get that through your thick skull. I love you. Do you hear me? I love you!"

A reluctant smile creased his face. "If you don't lower your voice, everybody in the valley's going to hear you."

"So?"

"So what happens when the novelty wears off, and you decide a cowboy just ain't as exciting as one of those fellows pining away for you back East?"

She knew she had to be patient. Jake was wary of her, even now, after all the joys they had shared. He had kept his heart closely guarded for many years. He had told her that much. He'd never been hurt by a woman because he'd never let a woman get that close to him. He had never really loved any woman—not until she came along. Now he was afraid. He'd never admit that, of course, but he was afraid all the same. He was afraid of giving too much of himself for fear that such a show of emotions would be his downfall.

Patience! She had to be patient, no matter what.

"In the first place, I'm not in love with the notion of being in love with a cowboy. I am not in love with just any cowboy. I am in love with you." She tried to keep her tone light. "And secondly, there are no fellows back East pining away for me because I never wasted my time with any of them. And finally, the novelty is not going to wear off because I will personally see to it that you and I have more excitement in our relationship than we can stand. Have I made myself clear, cowboy?''

''Yes, m'am, but what about when you get a hankering for New York?''

''If that hankering, as you call it, gets all that bad, then I'll go back for a visit and take you with me.''

Jake didn't smile. The furrows in his forehead deepened, and Araby knew at once that she had made a terrible mistake. Men like Jake didn't want to be taken anywhere!

''I need my wide open places, Araby. I could never be fenced in.''

Araby held her tongue, but it was a struggle. Was he talking about visiting New York or marrying her? She wished she had the courage to ask him! No, damn it! She would not sit by quietly and let him think he knew what was going on inside her mind.

She sat back down in the rocking chair, folded her hands in her lap, and looked him straight in the eye.

''You know something, Montana? Sometimes you make me so angry with these ridiculous notions of yours that I could choke you with my bare hands. I am not out to steal your precious wide open places or to fence you in.''

Araby paused, waiting for a response. When there was none, she decided she had come too far to turn back now.

''You are just like that black stallion you're

trying so hard to catch,'' she said calmly. ''He doesn't want to be caught any more than you do. What you don't realize is that I've never wanted to throw a lasso around you and have you jump on command. I love you just the way you are because you're the way you are.''

Jake squatted down in front of her. His face was only a breath from hers. ''You said everything you want to say?''

''Enough for now.''

Rough hard features relaxed into a grin that broadened as he pulled her to her feet and planted one seemingly endless kiss on her lips.

''Don't you know you already have me jumping on command?'' he said when their lips finally parted.

Araby breathed a sigh of relief that conversation had ended—at least for now. His doubts were not going to be easily dispelled, but she thought she had finally made a start.

She pulled his head back down to hers. ''Seems to me we have a little unfinished business from this afternoon.''

''Why, Miss Stone-Leigh, whatever are you talking about?''

A playful tongue darted in and out of his ear. ''Guess.''

Jake picked her up and swung her over to the bed. ''Oh, you mean before me and Slim went out wolf-hunting?''

''You know exactly what I mean, cowboy.'' She tugged at his belt. ''This time you can't blame Slim or some big, bad wolf for dragging you away from me.''

''What man in his right mind would want to get away from you?''

Jake was out of his denim shirt and trousers quicker than she could untie the bows on her creamy satin bed jacket. Soon the satin and bows joined the pile of work clothes at the foot of the bed.

Jake's kisses were deep and searching. Her own sizzled with promises of what was still to come. Jake knew her body well, much better than she did herself. It never ceased to amaze her that he knew just where all of her secret little pleasures spots were and how to go about making them dance at his touch. Under his practiced caresses, her body rose and fell, twisted and turned on command. His mere presence was intoxicating. How easy it would be to get drunk on his love!

Desire rose inside her. She could wait no longer for him to lay claim to the territory that only he would ever be given passage into. Legs interwoven with his, she guided him to his mark, and together in the hushed silence they fought to satisfy that rush of passion. Higher and higher they soared, searching for that burning sweetness that would bind them together. And when their love had peaked from one crescendo to another, they floated away together on a cloud of euphoria.

Jake closed her eyes with a kiss.

Araby fell asleep in the protective haven of his love, exhausted by so rapturous a bliss. A smile sighed from her lips. Surely heaven could be no sweeter than the paradise she had found in his arms. To think that he was worried about her leaving and returning to New York. Just where was New York, anyway?

When Araby awakened a little while later,

her lips were still curved in contentment. With a moan, she snuggled closer to his powerful form. It took a moment to realize something was wrong.

Jake was not sleeping, and she had a feeling he had not been asleep at all. His eyes were wide open, and he was staring up at the rafters deep in thought.

Her lips brushed over his chest. She could feel his muscles tighten. She started to whisper to him, to ask him what was wrong, but the thought that she might be the cause of his restlessness prevented her from speaking. Jake was a very private man. There had been times when he just wanted to be alone and retreat into his own thoughts. More than once, she'd had to respect that desire for solitude and refrain from asking questions he might feel were none of her concern. Whatever was bothering him would just have to wait until he was ready to tell her.

Jake was up well before daybreak. Araby watched him dress in silence through the gray haze enveloping the room. His sleep had been fitful. Hers had been as well, for every time he tossed and turned, she had tossed and turned right with him.

She watched in silence as he pulled on his boots. He was going to leave without saying good-bye, without giving her that one final kiss that would have to get her through the long hours until she saw him again. What was wrong? He couldn't leave without telling her, without giving her a chance to make amends if she were the one at fault. She wouldn't let him leave like that.

"Good morning, handsome." She tried her best to sound cheerful. "Didn't anybody ever tell you that you could get shot for leaving a lady's bed while she's still in it?''

His kiss was sincere, but his smile was anything but. ''Sorry, honey. I got to get an early start, and I didn't want to wake you up.''

He stooped down and scratched Tramp's stomach.

''By the way, I'll be gone for a couple of days. Me and Slim and Little Joe are going back up the ridge after the rest of that wolf pack. I doubt if we'll be back until Thursday night late.''

It didn't escape her notice that he was directing his eyes and his words to the dog instead of to her. Why hadn't he told her last night that he'd be going hunting again, she wanted to ask him, but she knew better than to question him. Besides, something told her he had only just decided that as he lay staring up at the rafters.

''I'll miss you,'' she said softly.

''Miss you, too.'' He gave Tramp a final pat, then stood up.

She couldn't let him go, not like that, not feeling whatever it was he was feeling. She had to stop him!

''I'll go with you.'' She jumped from the bed. ''I won't get in the way. I promise. I'd love to see more of the—''

He stopped her before she went on. ''Can't do that. Slim and the other fellows—well, they'll be along, too, and it won't be much fun for you. They might not . . .''

''Of course.'' Araby swallowed hard. ''I understand.''

She got back into bed. She understood a lot more than he thought. Things had become a lot clearer just then, when he put her arms back down to her side when they had reached out to hug him.

Jake sat down on the bed, hands on his knees and head hanging down. "The—uh, the fact of the matter is that I—well, I need a little time alone. To think about things."

"You don't have to explain anything to me, Jake. You do whatever you have to do." It took every theatrical skill she had ever mastered to pretend cool indifference. "I certainly don't own you. You can come and go as you please. It isn't my intention to . . . to fence you in."

Tears burning her eyes, Araby burrowed her head into the pillow, and when Jake leaned down to kiss her good-bye, she ignored him.

By the time she had composed herself enough to tell him good-bye and wish him a safe trip, it was too late. He was already out the window.

14

Araby walked along the river's edge, kicking stones and cursing her stupidity. Jake had been gone for three days, three unbearably long days and three unending nights. He had been gone that long from her. She knew he was back from wolf hunting. She had seen Slim in town yesterday when she went to visit Ruby and Mandy. He was back, and he just didn't want to see her.

She wanted to see him, but she was damned if she would swallow her pride and go to Cross Fork.

Then again, maybe she should do just that. . . . After all, he had tried to make amends before he left, and she had turned her back on him. . . . Still, he had been the one in the first place to push her aside. . . .

What was she going to do? Her mind was muddled with all kinds of conflicting thoughts. Should she go to him, or wait until he came to her? He might never come to her again!

Damn! Damn! Damn! What had been so all-fired important that he had to get away from her to think? She didn't want to tie him down and fence him in. Oh, yes—she wanted him, and she wouldn't say no if he asked her to marry him, but the choice would be his. She wouldn't force anything on him. He really was pigheaded!

Araby tried to comfort herself with the certainty that come Saturday, if she could last another twenty-four hours without him, she would see him, for that was the day he had promised to take her to Freezeout Mountain. He wouldn't go back on that promise, no matter what decisions he had made regarding them during his absence. Avenging Mike's murder was just as important to him as it was to her. He'd not let her down, he wouldn't let Mike down.

Come tomorrow, she'd have two full days with him, and during that time she would make it perfectly clear that she would take him anyway she could get him. If he didn't want any commitment, if he just wanted to come and go as he pleased, well, she'd just have to grin and bear it.

"Damn it to hell!"

Mike used to say that all the time when he was mad. He said it made him feel better, but it didn't work for her.

She might have to grin and bear it, but she didn't have to like it. Why did life's simplest joys have to be so complicated?

Curses! She was so mad she could scream!

She did.

That didn't make her feel any better, either.

She kicked at another rock. A pile of mud came up on the toe of her boot and splattered all over her skirt.

What else could go wrong? Jake had walked out on her, and if that wasn't bad enough, Devil's Darling had deserted her, too. That crazy chestnut had kicked down the door to her stall, and before any of the ranch hands could get a rope on her, she had jumped the fence and charged across the field snorting and bucking and rearing all the way like a beast possessed. That horse had been bound and determined to get to the hills, and there was no wondering why. By the time Araby had been roused by the commotion and jumped out of bed, it was too late. She had stepped out onto the porch outside her room and whistled. Any other time her whistle would have brought Darling galloping across the field at full speed. But not this time. Her crazy chestnut mare had been spirited away by the elusive black stallion.

Araby scratched Tramp's head. "It's just you and me now, pal. You won't desert me, will you?"

The dog's wet lick on the side of her face almost made her smile.

She walked on through the high willows thinking, remembering, and regretting. What an independent woman she had been in New York! She had paid her own way and relied on no one for support, emotional or otherwise. And now look at her! Her one and only love affair had gone sour, and now she was ready to end her misery by flinging herself into the swirling torrents.

Araby heard herself giggle. What swirling torrents? There could be none of those in the Saint Joe, the "gentle river."

"Good. I am glad to hear you laugh."

Araby whirled around. Standing behind her was an Indian woman who looked to be her own age. At least, Araby thought she was Indian. She was wearing a buckskin dress and moccasins, yet the braids hanging down her shoulders were the color of wheat.

Tramp barked.

Araby reached down to grab hold of his collar.

The Indian woman slowly walked up to the dog and held out her hand for him to sniff. As soon as she had satisfied him that she meant no harm, she stepped back and kept her distance.

"You looked so sad. I was afraid to leave you alone for fear you would throw yourself into the river."

"Then you've been following me?" Araby was surprised that she had neither seen nor heard the woman.

She nodded. "I was worried. I saw you crying underneath the big willow, and I did not want you to do something foolish. Bleeding souls sometimes force us to do that which we later regret."

Araby nodded her appreciation. From the sad way she said that, she thought the Indian must be speaking from experience.

"I am much relieved you do not intend to take your life," the woman said, coming a few tentative steps closer.

"Take my life? You mean kill myself? Oh, no." Araby smiled. "I am too much of a coward to do that."

"One often finds courage in the depths of despair."

Araby studied the dark-skinned figure in the beaded and fringed buckskin. She dressed like an

Indian, and her skin was the same copper brown, yet her hair was pale and her eyes were the soft blue of cornflowers. She didn't talk like an Indian, either. She spoke English. It was flawless, even if her words did come slowly and were very carefully pronounced.

"Who are you?" Araby stepped closer.

The woman did not back away. "The name I have been given is Fleeing Fawn."

"I am very pleased to meet you, Fleeing Fawn. My name is Araby Stone-Leigh." Araby held out her hand.

Fawn took the hand, but only after a few seconds' hesitation. "I know who you are. You are the daughter of Mike Stone's brother."

Araby smiled. She'd never thought of herself in that light before. "That's right. I'm Mike's niece."

"Ah, yes, niece. That is the word I was looking for."

The sun caught the silver glint of the knife hanging from the fringed belt around the woman's waist.

She saw Araby looked at the knife and explained, "I like to wander far away from my village on my own. Sometimes I follow the river as it weaves through the valleys and across the mountains. Wild animals are the least of my troubles."

Araby knew well what she meant. She lifted the hem of her skirt so her new friend could see that she, too, wore protection. "The two-legged animal can be much more dangerous than the four-legged kind."

"I see we think alike, you and I." Smiling, Fleeing Fawn took a leather pouch from around her shoulder. "I am hungry. Sit. I will share my food."

Araby followed her to a flat boulder underneath the drooping branches of a willow. She wasn't particularly hungry. Since Jake left, food had been the thought furthest from her mind. Still, Fleeing Fawn was kind to offer, and she didn't want to insult her by refusing her generosity.

Fleeing Fawn took from her bag a mound of brown bread, some beef jerky, and a small salmon that had been wrapped in leaves and smoked.

"Your uncle, Mike Stone, was a great man. He will be missed by everyone in this valley." Fleeing Fawn divided out the food. "My people call him the Great Protector. Had it not been for his kindness, my people would be forced to live and to die on government reservations like our neighbors the Spokane, the Kalispel, and the Nez Perce."

Araby listened quietly to Fawn's description of the horrors of reservation living.

"Indians on reservations are not allowed to hunt or to fish for their food," she told Araby. "Food enough to feed one man is given to feed families of six and seven. Indians die from white man's diseases, and our ancient medicine men are forbidden to seek their special medicinal herbs and roots on pain of death."

Fleeing Fawn spoke with much anger and emotion. "Children are sent to white man's school and forbidden to speak their own tongue. Only white man's words may be spoken or the child is severely punished. The braids of little boys are cut. The braids are symbolic of manhood, so in cutting them, the white man is emasculating the children. The Indians are stripped of their customs, their religion, and their tongue that had been passed down from generation after generation of our great forefathers.

"What gives white men the right to do this?" she asked, tears filling her eyes. "My people roamed and hunted these mountains and forests and fished these streams hundreds of years before the first settler ever found his way here. As long as the grass shall grow and the waters run . . . That is what the white man's government said each time they signed a new treaty. Then they turned around and pushed the Indian farther and farther away from his hunting grounds."

There was a long pause. Then Fleeing Fawn bowed her head. "Please, you must forgive me. Understand, I do not blame you for the Indian's suffering."

"What the white man has done to the Indian people in the name of progress is barbarian," Araby agreed. "I am ashamed of those of my own kind who condone such monstrous acts. I am a friend of the Indian people just as my uncle was a friend of the Indian people."

"My people will be honored to have you for a friend."

"And I will be proud and honored to have the friendship of the great Coeur d'Alene."

Once again, Araby listened attentively as Fleeing Fawn spoke of her people. Much of what she told her, Araby had already learned from Mike.

"The name of the tribe in Indian tongue is Schiquumish."

Araby repeated the name several times before

Fleeing Fawn was satisfied with her pronunciation. She already knew the name had been translated by the early French Canadian immigrants from the Hudson Bay Company to Coeur d'Alene, meaning heart of the awl.

"Unlike the name given by those immigrants," continued Fleeing Fawn, "the hearts of my people are not pointed and sharp. By nature, the Schiquumish are kind and gentle. Their courage and valor is widely known. However, when challenged, these stout-hearted people prove themselves to be valiant and fearsome foes."

Araby nodded. According to Mike, the only time the Coeur d'Alene, or the Schiquumish as Fleeing Fawn called them, ever shed white blood was when a few of their hot-headed braves joined a Yakima war party and raided white settlements along the river many years ago.

While Fleeing Fawn spoke more of the Indians she called "her people," Araby studied her with curious interest.

"There is something you wish to know about me, is there not?" Fleeing Fawn asked with a quiet smile. "But you are too polite to wonder your thoughts aloud."

Araby smiled. "Yes, there is."

A dark hand squeezed her arm.

"Do not be embarrassed, my newly found friend, because you find my pale hair and knowledge of the white man's tongue somewhat strange for an Indian."

Fleeing Fawn broke off more bread and handed it to Araby. "Eat. My skin is brown from the sun, not from birth. You see, the blood of the white man flows through my veins just as it flows through yours. Fleeing Fawn was the name given me by my Indian father. Lorna is the name I used to be called by the woman who gave birth to me.''

There was a sadness in her eyes as she spoke of her past.

''During the winter of my fourteenth year, I was stolen from my home by a Blackfoot war party. I became not only their prisoner, but their slave. Night after night I was beaten and raped and beaten some more. I was stripped naked and left in the snow to die. But I did not die. I wanted to die, I tried to die, but such was not my destiny. I was robbed of all pride and self-respect. I became an empty shell where a spirited young girl once lived. I thought they would kill me when they grew tired of tormenting me, but they did not. It was far crueler to let me go on living. They offered me for sale to another tribe at their big pow-wow. Chief Silver Bear took pity on me and traded six of his finest ponies for me.''

Fleeing Fawn paused to catch her breath. Her eyes began to mist, but she refused to let them weep.

''The chief of the Schiquumish was much angered by the actions of the Blackfoot. To make amends, he returned me to my family. My family did not want me. They acted as though I had somehow brought all those awful things that happened to me on myself. My brother, Johnny, called me a dirty Indian squaw. My mother and my father could not understand why I had not flung myself from the highest mountain peak rather than bring shame and disgrace on their name. They could not forgive me not coming back a corpse.''

Araby touched her friend's arm. ''Please,

Fleeing Fawn, do not put yourself through such agony of remembering."

"No, no, it is good for me to relieve my heart of so heavy a burden," she insisted as she took another deep breath. "I could not stay where I was not wanted. Yet I could not kill myself, either, so I left. I went to the only person who had showed me any kindness. Chief Silver Bear welcomed me into his tribe with open arms, not as a slave, but as his daughter. So as you see, Araby, I am a Schiquumish. I am a Coeur d'Alene, and I shall remain one until I die."

Araby was ashamed of herself. How petty her own troubles seemed in comparison to what Fleeing Fawn had endured!

"You have lived through hell and survived," she told Fleeing Fawn with much respect and admiration. "You are very, very brave. Few men would find such courage."

"Courage is not found. It is thrust upon us."

Fleeing Fawn pointed to the west. "The sun is starting to fall. I must go."

She took her necklace of eagle feathers from around her neck and placed it around Araby's.

"Now we are sisters of the soul. My people and I would be greatly honored if you would visit our village."

"It is I who am honored to recieve your invitation." Araby touched the necklace. "And your gift."

Fleeing Fawn pointed across the river to a fallen tree. Another tree was growing up from its trunk. "Beside the tree of two trees, you will find a path. Follow it up the hill to the site of the old mine. The path then forks. Take the north fork. You will cross two streams, the second smaller than the first. The climb through the forest is steep, but do not give up. Listen for the sound of the waterfall. It will take you to my village." She looked at Araby eagerly. "You will come soon?"

"I will come soon."

Fleeing Fawn held out her arm. Araby shook her hand.

Fleeing Fawn laughed, then clasped Araby's elbow and instructed her to do the same while their arms were positioned side by side. "I am glad the spirits brought us together."

"I am glad the spirits brought us together, too," Araby said.

Fleeing Fawn skipped across the river, her feet barely skimming the stepping stones. When she was on the other side at the tree of two trees, she turned around and gave a final wave.

Before Araby could lift her hand, Fleeing Fawn had vanished into the woods. Her friend had been aptly named!

Araby headed home in a far better mood than when she left. Fleeing Fawn had helped her to realize how small her problems really were. In spite of Jake's rejection and Darling's disappearance, she was one very lucky young woman indeed.

Nevertheless, it seemed her luck had just run out when she returned to see Jud sitting on her front porch. Damn! She had thought for sure that after her rudeness several days before, he would get the message and keep away. Obviously, she had been wrong!

Before she could cut across the field to the barn and hide there until he grew tired of waiting, she saw him come running out to meet her. His smile was as revolting as ever.

"Mattie said you've been gone all afternoon." He leaned over to kiss her cheek.

Araby quickly stooped down to pick an imaginary burr from Tramp's furry coat.

Jud keep right on talking as if nothing were wrong. "I was fixing to come out looking for you. We wouldn't want any of those red-skinned savages after your pretty scalp, now would we?"

When she stood up again, Jud gave her a quick peck on the cheek before she could stop him.

She felt dirty. Just the sight of him repulsed her, and his touch was sickening! She had seen Lena in town yesterday. The side of her face was all black and blue. Lena had told her she had been thrown from her horse, but Araby knew better.

"You want to walk some more?" Jud asked.

All she wanted was to be left alone! "No, I think I'll go up to the house. I'm a little tired. This heat, you know."

"Good, good. I'll go back up with you. We can sit on that nice front porch and have some cake and lemonade."

Araby frowned and kept on walking. She supposed she had little choice in the matter. After all, she wouldn't want Jud to get too suspicious before she was able to prove his guilt.

If he noticed her shrinking away from him when they sat down in the rockers on the porch, he gave no indication. Instead, he kept right on talking about some big deal he was going to close with a California company that wanted to buy his saw mill.

Mattie brought out a pitcher of lemonade and two pieces of cake.

"So where have you been walking?" Jud

wanted to know when he was finished touting his shrewdness in business.

"Oh, just down by the river." She set the cake plate down on the porch. She wasn't particularly hungry, but even if she were, just the sight of Jud would make her lose her appetite.

"What'd you do down there?"

Araby shrugged her shoulders. "Nothing much. Just walked and looked."

"I hear that crazy chestnut mare you've been riding took off the other night." His laugh was low and lusty. "That big stallion must have come courting. That little mare is long gone by now. It wasn't her you were looking for down at the river, was it Araby, honey? 'Cause if it was, you were just wasting your time."

Araby gritted her teeth. If he reached over to pat her hand once more, she'd Araby honey him!

Jud edged his rocking chair closer, but a snarl from Tramp made him think again.

"I don't know why you don't like me, Tramp, old boy. Me and your mama, we're great friends." Jud held out a piece of cake to coax him closer, but the dog stayed put at his mistress's feet. "Maybe next time I come courting your mama, I'd better bring a nice juicy steak instead of candy and flowers."

Maybe you'd better not come courting at all, Araby wanted to shout at him, but held her tongue.

"That cake sure is good," he said after a few minutes of silence.

Araby handed him hers. As long as he was eating, he wasn't talking. "Please, have another piece."

"Why, thank you, darling. That's real sweet

of you." He ate quickly. "I sure am sorry about that mare of yours. But you gotta admit, she was a little touched in the head. I must admit, the way you were able to stay on her put many of these cowpokes around here to shame. Did I tell you I'm going after that stallion myself? If I get him, I'll bring back Devil's Darling for you."

Araby forced a smile and said a prayer for the wild stallion. If somebody was going to catch him, she hoped it would be Jake. At least he'd treat him with some dignity. Jud would break his spirit as well as his neck in the process.

"Yes, m'am. I aim to have me that stallion. And do you know how I'm going to go about getting him?"

Araby shook her head. When was he going to leave?

"I'm going to get some of the boys together, and we're going to drive the whole herd up to Hell's Gulch. Once we get that ole boy cornered, there ain't but one way for him to go—straight down about three thousand feet. He ain't gonna take his herd down those rocks, so when he comes charging back out, I'll take him. Might have to shoot him to slow him down a little bit, but I'll get him one way or another."

Araby shivered at the thought of that magnificent beast plunging down into the canyon, taking most of his herd—including Devil's Darling—with him. She wouldn't put it past that brilliant beast to deliberately choose that way out of Jud Cord's clutches!

"What's the matter, dear—you getting a little chilly? There does seem to be a bit of a nip in the air. I'll go in and get Mattie to fetch you a wrap."

"No, no—please don't bother. I'm fine. I just

stayed out in the sun too long, that's all."

"What you need is a nice long soak in the tub and then an early bed." His brazen eyes conducted a thorough perusal of her every feature, in spite of her obvious discomfort.

"If you like, I could bring a supper tray up to your room," he said softly. His gaze lingered suggestively on the lilac ruffles closing her blouse. "We could continue our little chat there in private."

Those fictitious journal entries were coming back to haunt her, she decided, regretting now that she had made them quite so bold, even if they had served her purpose well.

She tried to keep her tone even. "I already have plans for this evening."

His smile did not fade. "Don't worry, my dear. There will be other evenings." He twirled the tip of his moustache. "At least, I hope there will be. You haven't by chance decided to return to New York, have you? Surely your ardent suitors will allow us poor cowboys the pleasure of your company a little while longer."

He was fishing for something, and Araby had a feeling she knew just what it was. She decided to play along with his little game.

"Well, now, I don't know how many ardent suitors I have left, but to be honest with you, I am starting to miss the excitement of New York. The night life here leaves much to be desired."

She smoothed a wrinkle from her skirt and kept right on talking, all the while looking right at him.

"Why, there are always parties or concerts or stage presentations going on every evening there, and by day there's shopping and visiting galleries and museums. . . ." She gave a heavy sigh that was filled with longing. "I guess I'm a city girl through and through. I was never meant for life's simpler pleasures."

"Then you will be returning to New York?" Jud was sitting on the edge of his chair.

"Even if I wanted to stay here, I couldn't," she said. "Rehearsals for my new play start in less than six weeks. I've been working like a demon trying to memorize my lines so I can go right into dress rehearsals when I get back."

If he only knew! The truth was she couldn't bear to look at the script and had finally shoved it into the back of the wardrobe.

She frowned, as if deep in thought. "I just don't know how I can possibly endure another two weeks here!"

Jud laughed. "You make it sound like a jail sentence."

"Well?"

When her own smile faded, she made sure an expression of forced resignation took its place.

"I suppose Uncle Mike had a reason for wanting me to stay here a whole month, though heaven only knows what it could be. The land holds very little fascination for me. Nor do the people, with the exception of one or two friends I have made during my stay."

Araby could have kicked herself for that last remark. She had always had a tendency to overplay a role!

"I would consider myself lucky indeed to be included in that select few."

Blushing was a trick of the trade she had long since perfected.

Jud started to take her hand, but decided

against it once again when Tramp raised his head and growled a warning.

"I sincerely hope you'll permit me to visit you in New York."

Araby played the innocent. "Oh I had no idea your business included traveling back East."

"I do make it a habit to separate business and pleasure from time to time. That is, if I am persuaded to do so by a beautiful woman such as yourself."

Dark lashes brushed her cheeks. Was the man ever going to leave?

"By the way, did you hear about the mining camp robbery?"

Araby shook her head.

"They just got their payroll in from Sacramento, and when Moe Gilley, the paymaster, went to divy it up, somebody shot him and stole the money."

She did not have to pretend concern. "How terrible! Have they caught the person responsible?"

"Not yet, but Sheriff Otter's got a good idea who did it, so it's just a question of rounding him up." Jud stood up and stretched. "You seen Jake Montana lately?"

She didn't have to lie. "No, not for quite a while."

A dark brow rose suspiciously. "You mean, he hasn't been coming around here?"

Araby countered with a raised brow of her own. "No, he has not been coming around here."

"You didn't let on that you were selling the ranch to me, did you?"

"That was one subject I thought best to avoid."

"Wise move." He put on his hat and smoothed down the brim. "When he does find out, we both better watch out. He's got a mean streak in him a mile long. There's no telling what he might do."

As Jud stepped off the porch, Araby couldn't resist asking about Sim and Lena.

"Oh, they're both fine. Just fine," he answered without missing a beat. "Sim's cut back some on his drinking, so he's a little easier to live with, and Lena—well, she's still a little hard to get along with at times, but you just got to know how to handle her."

Araby frowned. Jud handled her all right. Manhandled would be a better word!

"I saw Lena just the other day in town," Araby said as he got his horse from around the side of the house. "She looked like somebody had beaten her up. Her face was all black and blue."

Jud laughed. "I thought the same thing myself when I saw her, but she swears that paint of hers got spooked by a wild boar and threw her."

Araby could sense his laugh was more nervous than pleasant and decided to press him a little more. "You know, I saw her a few days ago as well. I almost forgot. She didn't see me, though." She could tell by the way Jud hesitated when he started to mount his horse that she had piqued his interest. "It was over at the old mission. I started to ride over and say hello, but I thought it best not to disturb her."

"Why? Was she with someone?"

"If she was I didn't see who." She was all but certain she heard Jud let out a sigh of relief. "I thought that if she had gone down there on her own, she probably just wanted to get away and didn't want to be disturbed."

Jud grinned. "I'm sure she would have enjoyed your company." Any worry he may have had passed quickly. "I feel sorry for that girl. Living with Sim ain't easy."

Araby said nothing. Living with Jud and Sim must be pure hell.

Jud leaned down from the saddle and eyed her necklace. "That's an unusual piece of jewelry. What kind of feathers are those? Eagle feathers?"

"Yes."

"Where'd you get it?" He eyed the necklace closer.

"I met a girl from the Coeur d'Alene tribe. She gave it to me."

"You watch out for those Coeur d'Alenes," he said, pointing his finger at her. "They may say they're friendly, but you cross one and you'll find a tomahawk in your back."

"Uncle Mike didn't think so."

Jud's frown hardened. "Never did know why he wasted all that fine timberland by just giving it to them. He could have sold that land and made a small fortune. Why, the company that's buying the sawmill from me, they—"

Jud cut himself off in mid-sentence. "There I go again, boring you with business talk. Forgive me?"

"Of course." Araby smiled. It was far easier being nice to him when he was on his way out!

"There's a church social a week from tonight," he said as he took up the reins. "You'd do me real proud if you'd go with me."

Araby smiled. In a week's time, if all went

well, he wouldn't have time to go anywhere. He'd be in jail awaiting his hanging! A church social, did he say? If Jud Cord ever set foot inside a church, surely he'd be struck down by lightning!

"That's very kind of you to ask, Jud. I'll certainly think about it."

He tapped the brim of his hat. "You do that. Coming for your answer will give me a good excuse to ride back out here to see you."

He whipped his horse into a gallop from a standstill, then took off. Araby watched him ride away. The farther he got from her, the easier it was to breathe!

With Tramp close on her heels, she went inside the house. A long, hot soak was just what she needed to feel good as new. Almost. She wasn't going to feel much better until she knew one way or another about Jake. Was it the thought of committing himself to a woman that drove him off, or was it committing himself to her that scared him off? If only he'd come around tonight so she could explain. She could resolve it all. There was no reason for Jake to feel that his freedom was threatened. He was just like that wild stallion—free as the wind. Nobody would ever tame either of them, even if they did get caught!

Araby looked into the parlor when she passed by. Mattie was dusting Mike's desk. She stuck her head inside the door and told the housekeeper she'd be having dinner in her room.

"Just a little something. Maybe some of that hoecake you fixed for breakfast."

"Yes, m'am."

Mattie looked as if she wanted to say something, but instead kept on rubbing the same spot on the desk.

Araby stepped inside the door. "Is something wrong, Mattie?"

Mattie hesitated, then nodded.

"Would you like to talk about it?"

The housekeeper put down her dust rag. "It's Miz Lena, m'am. I should have told you before now. I caught her snooping in your room. I gave her warning, but she just laughed and told me I'd better watch it or she'd have Mister Jud deal with me." She tugged at her apron. "He was the one that hired me, you know, so I didn't want to cause any trouble for myself in case you—well, in case you was to go back East and him and his brother and Miz Lena moved back in. I—I reckon you're going to fire me, ain't you?"

Araby tried to make the stern-faced woman feel at ease. "Fire you? Heavens, no. If I fired you, who'd make that good hoecake every morning?"

Mattie's tense features almost relaxed into a smile. "Thank you, Miss Stone-Leigh. I appreciate that. And don't you worry about them coming in here anymore. Whenever you ain't here, I'll make sure that door's kept locked."

Araby went on upstairs to her room.

An hour later, she emerged from a long, hot soak feeling refreshed but not particularly relaxed. The suds might have washed away Jud's grime, but it did nothing to get rid of her worries.

Jake! Why did he have to be so pigheaded? What was he trying to prove anyway? If he had something to say to her, why didn't he just get it over with? Whatever point he was trying to make he might as well make in person! Did he intend to stay away the next two weeks thinking that, come July twenty-ninth, she'd be on the train bound for

New York? Well, if he thought that, he had another thought coming! She wasn't going anywhere. Whether he wanted her to or not, she was going to stay right there at Tamarack! As Mike used to say, come hell or high water, she'd do it or die!

A little while later, Araby lay curled up in bed after making certain for the tenth time that the window onto the porch was unlocked. The night was hot, much too hot to wear a nightgown. If by chance Jake did decide to pay her a little visit, she wanted him to realize the error of his ways without her having to tell him.

She waited and waited, but he did not come. She closed her eyes. Perhaps when she opened them, he would be there.

She awakened again well on into the night. Her pillow was in her arms, and she was hugging it tight. Rubbing her eyes, she looked around the room. All was just as she had left it. Jake had not paid her a midnight visit after all. Only in her dreams would she be snug and cozy in his arms tonight.

15

"Miss Stone-Leigh! Miss Stone-Leigh, come quick!"

Araby rolled over and pulled the covers back over her head. All night she had chased Jake over the hills in her dreams, only to have him slip out of her grasp when she finally caught him. No more! She was tired.

The knock at her door sounded very real.

"Slim Watkins is downstairs! Says it's important."

She came to slowly. If the knock was real, then surely Mattie's voice was real, too.

Araby looked outside. It was daylight. Slim Watkins? What was he doing downstairs? Oh, no—something must have happened to Jake!

"Miss Stone-Leigh—"

"I'll be right down, Mattie."

Araby flung back the covers and threw on the first thing she saw, her dressing gown and the skirt she had worn yesterday.

Something had happened to Jake! She just knew it.

"I'm coming, I'm coming."

She tripped twice going down the stairs.

Slim was standing at the bottom of the staircase holding his hat in his hands.

Jake was dead! She just knew it.

She tripped on the last step.

Slim caught her. "Easy there, missy. You're liable to break a leg if'n you ain't careful."

"It's Jake, isn't it?" She sank down onto the nearest chair. "He's dead, isn't he?"

First Mike, now Jake!

"No m'am, he ain't dead—least, not yet."

"Thank God." For a moment, she breathed a little easier—but only for a moment. "What do you mean, not yet? Has he been shot? Has he been hurt? Is he dying?"

"Hold on, hold on a minute." Slim pulled up a chair from the dining room. "No, he ain't been shot, and he ain't dying. If you'll just give me a minute, I'll explain."

Araby nodded. *Hurry, please hurry,* she wanted to shout. Instead, she forced herself to be calm. As much as she wanted to, she couldn't drag the words from Slim's mouth.

"Me and him and Little Joe, we took off after the rest of the wolf pack. Well, when we got ready to come back down the mountain, Jake, he decides to stay up there a while. Says he's got some thinking to do, and he'd like to do it up there alone. Well, me and Little Joe, we come back down. Didn't think nothing of it 'cause Jake likes to go off on his own from time to time."

Araby nodded impatiently, urging him to go on.

"Well, he said he'd be back yesterday. When he wasn't, I didn't get too worried. Come last night, though, I was starting to get a little uneasy. Long about nine, ten o'clock, the Sheriff, he come looking for Jake. Said he wanted to ask him some questions about the mining camp robbery."

Araby's heart fell to her stomach. Jud had known yesterday who the prime suspect in that robbery was! She should have figured it out, too, from the way he was talking about Jake.

"Anyway," Slim continued, "Otter started nosing around through some of Jake's things. Wasn't much I could do to stop him, and after he left, I went to bed. Then just a little bit ago, Gus Fisher from over at the store sent his oldest boy out to tell me the Sheriff had just brung Jake in and was throwing him in jail for Moe Gilley's murder, and saying he was going to have himself a hanging come Sunday."

Araby came out of her seat. "That's the most ridiculous thing I've ever heard! Jake wouldn't hurt anybody."

"Try convincing Sheriff Otter of that! He says he found one of Jake's spurs just a few feet away from where poor old Moe was laying deader than a door nail."

"How convenient that spur just happened to be there," she remarked bitterly.

"That's just what I thought myself. A little too convenient if you asked me," said Slim, scratching his chin. "I don't know what to do. I thought you might be able to help, seeing as how you and Jake—well, seeing as how you two are such good friends. Got any ideas?"

Araby nodded. "I think the first thing we ought to do is have a little chat with Sheriff

Otter."

"Won't do no good. Otter's had it in for Jake for a long time now, and this is just the excuse he's been waiting on to get that noose ready."

"If the Sheriff knows what's good for him, he'd better think twice about lynching Jake."

Cross Fork's foreman shook his head. "Otter's not going to unlock that cell just because me and you go in and have a little chat with him."

"Oh, I think he might. After all, I've got some valuable evidence for him."

"Evidence?" Slim looked confused. "What kind of evidence?"

"Do you know why Jake Montana couldn't possibly have robbed the mining camp payroll and killed Mister Gilley? I'll tell you why." A smile spread across her face. "Because he was with me all day Thursday and all night Thursday, too."

Slim shook his head. "No, m'am. That can't be right because I . . ." A slow smile spread across his face. "Oh, I see."

"Come to think of it, I don't think he left Tamarack until eleven or twelve yesterday morning," Araby said.

"It was twelve, m'am," Mattie spoke up. "Right at noon."

It was Araby's turn to be surprised. That was the first time in two weeks Mattie had actually smiled.

"I'm sure of the time," said the housekeeper with a wink, "because Mister Jake asked me if I could cut him some bread and fry up some fatback for him to eat going home."

Araby turned to Slim and threw up her arms. "How can the Sheriff hang a man when there's two witnesses who will swear to his where-abouts?''

''That just might work, seeing as how Moe Gilley got shot some time between five o'clock, when he got back to the mine with the payroll, and eight o'clock, when the men came round to collect.'' Slim scratched his chin. ''And if'n Jake was with you during that time, he couldn't have possibly been two places at once, now could he?''

''No indeed.'' She started back up the stairs. ''How about getting Rowdy to hitch up the wagon, Slim? It'll just take me a minute to make myself a bit more presentable.'' She threw down another confident smile from the top stair. ''Then you and I and Mattie are going to take a trip into town.''

By ten o'clock, the three of them were standing in front of Sheriff Otter at the Castle Rock jail.

She had given special thought to her dress The image she wanted to present was one of the worldly actress, whose life was a never ending merry-go-round. The off-the-shoulder blouse and blue calico skirt split in the front to reveal petticoat ruffles and a hint of lace-stockinged legs fit the bill perfectly. The Sheriff had trouble keeping his eyes off her, and his deputy bumped into the desk and fell over a crate when he went to get Jake from the cell.

Hands folded across his paunch and legs stretched out on top of his desk, Sheriff Otter leaned back in his chair and stared suspiciously over the top of his wire-rimmed glasses.

''Now, just let me see if I got this straight, folks. Miss Stone-Leigh, you claim Montana was with you all day Thursday?''

Araby fluttered her lashes. "That's correct, Sheriff. Jake was with me all day Thursday and all night Thursday night."

"You sure of it?"

"I'm positive, Sheriff."

The Sheriff swung down his legs and leaned over his desk. "You'd swear to that, I reckon?"

"Indeed I would, sir."

"At no time was Montana out of your sight?"

Araby giggled. "That's right, Sheriff. I wouldn't let him go anywhere."

Sheriff Otter cleared his throat. "Oh, yes, I see."

The iron door leading down into the basement swung open.

Jake emerged from the darkness below rubbing his eyes with his handcuffed wrists. He was still wearing the clothes he had on Wednesday morning when he walked out of the room. They were torn and dirty. Several days' stubble darkened his face. He looked tired and haggard.

Araby ran over to him and threw her arms around his neck. "Jake, Jake, my darling!" She covered his face with kisses. "You were at Tamarack all day and night Thursday," she whispered. Then, in a loud, tearful voice she continued, "Look at you, you poor darling. Why didn't you tell the Sheriff where you really were?"

The Sheriff got out of his chair. "If you don't mind, Miss Stone-Leigh, I'd like to be the one asking the questions. Montana here told me he was up in the mountains alone looking for wolves." He stared Jake right in the eye.

Jake stared him right back. "That's right

Sheriff, but you didn't believe me.''

''Damn right I didn't believe you!'' He turned to Araby. ''Now you show up telling me he was with you all that time. Who am I supposed to believe?''

Araby took Jake's arm and held on tight. ''What a gentleman he is,'' she told the Sheriff. ''How many men do you know who'd risk being hanged rather than compromise a lady's honor?''

The Sheriff grunted.

Araby kissed Jake's cheek and brushed a few strands of thick black hair from his forehead. ''Oh, my darling, what a gallant gesture! What a sweet, sweet thing to do! But I will not let you die because you want to protect me from gossip. I've already told the Sheriff the truth about where you were Thursday—all of Thursday.''

Jake shrugged his shoulders and grinned at the Sheriff. ''What can I say?''

The Sheriff grunted again. ''I suppose you're here to verify all this?'' His question was directed at Mattie.

The look the Tamarack housekeeper shot Jake was one of complete disdain. ''If it were up to me, I'd let him hang. He should hang for what he's been doing. Why, he should have made an honest woman out of this poor child long ago!'' She pointed a finger at Jake and shook it. ''Don't you think for one minute I haven't seen you slipping up the stairs after dark! Why, it's a shame and a disgrace the way you come and go in that house as you please!''

Jake looked down at the floor. The toe of one boot kicked the heel of the foot in front. ''Heck, Mattie, I didn't mean for you to get all riled up.''

''Humph!'' Mattie crossed her arms and

turned her back to him. "It's a shame and a disgrace, Sheriff, how that man—"

"I think you've made your point, Mattie." The Sheriff took off his glasses, rubbed his eyes, then put them back on again. "Now, Slim, it seems to me like when I was out at Cross Fork last night, you told me you hadn't seen Montana since you left him up on the mountain. Where do you reckon he was from the time he left Tamarack at noon till the time I caught up with him late last night?"

Slim shook his head. "I'm just the foreman, Sheriff. Mr. Montana, he's the boss. He don't check in and out with me."

"Out of curiosity, Montana, where do you say you were all day yesterday? That is, from noon on?"

Before Jake could answer, Araby grabbed hold of him again. "I'm sorry we had that fight, darling. I promise I'll never try to tie you down again."

"What about Friday, Montana?" repeated the Sheriff.

"Let me think a minute. When I left Tamarack at noon . . ."

"Yeah, yeah, when you left Tamarack at noon munching on day-old bread and fat-back strips Mattie had fried up for you"—the Sheriff was showing his impatience—"then what?"

"No reason to go getting all upset, Sheriff. I was out trying to catch that wild stallion. I aim to get him, too."

"You and every other cowpoke in the territory."

"In the state," said the deputy. "Idaho's a state now. Remember, Sheriff?"

The Sheriff cut his eyes to his deputy in a warning glower, then directed his attention at Jake again. "I reckon you got an explanation, too, for your spur being found just a few feet away from Moe Gilley's body?"

Jake drew a long breath. "You got me stumped there."

Otter took out a silver spur from his desk drawer and shook it at Jake. "You gonna deny this is yours?"

"Don't see as I can, Sheriff. Not when it's got the Cross Forks brand and my initials cut into it." Jake frowned. "I don't know what it was doing there. I can only tell you I didn't put it there."

Araby held out her hand. "I'd like a look, please." She studied it closely. "It doesn't look broken to me."

The Sheriff yanked it back. "What's that got to do with it?"

"You can see for yourself that neither the strap nor the fastener is broken," she replied, showing him what she meant. "Doesn't it strike you as just a little peculiar that Jake would take off a spur before or after he killed a man?"

"Nothing Montana does strikes me peculiar," the Sheriff replied.

"If'n he wuz wearing spurs, don't you think he'd still have one of them on?" Slim pointed out.

Jake stuck out first one boot, then the other.

"Next thing you'll be trying to tell me is that one of your spurs was stolen," said the Sheriff, leaning back against his desk.

Araby and Jake exchanged knowing looks. Jud had put Lena up to sneaking up to her room to read her journal. Maybe he'd put her up to stealing one of Jake's spurs, too. If that were the case, then Jud must have killed Moe Gilley, or had him killed!

"Answer me, Montana," the Sheriff ordered. "Did you have a spur stolen?"

"It would appear that way, sir." Jake held up his handcuffed hands. "My wrists are getting awfully sore from being cuffed so tight. Maybe you could just—"

"Don't you tell me what to do," barked the Sheriff. "You're not going nowhere, Montana, so just get the idea right out of your head. I'm not finished with my interrogation yet!" He turned to Araby. "Funny thing. Jud Cord told me he was out to your place yesterday, and you told him you hadn't seen Montana in some time. Reckon you got an explanation for that?"

Araby fluttered her lashes again. "Well, Sheriff, surely you can figure that out on your own." She winked. "A girl's got to protect her interests."

Jake broke free of her arms. "Why don't you just tell me what that means? What's Jud Cord doing sniffing around you? Why'd you let him? Why'd you even talk to him? You know what kind of ideas he's liable to get. And what do you mean by protecting your interests? What interests? You just tell me that."

"I don't have to tell you anything, Jake Montana," Araby shouted right back. "You don't want any ties on you? Well, buster, I don't want any ties on me, either. What I do is my business, and what you do is—"

"Shut up! Both of you. Just hush up!" the Sheriff shouted. "What you two do or don't do, just keep it to yourselves! I don't want to hear it. I got enough troubles of my own without being caught in the middle of some fool lovers' quarrel.''

Araby kept her smile to herself. The Sheriff was weakening. She could hear the frustration in his tone. He knew he couldn't justify holding Jake in jail a minute longer.

''Unlock the cuffs,'' he instructed his deputy, drawing a labored breath with each word.

Araby gave him her most charming smile. ''I knew you were a noble man, Sheriff. I knew you wouldn't hang an innocent man.''

The Sheriff laughed. ''Montana, innocent? Ha! Tell me another one.'' He went back behind his desk and sat down the way they'd found him when they walked in. ''He's as guilty as sin. I know it. He knows it. The three of you know it, too. He robbed the payroll all right! Killed Moe Gilley, too. I'd stake my life on that. He robbed that nice Mr. Sullivan, too.'' He looked from Araby to Jake, then back to Araby. ''Seems to me like you make it a habit of coming to Montana's rescue, m'am.''

Araby struck a pose of naive innocence.

Jake rubbed his hands. ''You find out who stole that spur, Sheriff, and you'll find your murderer.''

''I know who the murderer is.'' The Sheriff sounded perfectly calm. ''All I got to do is prove it. I will, too. If I was you, Montana, I wouldn't get too used to breathing fresh air.''

The deputy got Jake's personal belongings from one of the cupboards and laid them down on the desk.

Smiling, Jake strapped his holster back around his hips, then returned his knife and coins to his pockets. ''I don't reckon there's anything I can say that will convince you I'm not the man you want.''

"You're right about that," the Sheriff agreed. He then directed his frown toward Araby, Mattie, and Slim. "If you folks start having trouble with your consciences, you know where to find me."

Mattie pretended to be insulted and stormed out of the jail, slamming the door behind her.

"Me and you's been friends for a long time, Sheriff." Slim's words were slow and deliberate. "But if'n it wuzn't for that silver star on your chest, I'd have already left my fist print up against the side of your head. I'm not a liar, Sheriff, and I don't aim to stand by and let somebody call me one."

The Sheriff stood up and held out his hand. "No hard feelings, Slim. I'm just doing my job."

Slim looked from the Sheriff's outstretched arm to his eyes, then walked out the door.

Araby gave another charming smile when she breezed past. "I don't care what Jud Cord said about you. I still think you're a very noble man."

"What's that supposed to mean? What did Jud say about me?"

Araby pretended not to hear his question. She did hear Jake telling him to have a pleasant day and nearly fell down laughing.

Once outside and a safe distance away from the jailhouse, Jake let out a loud "whoopie!" that made all the townsfolk stop and take notice.

"For a while there I was worried that the next time I walked down this street I'd be on my way to that hanging tree. Slim, Mattie, you don't know how much I appreciate what you did for me. I'll never forget it."

Both the housekeeper and the Cross Fork

foreman directed their smiles at Araby.

"As for you, Miss Araby Stone-Leigh—!" Jake lifted her up and swung her around and around.

Araby was laughing so hard that she couldn't get out the words to tell him to put her down.

Finally, Jake stopped swinging her around and planted her feet firmly back onto the ground. He kissed her square on the mouth with half the town watching.

"I owe you one mighty big debt of gratitude!"

It took a moment for her head to stop spinning, but then she informed him, "And don't you think for one minute I don't intend to collect!"

With that, she walked off leaving him with his mouth hanging open.

Just because she had saved his life was no reason for him to think all was forgiven. Jake had a lot of explaining to do!

16

Araby awakened with a smile and a sigh. This time she was not dreaming. Jake was lying beside her, snoring quietly, with an arm and a leg slung across her. What a glorious night they had spent rediscovering the intimate pleasures they had come to know so well! If only that night could be frozen in time so it would last forever. If only . . .

She felt his hand begin a delicious journey up her leg.

"Oh, no!" she said and laughed as she slipped out of reach. She pulled up the covers, careful to leave a bit of bare flesh exposed in a few choice places.

"Don't you think for one minute, cowboy, you can just walk in and out of my life whenever the urge hits you."

Jake nibbled at her thigh. She did not pull away.

"Now I thought we cleared up that little misunderstanding last night. Remember that discussion we had?"

Jake snuggled closer. Araby waited a few minutes more before pushing him away. After all, it did feel mighty good having him back in her bed where he belonged.

She allowed her fingers to curl themselves around the hair on his neck. What she remembered most about their little discussion of last night was that he had done all the talking while she had sat there and listened. The reason he hadn't returned with Slim and Little Joe from wolf hunting, he had told her, was that he had wanted some time alone. He needed time to think about him and her, time away from her to decide if he were ready to make a commitment. He said he thought she needed the time alone, too, to think about things and decide for herself just what it was she wanted. If he was what she wanted, then he felt she should realize once and for all that she'd have to stay in Idaho, for under no circumstances was she dragging him back to New York!

That was all well and good, Araby thought as her fingers ran through his hair, but not once during their little discussion had that all-important question been asked. If he had any intention at all of asking her to marry him, he had certainly not let on to her!

A hand crept under the covers and began caressing her breasts.

Try as hard as she might, she could not keep their rosy summits from standing at attention on his command.

Not too playfully, she pushed him away. "And just what makes you think you're forgiven, cowboy, may I ask?''

His smile was as slow as that western drawl of his.

''I'm here, ain't I?'' One hand started its descent.

Araby hesitated. She couldn't even think straight when he was doing that.

''I don't remember inviting you,'' she said finally.

''The door was unlocked.'' Ever so gently, he pried apart her legs.

''I'll have to remember to be more careful in the future about locking it.''

He caressed the velvet softness between her legs. ''I don't remember you putting up much of a struggle.''

The fires that had been kindled and rekindled before started to smoke again. How could she deny him anything?

''I was sleepy,'' she said weakly. ''I didn't know what was going on until it was too late.''

''Bull!'' Jake threw back the covers and feasted his eyes on the delicacies that were his alone to enjoy. ''You are one beautiful woman! I like to have drove myself crazy thinking about you when I was in jail.''

Araby jerked the covers back in place. ''Serves you right! I was worried sick about you.''

''I know, honey, and I promise I won't ever give you cause to worry like that ever again.''

Araby could feel herself start to weaken once more. He could be so convincing!

Jake sealed his vow with a deep, soul-searching kiss that went on and on.

''You understand why I had to get away, don't you, darling?'' he asked a couple of minutes later when their mouths finally did part.

Araby pretended to pout. "Now let me see if I can remember them. Oh, yes, you had to have time alone to think because, number one, I am too much of a distraction." She counted each off on her fingers. "Number two, my feminine wiles give me an unfair advantage over you. And number three, because I am a female, I can wield undue influence over those of the masculine type."

Araby kept her chuckles to herself. That undue influence was the reason he kept pressing harder and harder against her.

"You left something out," he said, grinning.

"Oh?"

Jake lunged at her and pinned her down against the bed. "Whenever you're anywhere nearby, I've got to have you! I can't keep my hands off you!" He showed her just what he meant.

Araby laughed. She threw her arms and legs around him and pulled him still closer. How she loved the feel of that strong, powerful body covering hers! That in itself was enough to drive a sane woman crazy!

More hot kisses rained down her belly.

"Am I forgiven?"

"Mmmm." She lay back and enjoyed the wonders his tongue was performing in the most secret nooks of her body.

"Well? Am I?"

"Are you what?" She was quickly growing weary of his questions.

A moment later, he was sprinkling kisses across the satiny mounds that fitted so easily into his hands.

''Am I forgiven?''

''Yes! Yes!'' She held him tight. ''How do you expect me to refuse you anything, Montana? Just who has the unfair advantage over whom?''

Legs wrenched around him in a vise-like hold, Araby directed him inside her without taking her hands from the hard muscles roping his shoulders. Moving against him slowly, tilting her body slowly forward, then back, she guided him to his sweet reunion once again. Every nerve, each muscle welcomed him home.

At first, they moved slowly into each other, teasing, taunting and tormenting. They gained momentum as their urgency increased, rocking wildly against each other, tossing one way, turning the next, their bodies possessed by the unrelenting lust consuming them. Self control gave way to a frantic frenzy of satisfying and satisfaction. And when at last it happened, when together they shared the ultimate climax of physical and mental being, earthquake-force tremors shuddered inside them in unison.

Even had she wanted to, Araby could not move. Never had she experienced such sweet exhaustion. Never had her body been pushed to the limits and so far beyond. Peace and contentment flowed between them.

Araby held on tight, afraid she might wake up still another time to discover he had only been a figment of her overactive imagination. How she loved that man! If he weren't so pigheaded, he would have figured out by now that all the fame and fortune New York had to offer could not make her happy. Only he possessed the power to do that. Perhaps doing it up right with the preacher and the ''I do's'' wasn't really all that important. After all, her body was already married to his, and as for their spirits—they, too, had been wed since their first meeting. Getting hitched, as Jake called it, for decency's sake would just have to wait until her cowboy was ready, and only he could decide when that would be.

"Damn it," Jake muttered softly as he rolled off her.

Araby rolled after him. "Is that a complaint?"

"Not about you. I ought to be horse-whipped." He pulled her over on top of him. "Only a fool would go off and leave you behind.

"I want to marry you, Araby," he said so quickly that all his words ran together. "If you'll have me, that is."

Araby looked up at him in disbelief. Surely she had not heard what she thought she'd just heard! Had he just ask her to marry him, or had she only imagined it?

Before she could ask him to repeat whatever it was he had just said, Jake was promising to be faithful and hardworking and a good husband and father when that time came.

"I swear I'll do my best to see to it you never regret taking the name Montana."

Araby Montana! Now that was a name that would give notice to New York and the theatre world! Araby Montana! Who needed big-city living? Who needed to be a star? Not Araby Montana. She had Jake Montana!

"I reckon what I'm saying is . . . well, that Mattie's right, I should make an honest woman out of you. Damn it, Araby, can't you help a fellow along? I'm asking you to marry me . . . don't you have anything to say?"

Araby held on to him tighter. Proposing obviously did not come easy to him. She was glad. Had he been adept at it, she might have cause to worry.

"Come on, Araby. Yes or no. Say it. Don't just keep me in suspense."

She traced the hard set of his mouth. What a boyish face he had when he was impatient. She'd never noticed that before. Imagine! She thought she knew all there was to know about him. No doubt each day spent with him would bring more and more of those revelations.

"Damn it, woman. Yes or no?"

She pounced on his chest, kissing him, hugging him and crying.

"Yes . . . Yes . . . *Yes!*" Each yes grew louder and louder.

Jake covered her mouth. "Shhhh. You're going to wake up the whole valley."

Araby bit his hand. "Who cares? I'm happy! I want the whole world to know."

She jumped to her feet and danced over the top of the bed. Only Jake's strong arms kept her from tumbling off head-first.

Out of breath, she collapsed into his arms. "You won't regret it, my darling Jake. I promise you that. I'll make you the happiest man in the whole world."

"You already have, darling. You already have."

Jake lifted her into position once more.

"Do you know what's going to be the best part of being married to you?" he asked.

Araby licked his lips. "I can guess, but tell me anyway."

"I can come into the bedroom through the

door," he said, grinning. "No more risking my fool neck shimmying up to the roof."

Araby frowned. "Sounds rather dull if you ask me."

Jake rolled her over and pinned her arms and legs against the bed. "I'll show you what—"

The bed fell.

They rolled onto the floor laughing, then reached for each other again.

Several hours later, they sneaked downstairs famished from their insatiable ardor.

"I am so hungry I could eat a horse," Jake whispered on the way down.

"Better not let Buck hear you say that."

In the dining room, they found the table already set with two plates, a pair of forks and knives, baskets of biscuits and apple turnovers, and a platter of fried potatoes and beef steak, all still hot.

They looked at each other and chuckled.

"Mattie must have known we'd be starved," said Araby quietly as she sat down and started filling the plates.

"I told you you were waking up the valley," Jake laughed as he attacked the food. "Tell me something. Does Mattie not like me or was she just pretending?"

"If Mattie didn't like you, she certainly wouldn't have gone into town with us."

"Yes, I guess you're right," he said, buttering a biscuit. "I really appreciate what the three of you did for me. Sheriff Otter is bound and determined to see me swing from that hanging tree."

"He must hate you an awful lot."

"He does. Shoot a man, and he'll forgive you,

but wound his pride—now that's something else entirely." Jake speared another steak. "The hell of it is I like ole Horace. He's a fine man. I've seen better as far as sheriffs go, but at least Castle Rock's got one." He stopped eating. "I sure hate that about Moe Gilley. Moe was as nice a fellar as you'd want to meet anywhere. He's left a wife and a house full of young'uns up at Cedar Creek. I sure hope Jaffe Mining provides for them. Think I might go myself and have a talk with George Jaffe."

Araby put down her fork. "I don't know if that's such a good idea. I mean, he may hold you responsible."

"Shoot! When George found out the Sheriff was holding me, he came right down there to that jail and told him he'd made a big mistake." Jake chuckled. "You can imagine how well that went over with Horace."

His tone grew solemn once again. "If the Sheriff don't find Moe's murderer soon, I'm going after him myself."

Araby swallowed hard but kept her thoughts to herself. As soon as word got out that Jake was out gunning for the murderer, there was no telling what might happen. He had told her stories of how boys hardly old enough to leave home would come looking for him just to make a name for themselves by challenging him to a draw in hopes they'd be lucky and be left standing.

Still, she couldn't stop him if his mind was made up. *A man's got to do what a man's got to do!* How many times had she heard that from Mike? She knew better than to interfere.

"You know what I been thinking, Araby?"

Jake remarked between bites. "Seeing as how my spur was planted near the body, I think whoever killed Moe did so because they wanted to pin the blame on me. The fact that there was a pile of money to steal was just an added bonus."

She didn't even have to ask who he suspected was behind it. "Do you think Jud did it, or do you think he paid to have it done?"

Jake laughed. "Jud's too much of a coward to dirty his hands. No, I think he paid somebody, and I have a feeling that somebody is Burley Wilkerson. A job like that is right up his alley!" He shook his head. "I sure hate to see Lena get involved in all of this. She's had a hard time ever since she was young. First with her pa, then Jud and Sim. But she ought to have enough sense to know what she's getting into."

"But why would Jud want you dead? Aside from the fact that he despises you," she added quickly. "I mean, he's convinced I'm selling Taramarck to him."

"Maybe so, but he knows that, even if he does take over Tamarack, he'll never take over the valley like he wants to do because I'll fight him tooth and nail every step of the way. No, I'm a thorn in Jud Cord's side. The sooner he's rid of me the better. It might look a little too suspicious for me just to turn up dead, but knowing how the Sheriff has just been itching to pin the train robbery on me, he most likely decided he'd be better off to let the Sheriff take care of me."

"So what do we do now?"

Araby held her breath. She prayed Jake would not do something foolish, like going after Burley and trying to get a confession out of him. Burley had a crazed look in his eye. Doing Jud's killing probably gave him some kind of a perverse thrill.

"We don't do anything," Jake said slowly. Hands folded across his chest, he leaned his chair back against the wall. "At least, not right yet. When Jud finds out I'm not in jail, and when he finds out why, he's liable to make another move. I'll just have to stay two steps in front of him and keep one eye over my shoulder all the time."

Araby pulled her dressing gown tight around her. One slip-up and Jake could be a dead man.

Seeing that such talk troubled her, Jake quickly changed the subject.

"You know that Indian Slim was telling us about the other day? Well, it seems he's been coming around every day since with some important message for me that he won't give to anybody else." He popped another turnover into his mouth. "Slim swears he's a Flathead, but it don't make any sense to me why one of them would come all the way down from Freezeout Mountain to see me. I think that Indian must be some messenger from Chief Silver Bear."

Araby told him of her new friendship with Fleeing Fawn. Jake already knew the woman's tragic story.

"She gave me her necklace of eagle feathers as a gift. She said we were sisters of the soul from that time forward."

Jake seemed pleased. "You should be honored. Only a few white people in this whole territory have ever been given such a gift by a Coeur d'Alene. A gift of eagle feathers is the highest tribute that can ever be paid a white woman."

He looked out the window. "It'll be daylight

soon. Today's the day we were going up to Freezeout, but Slim was telling me about some rock slides up along Toby Pass, so if it's all the same to you, I'd like to wait a day or two until the rocks stop falling."

Araby was disappointed, but she had to go along with his decision. The evidence they needed to prove Jud had murdered Uncle Mike was up on Freezeout Mountain. She knew it was! But they wouldn't get that proof any faster by breaking their necks or a horse's leg in the process. Jake was just as anxious as she·to get up there. He wasn't any happier than she about the delay.

"I can tell you're disappointed," he told her, "but I really do think we'd be better off in the long run if we wait another couple of days."

"Whatever you say, Jake. That's fine by me," she said, smiling. Funny, she had never thought she'd say that to any man!

Jake stood up and stretched, then leaned down and kissed her cheek. "I think I'll head up the mountain to Chief Silver Bear's village. If it was him that sent the messenger, I'd best go see what he wants. Care to keep a lonely cowpoke company?"

Araby held up her arms. "Talk me into it."

He smoothed her hair over one shoulder and began kissing her neck.

With a moan and a sigh, Araby began slipping down into her chair, taking him with her.

"Oh, no you don't." Jake ducked out of her hold and jerked her up to her feet. "I'm on to you, woman. Just because you know my weaknesses doesn't mean you can always get the best of me." He gave her backside a playful slap and pointed her towards the stairs. "You got five minutes to get ready."

Araby tossed him a wink over her shoulder. "If I'm not back down by then, does that mean you're coming up to get me?"

Jake put on his hat. "If I did that, we wouldn't get started until after noon."

"A kiss might help me get moving a little faster," she teased him.

Jake ran up the stairs, taking three at a time, and gave her a loud kiss. "Now, hurry up, woman. I ain't got all day."

Araby could feel the presence of the Indians long before she and Jake reached the mammoth waterfall that marked the entrance to Chief Silver Bear's village. Curious eyes followed them every step of the way from the moment they passed the old mine.

The horses, too, sensed vanishing figures in the bushes. Buck's ears were alert and pointed ahead, while Buddy, the handsome palomino Curley had traded two cowponies for, looked with interest at every twig that moved but made no effort to shy or take one step out of line.

If it were not for Fleeing Fawn's necklace, Araby was certain she would have felt even more uncomfortable than she already did being scrutinized by people hiding in the bushes. Having it around her neck did at least keep her imagination from conjuring up images of scalpings and massacres.

When the Indians finally did show themselves, it was with no warning. Stepping out onto the trail, they motioned for her and Jake to follow, then walked on ahead of them single-file, leading them around the back of the waterfall.

Araby studied each one as closely as she could without insulting them with her curiosity. How different they looked from the sad-faced Indians she had seen along the way! Those poor souls had been huddled together at the train stops to keep warm. Stripped of all dignity, they were forced to beg for whatever coin or bread crust was tossed their way.

The Coeur d'Alene, the Schiquumish as they were called by Fleeing Fawn and her people, still possessed the dignity of their forefathers. Their carriage was nothing short of regal. They held themselves tall and proud and stiffly erect. Long black braids hung down each shoulder, and when the sun hit them, they glistened blue. Their features were sharp and strong, their mannerisms noble. It was easy to imagine them galloping across the plains with their long-tailed war bonnets of eagle feathers streaming behind them.

The faces of the braves surrounding them were without the ceremonial war paint Araby had heard so much about, which was intended more to frighten their victims than for decoration. Nor were any of their heads adorned with the elaborate feathered headdresses symbolic of warfare in Western paintings by Eastern artists. They all wore moccasins and buckskin leggings that fell halfway down to their knees. Their chests were smooth and rock firm, their bare flesh the color of copper. Around one shoulder was a quiver of arrows, and slung over the other shoulder was a bow. One of the braves had a strip of leather around his neck, and dangling down from it was a silver star. From the way the others looked to him as if for instruction, Araby assumed he must be the leader.

Endless water cascades rushed down from the mountaintop, battering rocks and boulders and fallen trees in its path. The noise was so great Araby could hardly hear herself think, much less speak. Hand gestures were the only way she could communicate with Jake. When she motioned her concern over the braves forming a circle around them, he signaled back that there was no cause for alarm. By encircling them, the Indians were protecting their guests from any unexpected dangers.

Araby was about to ask what kind of danger when she saw Fleeing Fawn running out from the forest of sky-high pines to greet them. All her fears and worries were quickly put to rest.

Fleeing Fawn raised a hand in friendship. "Hello, Jake Montana. It is good to see you again. Araby Stone-Leigh, you do me much honor with your visit."

"Thank you, Fleeing Fawn. I am glad to see you."

Jake tipped the brim of his hat to Fleeing Fawn. "How is your father, the great chief?"

"He is eagerly awaiting your visit," she answered as she walked between them. "When we received news of your coming, he was very pleased."

Jake said something to one of the braves in the Indian tongue. The brave mumbled a few words in reply.

"My father is very anxious to meet you," Fleeing Fawn told Araby after declining her offer to ride Buddy with her. "He welcomes Mike Stone's niece into his village with open arms."

Fleeing Fawn's eyes settled on the eagle-

feather necklace, and even though she didn't say
so, Araby could tell she was honored she was
wearing it and that her father would be honored
as well.

"How did you know we were coming?"
asked Araby, curious.

"Very little escapes the watchful eyes of our
couragous warriors," replied Fleeing Fawn
proudly. "You have been observed ever since you
crossed the river. When it became evident you
were coming to our village, one of our braves ran
on ahead to announce your visit so we could
make ready."

Fleeing Fawn pointed to Jake and in a hushed
voice asked, "Is Jake Montana your man?"

Araby chuckled softly. She'd never really
thought of Jake in those terms before, but yes, she
supposed that was exactly what he was. When
she nodded, Fleeing Fawn pointed ahead to the
brave with the silver star dangling around his
neck.

"That is Running Wolf. He has spoken for
me. He will one day be chief of the great
Schiquumish," she announced proudly. "He is
good and brave and kind. No warrior is more
valiant in battle. He is good to me. He will take
care of me. I will give him many, many sons."

Araby gave her friend's shoulder an
affectionate squeeze as they walked on, chatting
about their prospective husbands. Sometimes it was
hard to remember Fleeing Fawn was not an Indian
by birth. If it were not for the braids, which were
the blond of Buddy's coat, it would be easy to forget. Fleeing Fawn's ideas about wifehood were considerably different from her own. Sure, she loved
Jake. She loved him more than anything in the
world, but somehow she could not quite see her-

self so willingly welcome a life of subservience, which from the way Fleeing Fawn was talking about her impending marriage, was exactly what she had to look forward to. Then again, Fleeing Fawn was genuinely happy, and that was all that mattered.

A caravan of Indian ponies bearing braves and squaws, some with papooses in cradleboards strapped to their backs, came out to greet them. Children ran alongside the ponies, and those who were too young were decorated with bright trinkets, while others were painted with colorful designs.

"The Schiquumish were the first of the Indian tribes to break the wild horses and train them to be useful," explained Fleeing Fawn. "The mark of honor and wealth among the Indian people is the number of ponies a brave possesses. Running Wolf has many ponies. When he captures the great black leader of the cayuses, he will have twelve ponies."

Araby exchanged smiles with Jake, whose ears had perked up at the mention of the stallion. If the magnificent black steed were a creature to be pitied, she would feel sorry for that horse. He was the target of many men's ambitions, even of men like Jud who would rather see him dead than have someone else revel in the glory of capturing him. The much talked about escapades of the black stallion had made him a legend. Lucky for the stallion, legends were not easily destroyed.

The caravan closed in around them. Everyone gathered closer for a better look at the white strangers.

Araby smiled at the children. They smiled back. She remembered what Fleeing Fawn had said about the miseries children in particular were forced to endure on reservations, and she felt deeply saddened. She was proud of her uncle for giving his friends their land, and she swore a silent vow to do all in her power to see to it that they kept those dense pine forests forever.

Several of the children reached out to her, wanting to touch her skin. When she touched them back, they giggled and ran to hide behind the ponies.

The village of Chief Silver Bear was just beyond the waterfall in the midst of the giant pines. Colorful drawings decorated each teepee. Fleeing Fawn explained that the blue at the point of the teepee represented the sky, the brown at the base, the earth, and spots of red indicated how many in that particular family had died. Galloping horses depicted the dweller's success in capturing wild ponies. She proudly pointed out the twelve ponies painted on the teepee where she would soon live. Every mark, each stroke of the paint brush represented a ceremonial ritual or prayer, and Fleeing Fawn explained each one.

Fleeing Fawn interrupted her lesson in the different good and bad spirits to point to a large boulder in the middle of the circle of teepees. Seated on its flat surface was an old man, whose snow-white braids hung all the way down his back and onto the rock. Around his head was a red band that held a single eagle feather. Hanging low on his bare chest was a strand of grizzly bear claws and buffalo teeth. The chief sat cross-legged with his arms crossed at his waist and stared into the fire pit beside him.

Running Bear motioned for everyone to halt and dismount. When they had done so, Fleeing

Fawn took Jake on one arm and Araby on the other and led them to her adopted father while the rest of the tribe looked on.

The chief and Jake exchanged greetings in the Indian tongue. Then Fleeing Fawn introduced Araby to Silver Bear.

The chief nodded, then smiled, and took Araby by the hand as he addressed her in words she could not understand.

Araby stood in awe of the Schiquumish leader. Even though he was an old man, his face was smooth and without wrinkles.

Fleeing Fawn translated his welcome. "Your visit greatly honors Chief Silver Bear and his people. He would like for you to know that he, too, suffered a great loss with the passing of his good friend, Mike Stone. Few white men have ever earned the respect of the Indian. Your uncle was one such white man. Your loss is our loss as well."

Araby gave the chief a warm smile. "Tell him for me, please, Fleeing Fawn, that my uncle spoke often of the great chief of the Schiquumish and of his admiration and respect for the chief. He considered him a very good friend."

When Fleeing Fawn had translated Araby's message, the chief returned her smile.

Araby excused herself to go back to where her horse was standing and reached inside the saddlebag for presents she had brought for the chief and his adopted daughter. She presented Silver Bear with a carving of a bear standing on its hind legs. She was certain Mike would not mind her taking it from his collection.

"Please tell the chief I would like very much for him to accept this gift of friendship from me."

The chief's smile broadened, and he bowed his head in appreciation.

"And these are for you," she said, giving Fleeing Fawn her gifts of a lacquer fan with Oriental designs, several tortoiseshell hair clasps, and a brightly colored scarf. Then she took a locket from around her neck and fastened it around Fleeing Fawn's. "I'd like for you to have this, as well. It has brought me much luck."

Tears came to Fleeing Fawn's eyes as she tenderly held the gold heart between her fingers. "You could not give me a more perfect gift. I had one like this when I was little. It broke my heart when I lost it." She threw her arms around Araby. "Thank you, my friend, my sister in spirit."

The chief shooed the curious onlookers away, then made signs that it was time for the visitors to sit down and join him for the noon meal.

Araby, Jake, and Fleeing Fawn sat down on blankets one of the older squaws had spread upon the ground and formed a semi-circle around the chief. Another squaw brought out from one of the teepees earthenware platters of smoked fish covered in leaves and surrounded by berries and yams and mounds of brown bread.

While the chief and Jake conversed in the Schiquumish tongue, Fleeing Fawn questioned Araby about life on the other side of the nation. Her eyes grew to the size of the bread mounds as Araby told her about New York's theaters, museums, shops and stores, and tall buildings.

"It is hard to imagine such a place," Fleeing Fawn kept repeating. "Yet, you say you are ready to leave all that behind and make your home here in the mountains. Perhaps New . . ."

"New York," Araby finished.

"Yes, New York. Perhaps New York is not as wonderful as it sounds."

Araby laughed. "Oh, it's wonderful, all right. It's just that there are some things here more wonderful." She looked in Jake's direction and smiled.

He caught her eye and returned her grin.

Fleeing Fawn gave a knowing nod. "Ah, perhaps I do understand." Then she took Araby by the hand and squeezed her fingers. "I am glad you will be remaining. We can spend many hours together talking while our children play beside the river."

Araby smiled. What a lovely picture that would make!

The chief motioned for Running Wolf to join them. When he passed behind Fleeing Fawn, his hand brushed her shoulder in a gesture of tender affection.

Fleeing Fawn followed every movement of her betrothed. Her smile and her eyes stayed on him as she listened to the men's discussion, but she waited until Jake, Running Wolf, and Chief Silver Bear had retired to the chief's teepee before translating the conversation.

"Chief Silver Bear did not send a messenger to Jake's ranch. However, he says he knows of such a messenger because his chief, Chief Brave Eagle, sent greetings to the Schiquumish people through that messenger. The messenger is a medicine man who has come to this side of the mountain to gather roots and herbs for his potions. The land is so barren and desolate on Freezeout Mountain that many of these roots and herbs have died out, just as the Flathead people have died out.''

Araby shook her head, deep in thought. Freezeout Mountain was home to many mysteries —first, Mike's murder and now the secret message that could be delivered only to Jake. Perhaps the two were somehow related. Could it be the medicine man had valuable information regarding Mike's death? Perhaps he knew Mike had been murdered by his step-sons. Maybe he even saw it happen . . .

''Araby, are you all right?''

Araby let out a long sigh. ''Yes, I'm fine.'' Sometimes her imagination simply ran away with her!

''Where is the medicine man now?'' she asked Fleeing Fawn.

''Three days have passed since he was last here. Perhaps he has returned to his tribe, though I doubt so if he has not been able to complete his mission.''

The three men appeared from inside the chief's teepee. Fleeing Fawn strained to hear what they were saying.

''They are still speaking of this medicine man,'' she said. ''Jake Montana believes the medicine man has information regarding your uncle's death.'' Her face bore a look of surprise. ''He just told my father that he suspects Mike Stone was murdered. Oh, Araby, how terrible. Who would do such a thing?''

Araby revealed their suspicions regarding Jud and Sim. Fleeing Fawn was noticeably disturbed at the mention of Jud Cord's name.

''That man is evil!'' Fleeing Fawn gritted her teeth and reached for her knife. ''He is why I wear this. Once, I was out following the river after the snows from the mountain tops began to fall, when all of a sudden Jud Cord galloped towards me on his horse and tried to run me down. He chased me, and when he finally caught me, he threw me down onto the ground and tried to make me do horrible things. Finally, another man happened along. Jud Cord knew him. Sim, I believe was the name he called out. He invited him to share in with him in the spoils of war, but the other man made him let me go. I ran. Next time, I will be ready for him," she said, patting her knife. "I could not tell any of this to my father or to Running Wolf, for they would kill him. If the blood of a white man is shed and the Schiquumish is held accountable, regardless the circumstances the entire tribe must suffer."

"If we can prove Jud was responsible for my uncle's death, then neither you nor any of your people will ever have to worry about him or his evil again," Araby promised.

"Ah, now they are talking about capturing the black horse leader." The smile returned to Fleeing Fawn's face. "Your man wants him as bad as mine. It appears they both have been outsmarted by the creature's cunning." She laughed. "My father just told them that if he were ten winters younger, he would capture the horse just to show them how it was done."

The three men disappeared once again.

"Jake Montana has promised cows to my father, and they have gone back inside the teepee to discuss this. My father will accept no handouts. He must earn all that he gets. That is why he would surely die if he were forced to take his people to live on a reservation," Fleeing Fawn said sadly.

Araby took her friend's hand. "Please tell your father that he will never have to go to the reservation. I fully intend to carry out all of my uncle's wishes. It was his heart's desire that the Coeur d'Alene—the Schiquumish people—remain on Tamarack land for many generations to come. I give you my word I shall see to it that agreement is never broken."

"Thank you, my sister. My father will sleep easier now, knowing that you do not intend to sell to one of those lumber companies that want only to destroy our great forests."

Araby swore once again that would never happen as long as Tamarack belonged to her.

Fleeing Fawn stood up and held out her hand. "Come. Let me show you the rest of my village."

The sun was setting by the time they were on their horses ready to leave.

"Please tell your father that I hope he will come to visit me at Tamarack, so I can return his kind hospitality and generosity."

Both Buddy and Buck were laden with gifts from the chief—brightly colored, woven blankets and tapestries, bowls and platters, all made with the same earthenware designs of eagles spread in flight, and a pair of mocassins for both Araby and Jake, as well as buckskin leggings and fringed and beaded dresses.

The chief wished them a safe journey, then took Araby's hand and clasped it tightly between his. She knew her message had been relayed. He said something to her in Schiquumish. She looked to Fleeing Fawn for translation.

"My father says Mike Stone was lucky to have you, just as he is lucky to have me."

"You will come visit me soon, won't you?"

Araby asked Fleeing Fawn as they started to walk away.

"Before the next full moon. I promise."

Jake was unusually quiet during the trip back down.

"Something's bothering you," Araby said lightly. "So you might as well tell me what it is, or I'm going to hound you all the way home."

"You think you know me pretty well, don't you?" Jake said right back. "Well you do, and you're right. Something is bothering me." He frowned. "It seems our friend Jud sent Burley up here a couple of days ago to deliver a message to the chief. It seems Jud has decided to put the chief and his tribe on notice that come August the first, they had better be gone from his land."

Araby could feel her blood start to boil. "Damn that Jud! When does he stop?"

"He doesn't," Jake answered solemnly. "Least, not until he's got everything he wants—or somebody stops him."

"I hope you told the chief that Jud will never own Tamarack land."

"I did, and that eased his mind considerably. I told him about Mike, too, and our suspicions about his death. His reply was that the bite of Jud Cord could be more fatal than that of a rattlesnake."

Araby nodded in agreement.

"And he's going to send Running Wolf in search of the Flathead medicine man so he can bring him to me and tell me what's so all-fired important that he can't tell anybody but me."

"It has something to do with Mike's death, doesn't it?"

Jake nodded.

"Maybe they have some evidence that will put Jud away for good," Araby said, once again letting her imagination run wild. "Maybe one of the Flatheads saw Jud and—"

"Whoa, there. Don't start maybeing this and maybeing that," Jake warned her. "If you do, you're bound to be disappointed."

"If only we could get to Freezeout Mountain," she said impatiently. "I know we'll find what we're looking for there. I just know it!"

Jake reached over and took her hand. "Wishing ain't gonna get us there any faster. Now, I tell you what let's do. If we haven't heard from the Flathead medicine man or Chief Silver Bear or Running Wolf by say, day after tomorrow, we'll head on up to Freezeout and pay a visit to Brave Eagle ourselves."

Araby was starting to feel a little better. "What about the rock slides?"

"I'd rather contend with a mountain falling than with you when you're all fired up like this," he said affectionately.

"I just want to get to the bottom of this once and for all, Jake," she said softly. "I know nothing I can do will bring Mike back, but I can damn sure see to it that Jud Cord is punished. An eye for an eye, a tooth for a tooth. That is one philosophy I believe in with all my heart."

"Jud'll pay, honey. You don't worry about that. If the law don't make him, I will."

Araby said nothing. It worried her when Jake talked like that. She didn't want to be a widow before she was a bride!

She decided it would be best if she changed the subject, and quickly!

"I felt so sorry for Fleeing Fawn," she said as the horses plodded down the mountain. "Did you notice the way the other Indian women were ignoring her? Her life must be so lonely."

"It's sad sure enough," agreed Jake. "She don't belong anywhere. Her family didn't want her, and except for Chief Silver Bear and Running Wolf, the Indians don't seem too pleased with her being among them, either. She's no longer white, but she's not Indian, either. Not a very easy life. All that will change, though, when Running Wolf becomes chief," he said confidently. "Fleeing Fawn might not have the friendship of the other women in the Coeur d'Alene tribe, but she will have their respect. To the Indians, that respect is far more important than friendship."

Araby gave Buddy a loose rein and let him set his own pace down the trail.

"Tell me, what were you two saying about children playing together by the river?" asked Jake.

"Shame on you for eavesdropping."

Jake's smile was devilishly one-sided. "Well? You thinking about starting a family? You ain't got yourself a husband yet."

Araby stuck out her tongue at him. "Who says a woman's got to have a husband first?"

"Is that the way they do things in New York?" he teased her.

"I wouldn't know."

He leaned as close to her as he could without coming out of his saddle. "Did you mean what you said the other day back at the cabin about having young'uns and all?"

Araby good-naturedly booted him away. "If I hadn't meant it, I wouldn't have said it."

351

"I think twelve's a nice number, don't you?"

Her look was one of mock horror. "It depends what you're talking about."

"Young 'uns," he replied with an even broader grin. "The more we have, the fewer ranch hands I'll have to hire."

"What do you think I am? A brood mare?"

"Well, I wouldn't make you have them all at once," he said, enjoying himself. "I'd give you a few months' rest in between."

"That's real gentlemanly of you, cowboy."

"Twelve boys just like their daddy! I can see them now."

Araby laughed. "I'm not sure Idaho is ready for a dozen Jake Montanas. I don't even know about the United States."

"All right then, eleven boys and one little girl as beautiful as her mama. How about that?"

"Wouldn't it be something if our girls looked like their daddy and the boys looked like their mama?" she teased him.

"We would be in one big mess of trouble." His face suddenly took on an uncharacteristic seriousness. "One thing's for sure. I'm not going to beat up on my young'uns the way my daddy did his. I reckon that's why I grew up so fast and took out on my own as soon as I could."

Araby listened quietly as Jake told her about his unhappy childhood with a father who would get drunk and take the strap to them and a mother who could only stand by and watch as her husband beat up on her as well as his children. Jake had never said much about his family. Maybe that was why. Even though he had few memories of his own childhood, she swore silently that he would have many happy memories of his own children to make up for it.

"Take me, now," she said with a deliberate laugh when Jake had finished. "I was an only child, so you can guess who got blamed for everything. Mind you, more often than not, I deserved it."

"I bet your folks spoiled you rotten, didn't they?"

Araby nodded. "But I was very lonely growing up. It seems that I was always being left with a nanny or a companion when I got older. Don't get me wrong, my parents were very good to me—are very good to me—but they believed very strongly that they should have their own lives, and even though they were quick to indulge me, they thought adults and children should only mingle at dinner time and before bed."

"What do you think they're going to say about their little darling marrying a cowboy?"

Araby kept her smile. She knew they'd not have too much good to say about it. *You're throwing away your chance. What, marrying a man who's a social nobody? How can you do this to us!*

"I take it they're not going to be too thrilled about it," Jake observed.

She laughed. "They'll be relieved I found a man to marry me. They were worried I'd end up an old maid like my mother's sister, Martha. Now that woman is a plague on the entire city of New York."

Jake took her hand. "I'll make them proud you're marrying a cowboy. I'll make you proud."

"You don't have to. I am already."

They brought their horses to a halt, and Jake reached over to give her a bear hug.

Araby held on tight. Who would have thought she would find true happiness in Idaho? Mike thought so. He knew so!

She lifted her head to the heavens and smiled. Thanks, Mike!

Jake reached down and rubbed her stomach. "Who knows? We may have started us a family already!"

Araby threw her arms back around his neck and smiled into his hair. Who knew, indeed?

17

Araby stood at the window, nose pressed against the pane, and watched the rain splattering the ground. For three days, there had been no break in the summer storm. If it weren't thundering, lightning was zig-zagging across the sky. One black cloud after another rolled across the sky. If only it would let up just long enough to get to Freezeout Mountain! It was beginning to seem as if some unknown force were deliberately keeping them away. First, Jake had been put in jail, then the rock slide had stopped them, and finally, on the day they were finally supposed to leave, the skies had opened up and didn't look as if they would close any time soon.

Curses! Were they never going to get to Freezeout Mountain? The proof they needed to present to the United States Marshal about Jud was up there. It could be found. It would be found, but first it had to stop raining, and that might be weeks!

She searched the sky for a hint of hope, but any patch of blue there might be somewhere up there in the heavens was very well hidden!

What had happened to that Flathead messenger, she wondered, trying to keep her mind off the weather. He must have known the rains were coming and headed back up the mountains towards home. At least, that had been Chief Silver Bear's explanation when Running Wolf failed to locate him. Perhaps the medicine man had just gotten tired of waiting to find Jake. Just what was it that had been so important that only Jake's ears could hear that message? It had to do with Mike and the murder. Of that she was certain.

Araby cautioned herself about being so impatient. She wasn't going to find those answers any faster by being so much on edge. The answers were there on Freezeout Mountain waiting for them. They'd be there when the rains stopped. So would the Flathead Indians.

She was about to go into the kitchen for a piece of the fudge pie Mattie had spent most of the day making, when she saw a horse galloping towards the house at full speed.

Hell-fire and damnation! She was in no mood to cope with Jud Cord today! If only he knew just how hard it was for her not to whip out her little pistol and shoot him, he'd not show his face at Tamarack for a long time coming!

Jud was all smiles, as usual, when he hopped off his horse and ran into the house through the rain.

Her own smile was delivered through clenched teeth.

"Lovely weather, ain't it?" He took off his

poncho, shook off the water, and hung it across the hitching post to dry. Then he stomped up the steps and plopped down in one of the rockers without invitation.

"To what do I owe this surprise?"

Araby made no effort to hide her sarcasm or her lack of enthusiasm, but if Jud noticed either, he showed no reaction.

"If it hadn't been for all this rain, I'd have come calling before now," he told her, still smiling.

Araby sat down in the other rocker and folded her hands over her lap. Surely he did not think she was being cool simply because he hadn't been out to visit her. What a conceited bastard! How women like Lena could fall all over him was beyond her understanding. Granted, his smile was devilish and his theatrical good looks could be irresistible, but he had a mean streak that would rival Satan's.

She wished he'd stop staring at her with that about-to-pounce look on his face and just say what he'd come to say—and leave!

"So what can I do for you, Jud?"

As usual, she had quickly grown weary of his compliments and his flattery and the way his brazen stares tried to strip her of everything, including her dignity.

He leaned closer. "That, my dear, Araby, is a dangerous question. You're lucky I'm a gentleman."

Araby held his stare. A gentleman? Ha!

Oblivious to the poison-arrow glances she was sending him, Jud pulled his chair still closer. "Perhaps a better question would be, what can I do for you?"

He took an envelope from inside his vest and handed it to her.

"What's this?"

Looking very pleased with himself, Jud twirled the tip of his moustache as he rocked slowly back and forth.

"That, my dear, is cash—cold, hard cash, and a lot of it. Remember that deal I was telling you about with that lumber company out of California? Well, that little bundle in your hands is the result of those business dealings."

Araby pretended not to know what he was getting at and handed the money back to him.

He shook his head and pushed her hand back. "No, no, dear. That money belongs to you. It's a bit more than Tamarack is worth, but I didn't want you to think I'd try to cheat you. What you think of me is very important, you know."

She stared long and hard at the cash. That was no money from any business deal. That was blood money. There was no wondering where that money had come from. Moe Gilley's innocent blood was smeared all over those bills.

"There's also a deed of sale inside the envelope," Jud announced smugly. "I took the liberty of having a lawyer over in Lewiston draw one up. I didn't want Wallace Ford to know what we were doing, considering the stipulation in your uncle's will."

Araby calmly handed the packet back to him without explanation.

His smile started to fade. "I don't understand."

"I think you do."

His frown disappeared the moment it appeared. "Oh, of course. You don't have to worry about that, my dear. Mike certainly isn't going to be any wiser. A week, ten days—he's not going to come back and haunt you just because the thirty days aren't quite up."

Araby started to reach for her pistol. He didn't deserve to go on living!

"Oh, dear, I see I've offended you. Please forgive me." Jud reached for her hand.

Araby pulled hers back, making it perfectly clear she needed no comforting from him.

"Forgive me for being so insensitive, Araby. Of course, you must do what you must do. I can understand that. It's just that I was certain you'd be anxious to head back to New York." He winked. "And I was anxious to head back there with you for a visit. Kind of hoping you'd show me the town."

Araby could not believe what she was hearing. Was he stupid, or was he just so vain that he could not fathom the thought that a woman would not prostrate herself at his feet!

He kept right on talking and smiling.

"I certainly can't do any courting at Tamarack, not the way that Jake Montana hangs out around here." His eyes roamed boldly over the floral print of her afternoon dress, all but singeing the cotton material. "Not that I blame him, mind you. Don't blame him at all. He's just not the right man for you."

Araby gritted her teeth. It was apparent just who he thought that right man would be. He didn't have to be licking his lips for her to know just what thoughts were going through his head!

"You obviously think you are," she couldn't resist.

"No, my dear. I don't think. I know, and you

know it, too," he said confidently. His frank appraisal of her physical attributes grew more daring, almost to the point of being obscene.

"Really, Jud," she said indifferently. "I don't know where you get these ideas of yours. I don't remember ever inviting you to go to New York with me."

"Oh, but you did. You did," he repeated, eying her up and down. "Perhaps not directly—not in so many words—at least not in words that were intended for me to hear."

Her cool composure remained intact. Once again those journal entries had come back to haunt her.

"Whatever message you think I sent, you were wrong. I am not interested in you, Jud, nor do I intend to encourage your interest in me."

He folded his arms over his chest. "I like a woman who plays hard to get. The chase is even more exciting then the—"

She didn't give him time to finish. "Than the kill?"

Dark shadows spread quickly across his face. "Actually, conquest was the word I had in mind."

"Whatever it is you have in mind, Jud, let me assure you I am interested in neither the chase nor the conquest. Have I made myself clear?" She almost wished he would make a move. It would be easier to kill him when he was lunging at her than to shoot him in cold blood, not that her conscience would bother her in either event.

"Araby. Dear, dear Araby. Your days here are numbered. Why don't you just give in to the desires of your heart? You and I were meant to be together. It'll be good. I promise you that."

She was anxious to change the subject before

he went into graphic detail about just what it was that would be so good.

"Do you know what bothers me the most about you, Jud?"

He shook his head. "If you tell me, I promise to do something to change it."

Lashes fluttering, she went on. "I don't know what it is you're interested in—me as a woman, or me as owner of Tamarack."

"All the more reason for you to sign the deed and take the money, my dear, so I can prove to you just what it is about you that attracts me."

"I have no intention of signing that deed," she said sweetly.

"I know. Not until the end of the month." He put the packet back inside his vest. "I respect your judgment in this matter."

She doubted he respected any woman at all! As far as he was concerned, a woman's only purpose was to be his slave so he could intimidate and humiliate her physically as well as mentally.

He closed his hand over hers. "Do you always get your way?" he asked cheerfully.

"Always." She pulled back her hand. "That's the advantage we women have over you men."

She could tell immediately that he not only disagreed with that remark, but it angered him greatly as well.

He was quick to regain his calm. "Only because we men allow it, my dear."

"Miss Araby?" Mattie called out from inside the house. "It's two-thirty. You wanted me to call you in an hour, remember? You got a lot of memorizing to do."

Araby smiled to herself. Mattie had just earned herself a raise!

''Memorizing?'' asked Jud. ''Memorizing what?''

''The script for my new play. It opens soon after I return to New York.''

Jud looked pleased. ''So you really are going back to New York?''

She feigned surprise. ''Was there ever any doubt? Surely you didn't think for a moment I intended to stay out in this no-man's land?''

Jud stood up. ''You're a hard woman to figure out. I guess that's what draws me to you.''

Araby said nothing. She stayed in her chair as he got up to leave.

''Promise me something,'' he said. ''These last days that you're here, promise me you'll give me a chance to show you just what you been missing. You never know. You might just be surprised.''

Araby chuckled. She wasn't the one who was going to be surprised these last few days. That she could promise him!

Jud fastened his poncho, then turned back to her. ''Out of curiosity, why did you tell the Sheriff Montana was with you when Moe Gilley was killed?''

She thought for a moment before answering. ''Let's just say Jake owes me something, and I couldn't collect if he were dead.''

He gave a knowing nod. ''I figured it was something like that. A woman like you couldn't be interested in a man like him, not romantically anyway.'' He leaned toward her again, his eyes boring through hers. ''Me and you, we're a lot alike, Araby Stone-Leigh. A lot alike. We'd be good together. Damn good! You just think about that.'' He blew her a kiss. ''You let me know when you want a real man to take care of you. You won't be sorry."

Araby watched in disgust as he rode away through the rain. He was right. She wasn't the one who was going to be sorry!

Araby dear, your days are numbered . . . your days are numbered . . . days are numbered.

That remark Jud made, seemingly just in passing, nagged at her for the rest of the day. At first, she didn't think much about it, but the longer it echoed inside her head, the more certain she became that there was a hidden message there. Jud did not mean her days at Tamarack or in Idaho were numbered. He meant her days were numbered, period! Not that that surprised her. Jud no doubt suspected he was fighting a losing battle to gain possession of Tamarack. He stood a much better chance of getting it if she were dead. He had killed Mike and Moe Gilley and only God knew who else, so there was nothing to keep him from adding one more victim to his list. One thing was certain. She had to get him before he got her!

At that moment, however, safe in the haven of Jake's arms, her body still trembling from the thrill of his lovemaking, she had never felt more secure. Still, she could take no chances.

"What's this?" asked Jake when she reached into her journal and brought out a piece of paper for him to read.

"It's my will."

"Your will? You're not planning on dying on me, are you?"

She shook her head. "Certainly not! I'm not letting you get out of your proposal that easily."

She could see the anger start to pulse in Jake's

temple.

"You told me Jud stopped by today," he said, sitting straight up in bed. "But you didn't tell me everything. Did he threaten you? Because if he did, I'll go break his good-for-nothing neck this minute. Araby?"

"No, he did not threaten me." Jake was reacting just as she thought he would. That was why she had already decided not to tell him about her days being numbered. All they needed now was for Jake to go after Jud in a fit of rage. Even if he didn't lay a finger on him, Sheriff Otter would lock him up in jail and throw away the key.

She managed a smile and, in a voice that was intended to soothe and calm, assured him she was just taking certain necessary precautions in case Jud did have that idea.

"Mind you, I don't think he did," she lied. "Not the way he was carrying on about me showing him the sights when he visited New York, but you can never be too sure."

"Especially where Jud Cord's concerned." Jake held her face up to his. "Don't you worry. To get to you, he'll have to get to me first, and I swear to you, darling, it'll be a freezing day in hell before that ever happens."

Araby snuggled close. As long as she was in his arms, she had no fears about anyone harming her, Jud included. But in the event something did happen, she felt better just knowing that even in death, she'd have the last word over Jud!

"Aren't you interested in what my will says?" she asked while Jake wound strands of her bright hair around his fingers.

"All I'm interested in right now is you!"

"Will you at least read it so I can explain?"

Jake laughed. "Read? Are you crazy, woman? There are times for reading, and believe me, this ain't one of them."

"Please, Jake."

"Oh, all right. If it's that all-fired important to you." He held the will up to the candle and read it aloud. "I, Araby Stone-Leigh, hereby being of sound will and mind leave all the properties known as Tamarack to Jake Montana of Cross Fork Ranch in the hope that he will run it just as my uncle, Mike Stone, intended."

"It's all legal. See. Hamstring and Mattie were my witnesses." She pointed out their signatures.

Before Jake could ask any questions, she explained. "You see, if something were to happen to me, then unless I had made other arrangements, the ranch was to go to my next of kin, my mother and father. Now, I love them dearly, but they have no intention of ever coming to Idaho—except to see their daughter married," she added quickly, hoping he had not guessed that not even that could bring them out. "My father would probably sell the ranch or have somebody run it for him. In either instance, you can bet your bottom dollar that Jud would find some way to finagle his way in. This is just to insure that he doesn't."

"But Araby . . ."

"Please, Jake, this is very important to me."

He nodded. "Don't you worry. If something were to happen to you, which it will not, Jud won't lay one claim on this land. Tamarack belongs to you and to Mike."

Araby took hold of his hand and kissed each finger. "And to you, my darling. After all, a husband does have certain rights over his wife.''

"Why do I have the feeling you're the kind of woman who insists on being on equal terms with her husband?'' he teased her.

"Does that bother you?''

"Heck no! Having a wife who kowtows to your every whim would make for a pretty dull marriage!''

Araby ran her hand down his leg and back up again. They had only just made love. Yet, she could tell an all-too-familiar desire was stirring in him once again. It was stirring in her as well!

A moment ago she had shivered at the thought of being Jud's next victim. She shivered again, but this time passion, not worry, was making her tremble.

Lovingly she caressed the source of her great passion. "You tell me whatever whim you want indulged, cowboy, and I'll be happy to oblige.''

"What you're doing right now is fine. Just fine, darling.''

The way he attacked her mouth with such savage hunger made her cry out in sweet ecstasy.

Araby rolled over, taking him with her. When he stretched out over her in all his naked glory, her urgency flamed higher and higher. The whisper of his breath in her ear all but melted her. One touch and she was sent hurling high into the heavens. Nothing else mattered, nothing—not when his love had her so gloriously entraptured.

Beginning at her head and easing their way down her curves, his hands knew what they were looking for and knew just where to find it. Where his hands journeyed, his lips were not far behind in his quest to pay homage to all those secret little love places. He kissed and caressed all along the way. Not one inch of her soft flesh was deprived of his promises of the even greater sensations yet to come.

Araby no longer belonged to herself alone. That was fine. She was his to do with as he wished, and she wouldn't have it any other way. He was her man. She was his woman.

Her hips rose suggestively, inviting him to plunge himself deep, within her. Hours seemed to pass before her invitation was answered.

Once inside the warmth of her velvety mound, he was in no hurry to stoke the flame raging inside her. Slow, deliberate thrusts left her begging for more. In his own time, he took her to the highest of peaks, then left her stranded, all but teetering on the towering precipices until finally he, too, was wavering on the ledge, and the only way to rescue them both was to drive himself home!

Araby held tight to her lover, imprisoning him in a web of love from which there was no escape. One shock after another tremored inside her, each more powerful than the last. Just when she thought she would surely faint from the tremendous impact, another tremor would surge through her, turning one moan after another into satisfied whimpers.

Araby was certain she must have passed out from such delicious torture, for when she came to, Jake was still atop her.

"You are one wicked devil, Montana."

"Wicked? I think amazing would be a far better description."

Her arms dangled lazily around his neck. "Such modesty!"

"I do aim to please." His lips sprinkled kisses

down the valley between her breasts. "Tired? A little exhausted?"

She laughed. "If I said yes, you'd not stop gloating."

His kisses grew more daring. "If you said no, then I'd take that to mean you didn't want to stop until you were worn out."

"Please. Spare me."

"Spare you? And deprive your luscious body of all those amazingly wicked pleasures I have to offer?"

"I may never move again." She gave a big yawn.

Jake slid his tongue down one breast and up the other. Rosy nipples peaked at his touch.

"Ah, your lips say one thing," he reminded her, "but your body says something else."

Araby could not keep a straight face. Exhausted or not, she was already looking forward to their next scintillating encounter, which just might come sooner than she had thought, considering that Jake's breathing was becoming more rapid by the minute.

Strength began inching back into her blood. The animal inside her was about to spring to life once more. Wicked! That was exactly how she felt.

Her hands slid down his chest and over his hard belly in a slow, gentle massage, then drifted still lower where her fingers tangled themselves in the forest of black curls.

"Don't start something you can't finish," Jake playfully warned her. "If you do, you'll be sorry."

Araby rolled onto him and pinned his shoulders down against the pillow. "I wouldn't dream of doing anything of the sort, cowboy. I ain't that kind of gal!''

"Then why don't you show me just what kind of a gal you are?''

Sitting astride him, she opened her arms and motioned him inside. "Just as long as you know what you're getting into.''

There was a knock at the door a little later.

"Miss Araby . . . You awake?''

Araby tried to make herself sound drowsy. Actually, she'd never felt more awake. "Something wrong, Mattie?''

"Send Mr. Montana down here quick.'' She sounded frantic. "Slim Watkins is at the door. He's got two Injuns with him.''

"Running Wolf and the Flathead medicine man.''

Araby wasn't sure which of them had said that.

Jake had his pants on and was at the door before Mattie could finish her next sentence. She slipped on her robe.

"You stay here,'' Jake told her.

Before she could protest he was down the hall and down the stairs.

He came back up a few minutes later with a peculiar look on his face.

"What's wrong?'' she kept asking, but her question went unanswered. "It was Running Bear and the Flathead messenger, wasn't it?''

After the longest while he nodded. Jake sat down on the edge of the bed. "I don't know how to tell you this.''

Araby sat down beside him and prepared herself for the worst. She already knew the news. The Flathead knew where Mike's body was. She and Jake would go up to Freezeout Mountain and bring him back home.

"It's Mike. We're going after him come daylight."

Even in the dark, Araby could see the tears start to fall from his eyes. They were streaming down her cheeks as well.

"I know, Jake." She swallowed hard and held tight to his arm. "We've got to bring him back. He won't be at peace until he's laid to rest in Tamarack soil."

"No, you don't understand." Jake knelt down in front of her and took her face in his hands. "Araby, Mike's alive. He's not dead. He's alive. And we're going after him."

It took a moment for Jake's announcement to sink in. Mike, alive? That wasn't possible. Was it?

She didn't know whether to laugh or cry.

Holding tight to each other, gently rocking back and forth in their embrace, they did a little of both.

Day's first light found them well on their way across the ridge. The day was going to be a scorcher. The sun had not yet started its climb across the east, and already the air was blistering hot against their faces in spite of the wide brimmed felt hats they were both wearing. Araby's hair hung in damp ringlets down her back. Her pale blue skirt was already wet, and the matching puffed-sleeved blouse clung to her steaming flesh. The hem of her skirt was up around her knees, and she was just getting ready to unbutton her blouse and tie it around the saddle horn and ride on in her camisole when

Jake warned her against it. In another hour, he told her, the sun would be out with a vengeance, and her bare flesh would roast under its rays.

Araby pointed ahead to the summit in the distance. "It doesn't look any closer now than it did when we started out."

"Just be patient, darling. We'll get there," Jake told her, his tone calm and soothing. "You getting all upset ain't going to get us to Freezeout Mountain any faster. Remember what I said about getting there being an all-day affair?"

She nodded.

"That's just what it is. An all-day affair," he reminded her again.

Araby nodded once more. It might be an all-day affair, but knowing so didn't make her feel any better. They had to get to Mike, and fast, too! He was waiting for them! He had been waiting for quite some time, too. He was alive, thank God. Uncle Mike was alive and well!

She had to keep reminding herself that impatience would not get them to Freezeout Mountain any faster. When she forgot, Jake was right there to tell her again what she already knew.

More than once she had to ignore the urge to whip Buddy into a mad gallop. Like Buck's, his walk was slow and ambling over the barren terrain where only rocks and a few scrub brushes made up the scenery. If only Jake would let them gallop—just for a little way, only for a minute or two! That way they could eat up a little of the ground and make the distance to the Flathead village seem less. But no, he didn't want to wear out the horses. She supposed he was right. If the climb up Freezeout were half as bad as he said it was, then the horses, as well as their riders, would have to conserve their strength for the worst part of their journey.

To get her mind off the long, hard miles they had yet to cover, Jake told her of the Salish Indians and why their neighbors gave them the name Flathead. Unlike the other tribes, the Salish Indians did not deform their heads so that their crowns would be pointed. Instead, they let the soft skulls of their newborn babies develop naturally and without any molding or shaping by their mothers.

Jake kept right on talking about the Flatheads, and Araby kept nodding every now and then, pretending to be hanging on to his every word. Any other time, she would have found the story of the Flatheads fascinating and would be asking question after question so that she could make detailed entries in her journal afterwards. But right now, the only story she was interested in was the one that involved her uncle.

It was a miracle that Uncle Mike was alive. According to the note Mike had scribbled out on a handkerchief and entrusted to the medicine man for delivery only to Jake Montana at the Cross Fork Ranch, the Flatheads had saved his life. Just as she and Jake had suspected all along, the destination of Mike's hunting trip with Jud and Sim had not been changed at the last minute. The only reason Jud had told everyone they had gone to Butte's Peak instead was that he knew that if anyone got curious and went to the peak to investigate, all they would find would be a mound of rocks marked by a crude cross. And as they had also suspected, Jud had shot Mike in the back and left him to die. One of the braves from the Flathead tribe had found him unconscious and carried him back to his village, where ancient rites and medicinal herbs had pulled him back from the edge of death.

It was truly a miracle considering what Mike had been through.

Araby heard her name and turned to Jake. "I'm sorry. What did you say?"

"Your worrying isn't going to get us there any faster."

"Maybe not," she sighed, "but it helps pass the time."

He pointed upward. The sun was straight overhead. "We better stop and give the horses a little rest. Some of those ham biscuits Mattie packed for us would taste mighty good along about now."

Araby knew that not even her feminine wiles would convince him to carry on a little farther, so she gave up without argument.

They tied their horses and the horse Jake was leading for Mike to ride back on in the shade under a tree where they could graze, then walked down to the creek, where they both ducked their heads into the water.

Araby splashed the cool water down the front of her blouse. "That's better! Much, much better. What time is it, anyway?"

This time Jake did not snap open his pocket watch. Instead, he looked up at the sky. "Oh, I reckon it must be fifteen, twenty minutes since the last time you asked." He gave her shoulders a rough squeeze. "Hey, don't look so sad. It won't be much longer before you see Mike."

"How long?"

"Five, six hours."

Araby sighed another exasperated sigh. "Just where is Freezeout Mountain anyway? Canada?"

"Pretty near." Jake dipped his bandanna into the water and rubbed it over her neck, his fingers gently caressing the smooth flesh. "Better?"

"Mmm." Slowly, she began to relax. The tension seemed to drip away with the water. Considering she didn't think she'd ever see Mike again, maybe five or six hours really wasn't that long a wait after all.

After their lunch of ham biscuits and cool mountain water from the stream, they stretched out on the grass, Jake's arm pillowing her head. His eyes had hardly closed before he was snoring.

Araby stared up at the clouds, piecing together faces and pictures of trees and flowers from their arrangements as she had done as a little girl. The minutes ticked by with excruciating slowness. She knew better than to wake Jake up and ask him the time again. Whoever said patience was a virtue had certainly never been in the situation she was in now!

A clicking sound coming from a clump of tall grass nearby caught her attention. She eased slowly from Jake's hold, careful not to make any sudden moves and praying he would do the same. She'd never seen a rattlesnake before, but that clicking sound was just as Mike had described it.

The hem of her skirt was already up to her knees. Ever so quietly, she ran her hand down her leg and slipped the pistol from its halter. Scarcely daring to breathe, she watched as the snake slithered closer. Another few feet and he'd be within striking distance of Jake's shoulder. Taking careful aim, she pulled the trigger.

"What the hell!" Jake was on his feet in an instant.

She pointed to the motionless coil near the spot where his head had been lying.

"Damn!" He looked from Araby to her pistol to the snake, all the while shaking his head. "Damn!"

Araby laughed and slipped the pistol back into its holster. "What's the matter? You knew I could shoot. Remember that day by the river when we were arguing about me going up to Butte's Peak with Jud?"

He nodded and looked at the snake again. "Sure. I remember, but shooting at a knot on a log is one thing. Hitting a snake about to strike is something else." He grabbed hold of her and smothered her with kisses. "Where did I ever get the idea you were some poor helpless female in need of a cowboy's protection?"

Araby made a face. "Certainly not from me. I can take care of myself just fine!"

"So I see. Looks like you don't even need me!"

She ran her hands down his back and gave his firm buttocks a rough squeeze. "Who says?"

Even though Jake sounded offended, she could tell from the expression on his face that he was proud of her, and more important, he was proud of her marksmanship as well. A lot of men she had known would have been insulted that she had overstepped the boundary between masculinity and femininity, even if it did mean that in doing so she had saved the man's life. But not Jake. He was not threatened by her at all. He really had been cut from a different mold, just as Mike had said.

With a lusty moan that assured her he liked the mischief his teasing fingers had gotten into, Jake wrapped her tightly in his embrace.

"You know, the Indians believe that if you save someone's life, your destinies are bound together in this life and on into the next."

"Sounds good to me." She snuggled closer. Jake was her present and her future. She could think of nothing more wonderful than for the two of them to be bound together forever.

At first their kiss was sweet with promises of the wonderful life they'd have together, but the longer their lips stayed locked together, the more impassioned their kiss became.

Araby dropped her arms back down to her sides at the same time that Jake stepped back. She knew the same sheepish grin that was on his face was on hers as well. She knew, too, that he was also thinking that there were far more important matters at hand than satisfying their never-ending need for each other. After all, they had an eternity to spend together. What difference would another twelve or fourteen hours make?

"Think the horses have rested enough?" asked Araby, still grinning.

"Whatever you say, m'am." Jake's grin stayed put as well. "You're the boss."

18

Araby stared at her uncle in disbelief. She could not believe the man sitting cross-legged on the ground beside her was actually Mike Stone—her Uncle Mike. His clothes were worn and baggy and tattered with holes. Gone was the barrel belly he always used to make jokes about. His hair was a lot grayer than she remembered, and his skin much paler, but Uncle Mike was there in the flesh. He was no dream. He was real, and he was alive, and he was going home!

Their reunion had been a joyous one. Leading the horses up Freezeout had taken everything out of her, just as Jake had warned it would. The steep climb to the top had been a grueling experience, one that she would not want to attempt again any time soon. But when she saw her uncle standing by the lake, leaning on a cane for support, her tired limbs were instantly revived, and she ran to him as fast as her legs could carry her.

Night had fallen quickly after their arrival, and now the sky of black velvet was alive with glittering jewels. The Salish were small in number—only twenty of their once great tribe still remained. Those were the ones who had escaped the reservation where most of their people had died from white man's diseases. Still, they welcomed their white visitors with the same open arms as they had Uncle Mike. What few children there were sang songs and played games around them. Chief Brave Eagle was a gracious host, eager to tend to his guests' every need. The horses had been curried and rubbed down with strong-smelling linaments to relax their tired legs. Baskets and trays of fresh-roasted venison and breads and cooked roots were set down in front of Araby, Jake, and Mike, and, with a signal from Chief Brave Eagle, his curious tribe members scattered, leaving him alone with his guests.

Araby held tight to Mike's arm and listened as he recounted that near-fatal hunting trip. She couldn't resist giving his tired old shoulders another hug, even though he was starting to complain of bruises from her exuberant affection.

"What a fool I was for thinking Jud was trying to mend his ways," Mike said, shaking his head. "I ought to have known all along what that rascal was up to. He knew he was going to put a bullet in my back. That's why he made out like we were going up to Butte's Peak. I didn't know he had been telling people that until I got up to leave that morning and Hamstring said something about my changing my mind. I should have known that bastard was up to no good. I should have known."

Chewing slowly, Mike stared into the fire and

continued, "Sim didn't want any part of it. I kept hearing him tell Jud to just forget everything, but I figured he was talking about the hunting trip. Anyway, we made camp not too far from here, and I was fixing to spread out my bed-roll when I saw Jud had his gun drawn. It dawned on me right then that ole Mike Stone was the only animal he intended to hunt. Sim still tried to talk him out of it, but Jud told him to shut up or he'd shoot him, too. Jud kept smiling and twirling the end of that moustache of his and telling me how much he had always despised me. Why, he didn't say. Lord knows I tried to help those boys all I could. That's the thanks I got."

He tore off some more meat from the joint. "Anyway, to make a long story short, I told him if he had some grudge to settle with me, he should at least be man enough to let me strap my guns back on so I could draw against him. He shot me before the words were out of my mouth. I fell back, and tried to grab my gun, and damned if he didn't shoot me in the back. He told Sim to check and make sure I was dead. I guess he was too much of a coward to get any closer to me himself. Anyway, Sim told him I wasn't breathing. I don't know if he was too drunk to see if I was or not, or if he thought he was doing me a favor by telling Jud I was deader than a door nail. I like to think Sim was trying to help me out.

"Right after that, he told Jud he wanted to get out of there fast. Jud joshed him about being afraid of ghosts, but he didn't stay around there any longer than he had to, either. So they left me for dead, lying in my blood. I heard Jud say something about not taking the time to bury me because by the next day, after the buzzards were through picking my bones, there'd be nothing left for anybody to recognize anyway."

Mike paused from his story long enough to take a couple of deep breaths. "Don't know how long I lay there. I knew that bullet in my hip wouldn't kill me, but the one in my belly I wasn't sure about. I'd figure I'd just lay there bleeding until there was no more blood to come out and then I'd die. But I was going to hang on just as long as I could. The one thing that kept me going was knowing that when I got my hands on Jud Cord, whether it was in this life or the next, I'd see that he'd do a lot more suffering than I was doing right then."

Mike pointed to a young brave standing with his squaw and three small children in front of the teepee across from where they were sitting.

"That's Quick Coyote. He's the chief's grandson. Lucky for me he was out hunting for deer that next morning. You can imagine how surprised these folks were when their best hunter came back with old Mike Stone thrown across his shoulders instead of a big buck deer."

Araby laughed along with her uncle. It was beyond her comprehension how he could still make jokes and laugh after the horrible ordeal he had been through. Then again, that was her uncle!

"The medicine man, the one I sent the note with to you, Jake, doctored me up with his herbs and foul-smelling roots that drew the hurt right out of my wounds. The bullets are still in there, but like that medicine man told me, the evil spirits that were in them are long gone."

Jake gave Mike a playful slap on the back.

"Those old fellows down at Fisher's will be hard pressed to top this story."

Mike laughed, but Araby could tell there was no humor in his laughter.

"I'd like to hear the story Jud Cord tries to concoct for the Sheriff. Hell, Horace Otter would probably believe him if he said I made the whole thing up."

"Oh, no he won't," Jake and Araby assured him at the same time.

Mike listened intently as Jake told him of how Jud had tried to frame him for Moe Gilley's murder.

"You can have at him when I get through with him," Mike said when Jake had finished. "Don't know how much of him will be left, but you're welcome to it."

Araby was starting to get concerned. If Mike did go after Jud, then nothing would keep the elder Cord from trying to kill him again, and this time he might be successful.

"I can't wait to see the look on that bastard's face when he sees me. He'll think I've rose from the dead for sure!"

"If you're not careful," Araby warned, "dead is just where you might still end up if you mess with Jud Cord."

Mike grabbed hold of his niece and pulled her closer. "Now don't you go worrying about that, Araby. I lived through two of his bullets. I don't intend to take a third. I already got me a plan formulating."

Jake laughed. "I'll just bet you have. You better count me in. I got one or two scores to settle with that bastard myself."

"Well, I'm not about to be left out," Araby

told them. It was pointless arguing with her uncle. He was just as pigheaded as her fiancé. "I've got some business to settle with him myself."

Mike got angrier and angrier with each passing minute as she told him how hard Jud had been trying to get Tamarack.

"So that's why he wanted me dead. I figured as much." Mike rammed his fist into the ground. "If he owned Tamarack and the river crossing he'd control the whole valley. Why, he could even revoke the agreement I made with the Coeur d'Alene and sell that forest to the lumber company from California that's been hounding me for so long. He's got one hell of a surprise in store for him. If the Sheriff don't lock him up, Jud will be begging to be put behind bars by the time I'm done with him!"

Araby and Jake exchanged troubled glances as Mike went on ranting and raving.

Finally, Jake stopped him in mid-sentence. "No use getting yourself all worked up, old buddy. Me and you, we'll take care of him. By the time Otter hears your story, he might just have second thoughts about Jud. If he doesn't, he sure as hell will when I get him proof that he killed Moe Gilley, or had him killed."

"How you gonna do that?" asked Mike, one graying brow cocked.

"I got my ways," Jake said. "Just don't you worry about that."

Araby rolled back her eyes. "Wonderful. Now I have two of you to worry about."

Mike poked his niece in the side. "So what do you think of my pal, here, sweetie? Pretty special, ain't he?"

Araby shrugged her shoulders. She could tell Mike was dying for her to make some big announcement. "He's all right, I guess," she said with no enthusiasm. "That is, if you like pig-headed, stubborn, arrogant cowboys who think they know everything."

For a moment, Mike was taken aback. He looked at Jake as if he was silently apologizing to his friend for having asked the question in the first place. Jake hung his head trying to hold back his laughter.

Araby threw her arms around her uncle, then shook an accusing finger in his face. "You sly devil," she said. "Don't you think I don't know what you were up to when you wrote that will of yours! You knew that if you died before you got me and Jake together, I'd come live at Tamarack out of guilt. That's right. You played on my guilt for not having visited you before. You knew I'd come, didn't you? Don't give me that innocent look!"

Mike chuckled and looked from one to the other. "Well, did it work?"

Araby looked at him and grinned.

"Don't keep me in suspense, gal!" he exclaimed. "Tell me. Did it work or not?"

Jake took Araby's hand. "Do you want to tell him or you want me to?"

"Tell me what?"

"You tell him," grinned Jake.

"Jake's asked me to marry him, Uncle Mike."

Mike let out a bellowing "yippeee!" "You said yes, didn't you?" he asked as an afterthought.

"What do you think?" Araby gave Jake a hug. "You don't have a fool for a niece, I can assure you of that!''

Mike threw his faded felt hat high into the air. ''I knew it! I knew it! All I had to do was get you two together, and there'd be more sparks flying than on the Fourth of July. Once you laid eyes on Jake and he caught a good look at you, there'd be no place for you to go but to the altar! Hot damn! We're gonna have us a wedding!''

''Whoa there, partner!'' Jake retrieved his hat and put it back on Mike's head. ''Just hold your horses. First things first. And the first thing we got to do is get you back down this mountain.''

''Hell, son, that ain't no problem.''

Araby and Jake exchanged questioning glances.

''I know what you two are thinking, and no, there is nothing wrong with my head. I see you brought up a horse for me. That's fine and dandy. You just help me in the saddle, and I'll stay there till we get home. I'd have gone home already, but that fool gelding I was riding took off when I was lying on the ground, and I didn't want to leave the chief short of a pony. They ain't got much as it is.'' His eyes lit up. ''As a matter of fact, when I get back home I have a good notion to load up a couple of pack mules with supplies and bring them up to these folks to help them get through the winter. Yeah, that's just what I'll do.''

''That's wonderful, Mike. I'll help you,'' Araby told her uncle. ''We'll help you,'' she said, including Jake. ''But first, you have to get home and take it easy for a while.''

''Take it easy? You crazy, gal?''

''You better listen to what she says, Mike. Believe me, that's a lesson I had to learn the hard way!'' Jake warned him.

384

Mike took Araby's hand. "You know, honey, I ain't dead yet. Besides, all those evil spirits that went into my body on those two bullets are all gone now. You ask the chief. He'll tell you."

Jake and Araby nodded. Both of them knew there was no point in arguing with Mike Stone. Nobody ever won who'd tried because Mike always got the last word.

"So what do you say, partners? How about us heading out at daylight?"

"You're the boss, Mike," Jake said, throwing up his hands.

Araby hugged her uncle once again. "Do you know something, Mike Stone? You are incorrigible! Absolutely incorrigible!"

"If I weren't, you wouldn't love me nearly as much, would you?" Mike hugged his niece with one arm and gave Jake a slap on the leg with the other. "What'd I tell you? Ain't she just the prettiest thing you ever seen? And smart, too. Takes the looks after her mama. Her mama wasn't too smart, though. She let me get away." Mike laughed. "Just as well. I'd hate getting all doodied up and going to all them fancy parties every night anyway."

Araby was about to tell him how much she liked Ruby and that if he didn't make that woman marry him even under protest when he got back to town, she was personally going to give him a kick in the pants, but someone behind them clapped his hands, and Mike motioned for quiet.

What few members there were left of the Salish Indian tribe gathered around them. Then six of the young braves and their chief passed in front of them. Their faces and bodies were painted a ghostly white.

Mike leaned over and whispered, "Chief Brave Eagle and his warriors are about to perform their ghost dance. This is something for you to put down in that journal of yours," he said to Araby. "Not many white folks have ever been privy to this ceremony. Its dedicated to all the guardian spirits of the Salish."

The chief appeared first, wearing a cape of buffalo hide and the horned head and tail of that great creature that had once roamed the plains in abundance. The four braves in the center were dressed for the hunt in moccasins, thigh-length leggings, and strips of rawhide crossing their pale chests. They carried spears and bows and arrows and walked carefully and with great stealth, as though they were tracking their prey. The medicine man at the rear, the same one who had been sent to find Jake, wielded a lance and had a painted shield hanging from his shoulder. As the hunters walked several steps ahead, the medicine man showered them with ground-up root powder and leaves. From somewhere in the dark distance came the sound of drums, whistles, flutes and rattles.

The sound of the chief's voice mesmerized Araby, even though she could not understand a word he was saying. From the sorrowful intonation of his words, she knew the story he was relating involved much sadness.

Mike quietly explained every gesture and translated the great chief's monologue. Brave Eagle spoke longingly of the days when the buffalo roamed the plains in great number, the days when his tribe had flourished as a nation much respected. Long ago, even before the Indians had ponies, they hunted those great, hairy beasts with only bows and arrows for protection. The one brave who had proven himself to have the most courage in battle would be given the honor of wearing the robes of the buffalo. It was his task to go among the buffalo herd dressed up like one of them and cause a stampede. In their crazed frenzy, the buffaloes would not be aware that they were all heading toward a cliff and would plummet to their deaths.

Araby shivered. Now she knew where Jud had gotten his idea to capture the black stallion.

"Then came the white man," Mike continued in a whisper. "His greed and hatred caused the herds of buffalo to dwindle until they had all disappeared. It wasn't long before the valiant Indians followed the same course as the buffalo."

The chief motioned for all to bow their heads.

"Now he's praying to the spirits to destroy the white man so that the buffalo will return." Mike chuckled. "He's adding a little something for our benefit. He just told the spirits to spare the three of us."

The ghost dance ended as solemnly as it had begun. The chief and his warriors walked quietly off into the woods. Araby was left with a heavy feeling that, like the buffalo, the entire Indian nation would one day be extinct. They, like the great bison they once hunted, were a vanishing breed.

The next morning, after bidding good-bye to their Salish friends and promising to return before winter with blankets and food, Mike, Jake, and Araby began their long trip back home.

Just as it had done the day before, the early morning sun showed no mercy. There were no trees for shelter, just rock after rock. Leading their horses back down was far trickier than it had been going up. Mike refused to stay in the saddle and insisted on lightening the load on his horse's back as well.

Araby cringed the entire way down. One slip, and the results could be fatal.

It seemed forever before they reached the base of the bald summit. When they did, all three breathed sighs of relief.

Once back in the saddle, they rode abreast, laughing and talking over old times and planning their strategy for revenge on Jud Cord.

What a surprise everyone at Tamarack and Cross Fork was in for! No one knew Mike was alive. Jake had wanted to tell Slim, and Araby had wanted to get word to Ruby, but the risks of doing so were just too great. It was far better to sneak Mike back onto the ranch and, when the right time came, announce his return. But that would be only after Jud had paid for what he had done.

"I can't wait to hear the cock-and-bull story Jud tells Otter when he tries to get off the hook," Mike said as they rode along. "Hell-fire, I'm not even going to mess with Horace Otter. Jake, the minute you get back, you send word for the Marshal to come to Tamarack. That's one fellow Jud won't be able to sweet-talk."

Jake nodded. "Good idea. But I can't for the life of me see how Jud can weasel out of this one. He shot you. As far as he knows, you're dead. He's a murderer. He ought to be hanged like one."

"He will be," said Mike confidently. "Marshal Will Riley will see to that, I promise you. That Jud Cord is meaner than any rattler ever dared to be. He might not hang for doing what he did to me, but by God, if we can connect him with Moe Gilley's death, he'll be swinging from that hanging tree come August.''

''I hope you're right, Uncle Mike.'' Araby couldn't help but be skeptical. Jud was sly. If there were a way he could get out of it, he would. No one should underestimate that snake in the grass or think they could put something over on him.

''I know I'm right, missy. Your old uncle ain't let you down yet, and he ain't about to now. Right now, the only stop I want to make is when I get home. Anybody want to place a small wager on who'll get to the gate first?''

Without waiting for an answer, Mike took off at a gallop, giving a loud ''Yippeeee!''

''Hey, no fair!'' Araby took off after him. ''You got a head start.''

''I'm crippled,'' he yelled back over his shoulder. ''I deserve a little advantage.''

Araby galloped faster. ''You want an advantage, I'll give it to you,'' she said when she had caught up. ''To win I'll have to beat you by a half mile. How's that?''

Jake galloped up alongside them. ''Don't encourage him, Araby,'' he said, laughing. ''He's a sick man.''

''Not too sick to give you a good licking any time of day,'' Mike shouted back. ''Come on, now. Time's a-wasting.''

Before either of them could warn him to be careful, Mike had shot out in front of them and disappeared in his own dust.

''Seems to me those Indians left a couple of those evil spirits in him,'' said Jake, taking off after him.

Araby rode hard to catch up. She had Jake, and now she had her uncle back! Life was wonderful after all!

By the time they reached Tamarack, it was well after dark. The cowboys had already bedded down in the bunk house, and not even the wail of the harmonica disturbed the quiet darkness.

While Jake unsaddled the horses and turned them out in the field to graze, Araby sneaked Mike into the house and up the stairs to his room. The lights in the front room had been blown out, and Mattie was asleep.

Mike walked into his house looking as though he had never seen it before. He had to touch everything to make sure he was really home. Araby could see the tears misting his eyes, but she said nothing. An occasional hug or squeeze of his arm was all that was needed for him to know she was there and she loved him.

In his room, he fell across the bed making such a noise that she was certain it would collapse from all the commotion.

"Hot damn! But it's good to be home!" he exclaimed again and again. "You just don't know how much I dreamed about this moment. Lying there on the mountain, all but drowning in my own blood, I didn't think I'd . . . Ah, hell, there's no reason to bring back bad memories! I'm here, and that's all that matters."

Araby hugged him again. "You're here, Mike. You really are here."

"So are you, little girl. Though I don't guess you're a little girl any more, are you?" He plopped back down onto the bed and started pulling off his boots. "You love him, don't you, sugar?"

Araby motioned for him to lower his voice. "If you don't watch it, the whole valley's going to know you're home."

"All right, all right," he grumbled. "Answer my question."

"Yes, I do love him." She sat down beside him. "You were right. The moment I met him, I didn't ever want to let him out of my sight again."

"Jake's a fine man, honey. A mighty fine man. You won't find the likes of him in New York, that's for sure."

"You're not telling me anything I don't already know, Uncle Mike."

"Why, we'll have the finest wedding this territory's ever seen!" Folks from miles and miles around—what's wrong?"

"Nothing. Except Idaho isn't a territory any more. It's a state."

She could tell from his expression that the news did not particularly please him.

"Ah, hell, it had to happen sooner or later," he said cheerfully. "I'm just lucky I lived long enough to see it. Now about that wedding. I think we—"

Araby pushed him back onto the bed. "I think you had better get some rest."

"But—"

"No buts about it. You just lie down and close your eyes. That's an order."

"Says who?"

"Says me," she replied firmly.

"Don't you want to hear about my plan for getting Jud?"

"Tomorrow. Good night, Uncle Mike."

"Hey, Araby . . . I'm glad you're here."

Her stern expression broke into a smile. "I'm

glad you're here, too. Now get some sleep!"

Araby blew her uncle a kiss, then closed the door quietly.

She found Jake downstairs pouring himself a cup of coffee and slipped up behind him. Teasing fingers popped a few buttons, then ventured on inside his shirt. She could feel his flesh come alive at her touch.

"Want to have a real good time, cowboy?"

Jake all but choked on his coffee. "You want to get me killed? Mike Stone catches us fooling around, and you'll be a widow before you're a bride."

Determined hands caressed the warm skin above his belly. "But Mike likes you. You're the son he never had. He wouldn't hurt you."

Jake took her hands and put them down by her side. "Hurt me? He'd kill me if he thought I had taken advantage of you."

"Taken advantage of me? Ha! I don't remember you twisting my arm."

He gave her a quick kiss, then held her at arm's length. "It was the other way around, but he wouldn't believe that either."

"Then I'll tell him. He'll believe me."

"Don't you dare." He caught her by the waist and wouldn't let her go.

"Then kiss me."

"Araby . . ."

"If you don't, I'll scream as loud as I can."

"Araby . . ."

She opened her mouth, but Jake's kiss closed it just as she had intended.

"Not bad." She started to unbuckle his belt. "Show me what else you can do, cowboy."

"Oh, no, you don't." Jake held tight to her wrists.

"Chicken."

"You bet I am, and I don't intend to get my neck wrung!"

"Oh, all right, then." She walked away without futher protest. "Good night."

Once inside her room, she undressed quickly and crawled under the covers.

A little while later, the door opened and closed quietly, just as she knew it would, given a little time. Jake tiptoed across the room, and she slipped further under the covers pretending to be sound asleep. Her bare flesh tingled with anticipation as she watched him undress in the dark. If they were together for the next hundred years, she knew the sight of him getting out of his clothes would never cease to excite her.

Jake slipped in beside her and softly called her name while his hands roamed freely over her naked flesh, making each spot his wicked fingers caressed sizzle with desire.

"Go 'way, Tramp," she muttered sleepily.

Jake called her name again and tried to rouse her with touches and kisses, but she kept slapping him away.

"Go get in your corner, Tramp."

Araby heard him expell an exasperated sigh, and she couldn't resist a giggle.

Jake dove under the covers after her and started tickling her in the ribs. "You rascal! I ought to turn you across my knee and give you a good beating."

"Shhh! You'll wake up Mike," she reminded him. "He'll kill you if he catches you messing with his niece.''

''The way he's sawing logs, he wouldn't hear a stampede if it came right through his room!''

Araby tried to keep her responses cool and uninterested as he kissed and stroked and whispered sweet words of love. When he slipped his hand between her legs and ignited once again the blaze smouldering inside, she could feign indifference no longer.

With a soft moan, she pulled him down on top of her, calling his name over and over as her tongue flirted with his.

Jake entered her quickly, but once the delicious mating had begun, he moved slowly in an eagerness to prolong her ecstasy with deep and unhurried movements.

Greedy for the wonders he performed inside her, Araby pulled him closer and closer. The pounding of his heart was an echo of her own. She never would let him go! Even after all the glorious nights they had shared, she still trembled each time he touched her, each time he thrilled her with bold caresses, each more arousing than the last. She belonged to him, just as he belonged to her, body and soul, forever and ever.

Heartbeats fluttered in unison, then quickened only to stop in mid-beat. Muffled cries of rapture filled the room as the bed, the wardrobe and all the rest of the furnishings crammed into the tiny room spun round and round.

The clock on the mantle had long since struck midnight when Jake finally roused himself from a satisfied slumber and, after a good-night kiss, slipped on his pants and shirt and tiptoed down the stairs carrying his boots.

Araby wanted to stop him, to reach out and

pull him back to her bed, but she could not find the strength. Her limbs had already given way to the heavy weakness seeping into them.

"Rise and shine, missy. You gonna sleep your life away?"

Araby opened the door, dressed and ready to go for her usual morning ride. She pulled her uncle inside the room, then looked up the hall, down the hall, and back up again to make sure he hadn't been seen.

"I thought you wanted your resurrection to be a surprise to Jud," she scolded him. "You keep this up, and everybody's going to know you're back—including Jud."

Mike scanned the room quickly, then gave it another, more thorough, check.

"Are you looking for something?" Araby asked her uncle.

"No, no, just wondering . . ." He limped across the room and picked up a red bandanna from the beside table. "Ah ha!"

"Ah ha, what?"

Mike waved the bandanna in front of her face. "Ah ha, this."

Araby plucked it from his grasp and tied it around her neck. "Thanks. I was wondering what I'd done with this."

"Huh!"

"Uncle Mike, if you have something to say, please say it." She met his questioning stare with a pert smile.

Mike rubbed his stomach. "I sure am hungry. I could eat a dozen flapjacks. Reckon I'll go downstairs and get what's-her-name to whip me up some."

"Her name is Mattie, and if I were you, I'd stay out of sight in case Jud decides to come calling."

"But what about breakfast? I'm starved." He showed her how baggy his trousers were. "I'm fading fast. See."

Araby took him by the arm and led him back into the hall. "Tell you what. You get back in bed and catch up on your rest, and I'll have Mattie bring up a dozen flapjacks."

"You ain't afraid of her knowing I've come back from the dead?"

Araby shook her head. "She can be trusted." She told her uncle how the housekeeper had verified her story about Jake's whereabouts when Moe Gilley was murdered.

Mike nodded his approval. "If we had to lose Missus Slim, this Mattie sounds like she'll fit the bill just fine."

Araby walked him to his room and pointed him toward the bed.

"Ah, heck, honey, I ain't tired."

Araby folded her arms across her waist. "Do you want to keep that good leg or do you want it lamed to match the other one?"

Mike crawled back into bed fully dressed. "What about my welcome-home party?"

"Jake's going for the Marshal right now. You leave it all up to us."

"You gonna do what I suggested?"

Araby nodded. "If we're lucky, Jud will drop dead from a heart attack right on the spot, and the Marshal will be spared the trouble of taking him in."

"Wait—just one more thing. Let me get my—"

"You stay in bed." Araby shook her fist at him. "Do you understand me?"

"A dozen flapjacks. Do you understand me?"

"Yes, sir."

"And plenty of honey to go with them."

"Whatever you want, Uncle Mike."

"Oh, maybe a dozen strips of bacon and a couple of eggs?"

"You got it. Anything else?"

"Maybe some fried potatoes?" He grinned.

Araby heaved an exasperated sigh. "I'll tell Mattie."

"Good, and maybe if—"

"If you don't watch it, I'll tell Mattie to beat you over the head with the frying pan if you don't behave."

"Well, don't that just beat all." Mike shook his head and frowned. "Won't you even keep me company while I eat my breakfast?"

"You need your rest. Oh, all right," she grumbled good-naturedly. "I suppose I could sit and talk for a while. But you have to promise me that as soon as you've eaten, you'll take a nap."

"Promise."

"All right, let me go downstairs and get Mattie started cooking, and I'll be right back up."

"Hurry up."

"Yes, sir, Uncle Mike. Whatever you say, Uncle Mike! Tramp, you stay here," she told her dog. "If he tries to get back out of bed, you bite him."

Laughing to herself, Araby ran down the stairs. Thank God, Uncle Mike was alive and well and back to his usual robust self!

19

It was nearly nine o'clock by the time Araby was atop Buddy and galloping through the pines to the river's edge. She was two hours late for her usual morning ride down by the Saint Joe, but the time had been well spent reminiscing about the days when she was a little girl. Mike took such delight in telling her over and over again how he had taught her to ride. When he put her on her first pony—his Christmas gift when she was two—she had known just what to do, grabbing hold of the mane and holding on. Finally, after several hours of talking over old times, Mike had yawned and admitted he was getting a little sleepy. This time when she left him to get some rest, he made no protest.

Araby turned down the trail and headed for the river. She had time only for a quick ride, for there were many preparations to be made for the evening's festivities. And the guest of honor had yet to be invited. That was one invitation she wanted the pleasure of delivering in person. Knowing Jud, he'd be sure to think she had finally come to her senses and was coming to him on bended knees begging him to throw her down on the floor and make love to her. Ugh! The thought of him touching her was repulsive! What a surprise he was in for! No doubt he really would think the man he murdered had risen from his grave to haunt him!

Araby reigned Buddy in to a quick halt, then jerked around expecting to see someone behind her. Strange! No one was there. She could have sworn she wasn't alone. She hadn't seen anyone, but nevertheless the eeriest feeling had come over her just then. She could sense someone watching even now as she peered closely at every overturned boulder and clump of shrub. Whoever it was had chosen his hiding place well. And there could only be one reason to hide. Anyone whose intentions were friendly would have already made known his presence.

Araby picked up the rein and trotted on. Tamarack and Cross Fork were about the same distance away. She could take off in a gallop toward one of the ranches and hope her horse was faster than the one whoever was following her was on. If she were on Darling, she'd not hesitate in doing just that, but Buddy lacked the chestnut mare's speed and endurance. The only other thing she could do was to take whoever was following her by surprise and become the hunter instead of the hunted.

The little pistol strapped above her boot helped make the decision for her. No one was going to intimidate her and get away with it. Not without a fight, anyway!

Araby jerked her horse around and headed toward home. Acting on a hunch, she veered suddenly off the path and charged through the tamaracks.

Her hunch paid off! A little way in front of her, a white horse stood tethered to a low-hanging branch. A white horse . . . who had a white . . . ? Oh, yes, Burley Wilkerson. She thought she had seen the last of him. Now there could only be one reason that he was still hanging around. Jud obviously had a job for him to do, and she was that job! Burley had probably been the one who killed Moe Gilley for Jud, too. One thing was certain. When Jud told her her days at Tamarack were numbered, he hadn't been referring to the time when her thirty days were up.

Her stomach plunged to her toes, but only for a minute. If she were going to be the one who came out of this alive, she mustn't give in to fear! She couldn't be caught off guard!

"Burley Wilkerson! I know you're in here," she called out cheerfully.

Her voice trembled, but only a little. After all, she was an actress. Unfortunately, this was one performance that might well determine whether she lived or died!

"Now, Burley, I know you're in here somewhere," she called out playfully. "Are you going to make me come looking for you? I've been hoping I'd run into you again. I bet you've been wishing the same thing, haven't you? I know you've been following me, and I know why, too. You want to see what city gals do that country gals don't. Right, Burley?"

Holding tight to the reins, she scanned the pines carefully. If she could only find where he was hiding. As long as he could see her, and she couldn't see him, she was in danger.

"Burley Wilkerson, are you going to stay hidden in the bush all day?"

Araby held her breath and waited. All she could hear was the sound of her heart thumping.

She nudged Buddy a little closer to Burley's horse.

"Now, Burley, honey, what kind of a game are you playing with me? If you're not interested in having a little fun, just say so. You're not going to hurt my feelings!"

Damn! She had expected Burley to show himself before now. What was taking him so long? As long as he remained hidden and she was a wide-open target, her minutes might well be numbered.

Araby took a deep breath. No, if he were going to shoot, he would have done so before now. He was playing a cat-and-mouse game with her. She'd just have to show him who the cat was!

"Oh, Burley. I'm waiting. If you can't come out soon, I'm just going to go back home."

Her smile froze on her face. Hanging from the saddle horn on the white horse was a necklace of eagle feathers similar to the one Fleeing Fawn had given her.

Now, she knew just what Jud had in mind. If he got his way, she'd never leave that stand of pines alive. He was confident that if she were dead, Tamarack would end up in his hands. She remembered what Jud had said about some California logging company being interested in his saw mill and wondered if that were the same company that Mike had turned down time and time again about selling the land he had deeded the Coeur d'Alene. "As long as the Indians lived in peace and harmony with their neighbors" —that was the stipulation the government had placed on Mike's gift of the great forests to Chief Silver Bear and his people. This time it would be the peaceful Coeur d'Alene who were framed for murder—her murder!

Burley walked out from the bushes in front of her. The sharp point of the hunting knife strapped to his waist caught the sun filtering in through the pines and glistened threateningly.

Araby drew a quick breath. She wondered if the plan was for him to scalp her after slicing her throat.

"You don't have no cause to be scared of me, little lady," said Burley with a big smile. "Specially since me and you seem to be thinking along the same lines."

He stood blocking her way. His hands rested on his hips and a wolf-like grin contorted his mouth.

Araby felt her heart sink once more, then quickly regained control. She couldn't back out now. She had to play up to him, and she had to do so convincingly!

"You think I'm breathing this hard because I'm scared? I'm not scared of you, Burley."

Her smile traveled up and down his imposing frame, but she made sure she kept a firm hold on the reins. If he didn't fall for her little act, she'd have to kick him in the gut and take off for home mighty fast!

"Where you been keeping yourself, Burley? Why'd you leave Tamarack? Were you afraid to have a lady for a boss?"

Araby sat up straight in the saddle. Lips

pursed, she unbuttoned the top button of her blouse.

"Oh, I liked having a lady for a boss just fine." Burley held his stance. "Trouble was, I heard that lady didn't much like me."

Araby flashed him another inviting smile as she rubbed her throat. Good! He was playing right into her hands. He might have killing her on his mind, but from the way his hand kept dropping below his belt he would not have any objection to having a little fun first!

"I bet I know who told you that. It was Jud, wasn't it?" Araby met his stare with one that was just as hungry as his. "He was jealous of you," she giggled. "I think he was afraid he'd have to compete with a real man if you stayed on."

Araby reached over and gave Buddy's neck a pat knowing that what lay beneath those few buttons that had popped on her blouse would keep Burley's mind off what he had come there to do.

"Yeah, well, if me and Jud ever tangled, he'd be the one who got whopped!"

"I'm sure he would." Lips full and suggestive, Araby gave him a pout and a smile as seductive as she could manage under the circumstances. "I'll bet nobody tangles with you."

"Nobody with any sense." Burley strutted closer. He made no secret of what his hands were groping for beneath his big silver belt buckle. "You get down from there, and I'll give you something a whole lot nicer to ride."

Araby slipped her right foot out of the stirrup ready to kick.

"Why don't we go back to Tamarack?" she suggested. "Somebody might see us here."

Burley's laugh was lusty and low. "Honey, there ain't nobody around for miles but me and you. Now get down off that horse," he said roughly. "Take off that blouse."

Araby played with the ruffles, stalling for time. "How do you like this blouse? It's the latest in New York fashion. Why, these ruffles—"

"It ain't the ruffles I want to see. Now git it off."

She could tell he was growing tired of her game very quickly.

"Just what do you want to see, Burley honey?"

His hand slipped inside his pants. "Git down, and git out of those clothes. I'll show you what a real man can do."

"No reason to get mad, Burley. I want to have a little fun as much as you do. A girl just likes to be played with a little first. You gonna play with me, Burley?"

His breathing became more labored.

"Git off, damn it! What I got fer you can't wait all day."

Araby slid off the other side. Her pistol was out of the holster and in her hand before her feet touched the ground.

Burley was busy unbuckling his belt when she walked around the horse to where he was standing.

"Why don't you put on a little show for old Burley here?" he suggested as he dropped his pants and stepped out of them.

"You just go over there and sit down," she told him, stepping back a little, "and I'll put on a show for you that you won't ever forget."

Burley grumbled a little, but did as she said.

"You're going to really enjoy this, Burley honey," she told him in her most seductive voice. "That's it. You just sit down right there. I'll put on a show for you like you've never seen before. Ready?"

Burley had both hands between his legs. "Hurry, damn it."

"Whatever you say." Araby raised the pistol and aimed it right at his head.

"What the hell?"

"You better sit back down if you know what's good for you." Araby looked him straight in the eye. "Because if you don't, hell is exactly where you're going to end up!"

Laughing a nervous laugh, Burley raised his hands over his head. "Hey, there ain't no need to get upset, honey. I was just funning you, that's all. Hell fire, I thought you wanted a little loving. Can't shoot a fellow for trying to oblige, now can you?"

"Are you willing to stake your life on that?"

Burley sat back down.

"You just tell me what to do, little lady." His laugh was husky, but she could tell that he was a little nervous.

"I'd like for you and me to have us a little talk."

"Sure honey, whatever you say," he told her, watching the pistol. "Talk ain't exactly what I had in mind, though."

Araby kept the pistol leveled at his head. "Jud sent you out here to kill me, didn't he?" She cocked the trigger. "Didn't he?"

Panic flooded Burley's face. "You just put that gun away, and I'll tell you what you want to know."

Araby kept the pistol aimed at his head. "Talk."

"All right, all right. Sure, Jud sent me out here, but not to kill you. He just wanted me to rough you up enough to scare you so you'd leave."

"Is that what you did to poor Moe Gilley, just rough him up a little bit?"

From the stunned look on Burley's face, Araby knew her hunch had been right.

"I ain't no killer."

His declaration was far from convincing.

"I guess you'll just have to let the Marshal decide that." Araby waved the gun at him. "Why don't you stand up, turn your back to me, and start walking."

Burley was quick to oblige. Much too quick for her liking! When he started to walk away from her, his steps were short and slow. She was ready for him when he whirled back around and threw himself at her.

Araby pulled the trigger without a moment's hesitation.

Burley's screaming curses echoed through the pines. Grabbing his stomach, he stumbled and fell to the ground. His evil smile faded fast.

She let him lie where he fell. There was a lot of blood spurting out, but she knew she had only clipped him. She could just as easily have pumped the bullet into his heart, but with him dead, Jud would never visit that hanging tree. Maybe the threat of his accompanying his good friend there would be all the encouragement Burley needed to tell all.

Araby walked over to her horse, all the while keeping the pistol on Burley.

"You ain't leaving me, are you? You just gonna leave me to die?" he groaned loudly.

"You're not going to die, Burley. At least, not yet. Not until the Marshal decides what he's going to do with you."

She mounted her horse, then started to throw down her canteen of water, but changed her mind. Given half the chance, he would have killed her without so much as a blink. Why should she care whether he was thirsty or not?

Araby pointed up at the buzzards that were already circling around. "Looks like you'll be getting some company before long."

Burley stopped cussing long enough to look where she was pointing. His face went white. "You can't leave me here to die. You hear me? You can't do that."

"Why can't I?" One hand held the reins, the other the pistol. She stared down at him, feeling no pity at all. "That's just what you were going to do to me, wasn't it?"

"No, no, I swear I wasn't. You got to believe me! Don't leave me here."

Araby looked down at him and smiled. "Tell you what I'll do. I'll send you some help. And while I'm gone, you can be deciding whether you want to talk to the Marshal and save your own neck, or whether you want to hang right along with Jud."

She nudged Buddy on, making sure to swing wide from where Burley was lying, and untied the white horse.

"Leave my horse here!" he called out. "You got no right to take it."

"I don't think you're in any position to tell me what I can or can't do." She led the horse behind her. If Burley did try to get up and walk away, he wouldn't get far, not the way he was bleeding. Besides, a trail of blood would be easy to follow.

Burley tried to crawl after her. "At least leave me my rifle so I can shoot at those damned buzzards."

"Use your knife," she called out over her shoulder.

"Hey, listen to me. I'll talk! I'll tell you about Jud and Moe Gilley. He paid me to kill him and take the money and leave Montana's spur.

"I'll tell you about what he wanted me to do to you!" he called out after her. "And how he wanted me to leave that eagle necklace so every-body'd think the Injuns done it. Are you listening to me? Listen to me, damn it! Don't just leave me here. Those damned buzzards'll pick my eyes out. Wait! Stop!"

Araby kept right on riding away in the direction of Tamarack. No doubt the Marshal was going to be very interested in everything Burley had to say!

A little after sunset, Araby started pacing from one end of the parlor to the other, stopping along the way to straighten paintings that Jake kept telling her were already straight.

Amused, Jake kept one eye on the window and the other one on her. "Did I tell you how pretty you look tonight?"

"Oh, about fifty times." She put the book she was thumbing through back into the bookcase. "But tell me again."

"Give me a hug, and I will."

"You'll not have to ask me twice, cowboy."
After hugging him the second time, Araby peered

out over his shoulder. "No sign of them yet."

"Not yet, but they'll be here. You can bet on that. Jud wouldn't miss it for the world. Not after this afternoon. Lordy, I'd have given my eye teeth to have seen the look on his face when he opened his door and found you standing there."

Araby reached around Jake's waist and rested her chin on his shoulder. Jud had looked as if he had seen a ghost when she delivered the invitation for him, Sim and Lena to join her at Tamarack that night to discuss the sale of the ranch. That was the only time since she met him that he had been at a loss for words. He could hardly do more than stutter his acceptance.

Araby chuckled out loud. "Poor Jud. Two of his victims resurrected the same day. He's going to think he's lost his mind."

"He's already crazy," said Jake frowning. "Only a crazy man would think he could get away with doing what he's done."

"That was some change of heart Sheriff Otter had, wasn't it?" Araby asked with a smile, remembering the chat she, Jake and Burley had with the Marshal and the Sheriff that afternoon. Mike had wanted so badly to go into town with them, they all but had to tie him to the bed to keep him at home! The Marshal's assurance that Jud would get just what he deserved convinced him to stay at home out of sight, at least until that night.

"Burley sure was anxious to spill his guts to the Sheriff and the Marshal, wasn't he?" Jake said. "I noticed he kept his distance from you. Not that I blame him. Any woman that puts a bullet in my gut I'd be wary of, too."

Araby nipped at his neck. "So what were you

and Sheriff Otter talking about when we got ready to go?''

''Oh, he admitted he might have made a mistake or two where I was concerned, and told me what a lucky cuss I was to be getting hitched up to you. Of course, he threw in a warning here and there, and said he wouldn't worry about having to keep me in line anymore since you could do the job just fine.''

''He did, did he?'' Araby was pleased. Maybe the Sheriff wasn't so bad after all. ''Any time you think about doing me wrong, as these country girls say, you just remember that bullet I put in Burley's belly could just as easily have gone into his heart.''

''You got me trembling in my boots, sugar.'' He grabbed hold of her and kissed her. ''You don't watch it, and something else is gonna start trembling too.''

Araby gave him a playful slap, but rubbed herself closer. ''You better watch it, cowboy. I know how to deal with the likes of you. Just ask Burley Wilkerson!''

Araby was just getting comfortable when Jake made the announcement that she had been so impatient to hear.

''Jud's coming. He's alone. Wonder where Sim and Lena are?'' He jerked the curtain closed. ''Think you can handle it on your own for a little while?''

Araby patted the pistol that had gone from the leg holster to the pocket of her skirt. ''I took care of Burley, didn't I?''

''That you did, my sweet. That you did!''

She could not resist giving his backside a pinch when he passed by. ''Know something, cowboy? You got yourself a real nice *derriere.*"

His tight-fitting dungarees made his backside look even more inviting. Later, she promised herself.

Jake grinned. "If *derriere* means what I think it means, yours ain't so bad either."

After watching him disappear up the stairs, Araby checked the hall mirror one last time. She was nervous, but the lessons of her profession had been well learned.

Hands folded in front of her, she waited for the knock. Mattie was in her room under specific instructions not to show herself until Jud was in cuffs and being taken away. She glanced into the dining room. The table was set with the company linen and china plates, cups and saucers, but there was nothing cooking on the stove. Jud might think he was coming for supper, but little did he know he was being served up as the main course! Afterwards, with Jud under lock and key, Mike was taking her and Jake, the Sheriff and Marshal Riley all out to dinner in town, then on to the Ruby Rose. Mike had already been given ample warning that if he didn't make Ruby marry him, he'd have two bad legs instead of one.

A knock sounded at the door.

Araby took a deep breath to collect herself. Before they could all go out for their night on the town, there was one small matter that had to be resolved.

With a smile on her face, she opened the door. "Hello, Jud. I'm so pleased you could come." She turned up her cheek for Jud to kiss, but was not at all surprised when he chose not to. "Where's Sim and Lena? I so hoped they'd come join us."

Jud managed a smile, but it was not his usual charming smile. "Lena sends her apologies. Sim's on another drunk, and she's home taking care of him." He walked into the parlor, hat in hand, and took a wary look around. "Just me and you?"

"Why, yes. And Mattie, of course. She's busy in the dining room." Smiling, Araby walked to the sideboard and took the cork out of the whiskey decanter. "Can I pour you a drink, Jud?"

"No. No, thanks." He kept looking around the room.

Araby wondered if he sensed that he had just walked into a trap. "Do sit down, Jud, dear. Make yourself at home. After all, this will be your home in another week. That is, if you still want Tamarack. You do want it, don't you, Jud?"

"Oh, yes—yes, I still want it."

"Well, gracious, have a seat. You make me nervous pacing like some wild animal." She motioned to one of the wing-back chairs.

Jud sat down.

Araby positioned herself opposite him in the matching chair.

"Are you sure there's nothing bothering you, Jud?"

He nodded. "I'm sure."

"How about a glass of wine, then?"

"Maybe later."

She smiled. "Suit yourself." She leaned against the Indian blanket draped over the back of her chair. "You seem so preoccupied. Are you sure there's nothing wrong?"

His smile was cold and calculating. "I just have a lot on my mind."

"Of course. The saw mill, Sim, your sister-in-law . . . You certainly do have your share of troubles, don't you?'' Araby smoothed a wrinkle from her shirt. "Speaking of troubles, that fellow who used to be the foreman around here—um, Burley, Burley Wilkerson—got himself in quite a mess, I hear.''

The hard set of his jaw tightened even more. "Mess? What kind of a mess?''

"You mean you haven't heard?''

"Haven't heard what?'' he demanded impatiently, then added in a kinder tone, "I didn't have a chance to get into town today so I don't know what's going on.''

Araby folded her hands demurely in her lap and continued. "You know, I never did like that man. I was so relieved when he left. Why, the way he kept looking at me, I was afraid he was going to jump me and drag me out behind the barn. It doesn't surprise me at all what they say he's done.''

Jud was on the edge of his chair. "Exactly what has he done?''

Araby shook her head. "Why, he was the one who killed Moe Gilley. He's in jail right now.''

Jud's face turned gray. "How do they know he did it?''

Araby took great delight in watching him squirm. "He confessed.''

She could almost hear his stomach lurch!

"He confessed? You sure?''

"That's what I hear.'' Araby flashed him another gracious smile and lounged back into her chair. "Jud, dear, are you sure I can't fix you a drink before dinner? Just a little one? Something to whet your appetite?''

"No, no, I'm not hungry—uh, thirsty.'' Jud

tugged at his chin. "What else did you hear about Burley?"

"Well, I heard somebody put him up to it. Somebody paid him to do it. Wonder who'd do that? Anyway, I'm sure he must have had a partner," she said smugly. "Burley didn't strike me as being particularly smart. I suppose if he did have a partner, he's already told the Sheriff who it was. Things would go easier on him then, I believe. Don't you?"

"What? Oh, yeah, yeah. That's right."

Araby couldn't resist one last cutting remark. "Can't blame him, can you? I know I sure wouldn't go to that hanging tree alone. I'd be wanting some company if I were him.

"Excuse me for a moment," she said, standing up. "Just let me see what's keeping Mattie. I don't know about you, but I am starved."

Smiling to herself, Araby walked out of the room and toward the kitchen. She looked up at the top of the stairs and gave a smile and a nod to the four men standing there, then headed back to the parlor. She met Jud coming out of the room.

"Mattie assures me it's only going to be another minute or two. Are you going somewhere?" she asked innocently.

"I'll—uh, I'll be right back. I just need to get something out of my saddlebag." He pushed her out of the way.

"Going somewhere, boy?"

Jud whirled around. His face turned a ghastly color when he caught sight of Mike Stone.

Smiling, Mike limped down the stairs holding tight to the railing with one hand. Jake followed closely behind.

"Sorry to disappoint you, Jud, but I ain't dead. Lucky for me you never could hit the broad side of the barn."

Jud lunged for the door, but Jake got there ahead of him and blocked his exit. "Where you going, Jud? Ain't you staying for dinner?"

"Get out of my way, Montana, or I'll—"

"You'll what? Sic Burley on me? Sorry, pal, but he won't be doing any more of your dirty work for a long, long time."

Jud's right hand eased up his leg.

Araby held her breath.

Jake's stare went cold and stone hard. "Go ahead, Jud. You just try that. I'll put you out of your misery a lot quicker than you thought."

Jud stared right back. Finally, he looked away and laughed.

"I don't know what you folks are getting so uppity about."

It took him a moment to regain his composure, and when he did he was just as arrogant and despicable as ever.

"You don't have nothing on me, Jake Montana. You neither, old man. It's my word against yours, and I got me a witness. Sim was there, too, remember? You got drunk and went crazy. Tried to kill me and him both. I shot you in self-defense." Jud's smile grew wider. "Yeah, that's right, it was self-defense."

"It was murder, Jud," Mike said with solemn anger. "Murder plain and simple. At least you thought it was. I was lucky. I rose from the dead. Moe Gilley, he's cold in his grave."

Jud rolled the tip of his moustache between his thumb and forefinger. "It's my word against Burley's on that one, too. Reckon I know which one of us the good sheriff will believe.''

''Pretty sure of yourself, aren't you, Jud?''

Jud stopped twirling his moustache. ''Horace! What are you doing here?''

The sheriff walked down the stairs slowly shaking his head. Will Riley, the marshal, followed him.

''You sure played me for a sucker, didn't you, Jud? I'll not be made a fool again.''

Jud's laugh was nervous. ''Horace, old buddy, what are you talking about? Remember all those nights we used to stay out gambling and chasing women? Hell, you know I wouldn't kill nobody. You ask Sim. You ask my brother. He'll tell you I shot Mike Stone in self-defense before he could kill us. He was in a drunken rage. He don't remember it now, but he was.''

''What about Moe Gilley?''

Araby watched the marshal come down the stairs. Mike's description of him couldn't have been better. Will Riley really was a grizzly of a man. The room shook when he spoke.

''Ah, hell, Marshal, you just ask anybody around here about Burley Wilkerson. They'll tell you what a no-good, low-down saddle tramp he is,'' Jud answered quickly.

Araby studied Mike's stepson. He would have made one hell of an actor!

''I'm not at all surprised Burley's trying to drag me into that mess he's gotten himself into. You see, I—''

The Sheriff interrupted. ''His exact words were, 'If I swing, he swings.''

Jud's hesitation was short-lived. ''I fired him. You ask Araby. I fired him because he'd been rude to her. That's right. He made some suggestive remarks to her. When I fired him, he told me he'd get even. I reckon this is how he's planning on getting his revenge."

Thumbs hooked onto his vest, Jud stared at each of them in turn, long and hard.

Finally, when no one said anything, he smiled. "So you see, Burley's not a very reliable witness anyway."

"I suppose you didn't send him after me this morning, either, did you?" Araby asked him calmly.

Jud's smile faded, then reappeared quickly. "Now why would I do that?"

"You tell me." Marshal Riley grabbed one arm. Sheriff Otter grabbed the other.

Jud didn't put up a struggle. "You've made a mistake, gentlemen."

"Shut up, Jud. I'm tired of listening to you."

"But Horace—"

"Shut up, Jud," repeated the Sheriff. "Or I'll have to shut you up."

Jud laughed. "Sure, Horace, whatever you say. I reckon we'll just have to let the jury decide whether I'm guilty or innocent, won't we?"

Araby watched as the two lawmen cuffed his hands behind his back, then led Jud away on his horse. "He's pretty sure of himself, isn't he?"

"Won't do any good. If he doesn't hang, he'll be locked up for the rest of his life," said Mike confidently.

Jake slipped his arm around Araby's shoulder. "No matter what happens to him, he won't be bothering us ever again."

"That Jud is rotten to the core," Mike said, staring out the window and shaking his head.

"His ma knew it, but wouldn't admit it. Then again, what mother would?"

"What's going to happen to Sim and Lena?" Araby asked.

"Sim's going to drink himself to death," Jake answered quietly. "It won't really matter whether he's put in jail as an accomplice or not. And I don't expect Lena will be staying around here, not without Jud."

"Hey, why the long faces?" Mike grabbed Araby out of Jake's arms and whirled her around the room. "We got us a party to go to. Mine! Yeee, doggies!"

He swung her around again. "Wait until I strut into the Ruby Rose. Those good-for-nothing drunks are gonna think they died and went to heaven. No, I take that back. Heaven ain't where any of those saddle tramps are headed. Well, what are you waiting for?"

Jake nudged Araby. "He's still got two bullets in him, and he's not slowing down a bit."

"I can whop you any day of the week, sonny boy, and don't you forget it." Mike gave Jake a playful shove. "You mess with me, and I won't let my niece marry you. I'll tell her about the time when me and you went down to Mexico, and those little senoritas—"

Jake cupped his hand over Mike's mouth. "You gonna stand there and gab all day? I thought you were buying us drinks and supper."

Araby refused to move. "I want to hear about those Mexican senoritas."

Mike grabbed one arm. Jake grabbed the other.

"Come on, missy," bellowed Mike. "We got

us some celebrating to do.''

Araby gave Jake a wink. She could tell that he was thinking the same thing she was. The real celebrating would come later—much later.

20

A raby stood at the bedroom window looking out across the valley. Daylight was just breaking over the hills. An aura of peace and contentment lay over Tamarack.

What a wonderful day for a wedding! Smiling, Araby flung open the door and stepped outside onto the tiny balcony. The day could not be any more perfect had she ordered it special. Nothing and no one could put a damper on her happiness. That afternoon she would become Mrs. Jake Montana. A new phase of her life was about to begin. Her stage days were behind her. She might miss the glamour and excitement she had known and enjoyed from time to time, but she would not trade her newly found happiness for any amount of fame or fortune. She was going to be a wife. Her smile widened. And a mother! Of course, she hadn't told Jake yet. He'd be thrilled. Perhaps she should have told him last night. Then again, she'd only just become absolutely positive of it herself. No, it was better to wait until the preacher pronounced them man and wife. After all, a mother-to-be really should be a bride first! What a fine father Jake would make! What a fine husband, too. She was one lucky woman.

Leaning over the wooden railing, Araby breathed in the crisp, pine-scented morning air. The air really was sweeter in Idaho. Mike had been right about that. Come to think of it, Mike had been right about everything. *If you ever come to Tamarack, you'll never want to leave.* For years he had promised her that. *If you want a real man, you have to come West to find him!* No man could be any more of a real man than Jake Montana, and he was all hers!

What a wonderful life they'd have together!

Poor Jake had worried so much that the cabin wasn't nearly good enough for his bride that he had wanted to commence work right away on a house that would rival Tamarack. She had had a hard time convincing him that the cabin's quaintness suited her just fine. There was something very romantic in its coziness. Besides, as she had told him before, grandeur did not make a house a home. Only love could do that, and she and Jake had enough love to turn that cabin into a palace!

She still could not believe her good fortune. It was all just too good to be true. She had pinched herself black and blue just to make sure she wasn't dreaming.

What a wedding it was going to be! All her friends from town would be there—Ruby, Belle, Charlie, Mandy, Felix, and the girls from the Ruby Rose, as well as Hamstring, Rowdy, and all

the fellows from Tamarack and Cross Fork.
Fleeing Fawn, Chief Silver Bear, and Running
Wolf had been invited as well and promised to
attend.

Back inside her room, Araby took her
wedding dress out of the wardrobe and carefully
arranged the embroidered silk organza gown and
fillet lace veil across the bed. Mattie had sworn
that if she didn't stop touching it, the gown would
be threadbare before it was even worn. Still, she
couldn't resist the urge to run her fingers over it
once more.

She was dying to try it on, but Mrs. Devoe,
the seamstress, had already warned her that the
marriage would be doomed before the "I do's"
were said if she so much as held it up to her and
admired her reflection in the mirror. Even during
the final fitting, Mrs. Devoe had not allowed her
so much as a peak! Araby wasn't superstitious,
but she had done as the seamstress instructed.
There was no point in tempting fate!

Araby could not resist one last feel of the fillet
lace veil. Certainly no more beautiful and stylish
a wedding gown could be found anywhere,
including those fancy ladies' stores in New York.
The skirt fell in two tiers with each hem scalloped
and beaded in tiny seed pearls. An off-the-
shoulder shawl neckline and tight wristed leg-of-
mutton sleeves graced the fullness of the bodice.
When Mike saw it, he had told her it would make
her look like an angel. Well, an angel at the altar
was one thing, but on her wedding night, there
would be no room in the bed for any angels! Just
the thought of what would come after the
wedding and the reception made her knees go
weak and quiver!

Another longing look and a few more quick caresses here and there, and the gown was returned to the wardrobe before she gave way to temptation and doomed their marriage!

Araby glanced at the bedside clock and frowned. It wasn't even six yet. Two o'clock that afternoon would never get there! Eight whole hours! It might as well be eight days. How on earth was she supposed to keep herself busy from now until then? Her trunks were all packed and ready for Hamstring to take to Cross Fork. The food for the reception was already prepared, and the table it would be served on had been set up the evening before. One thing was certain. If she stayed in her room pacing the floor and watching the clock, she'd go crazy, and Jake would have a raving lunatic on his hands instead of a blushing bride. A ride! That's what she needed to calm her nerves and relax! Yes, a nice long ride up into the hills would be the perfect way to help pass time.

It wasn't long before she was astride Buddy and galloping towards nowhere in particular but anywhere she might end up. She had been right! A ride was just what she needed to clear from her mind the excited thoughts racing inside. Still, she could not help but feel a little sad. It was at times like these that she missed Darling the most. She longed for those mornings when they chased the sun up to the top of Indian Peak. Buddy was a polite, reliable mount, and she certainly had no complaint about him or his manners, but there was something about that spirited chestnut mare she'd never forget. Riding on Devil's Darling was like riding the wind.

Leaving Buddy to graze on the clover and buttercups dotting the grassy base of the peak,

Araby set out on foot for the top. The view from Indian Peak was breathtaking. She and Jake had hiked up there and picnicked on the summit many times before. Jake said you could see Montana, Washington, and Canada all from that one peak. Legend had it that a pair of Indian lovers from warring tribes had jumped off the cliff to their deaths rather than be parted by their families.

At the end of her long climb, she was surprised to see Jake standing on one of the overhangs that overlooked the Saint Joe Valley.

Araby smiled to herself. It was as if thinking about her future husband had willed him to appear in front of her.

He must have come up the back side of the summit, she decided, pausing to look at him for a moment before calling out. Buck loomed up from his grazing, then lowered his head and kept on eating.

Finally, she called out Jake's name.

Jake turned around, smiling. He seemed just as pleased to see her as she was to see him.

"You're not having second thoughts, are you?" she teased him, walking closer.

Jake opened his arms and beckoned her inside. "Don't think you're getting out of this that easy."

"Who said I wanted out?" Arms tight around his waist, she pressed close to him and smiled. He was hers, all hers. She could revel in his embrace all day!

"What are you doing up here?" she asked quietly when their arms had finally let each other go.

Jake smiled. "Probably the same thing you

are." He led her to a rock, and they sat down. "I didn't think two o'clock was ever going to get here, so I decided to come out on a little ride."

Araby snuggled close to his shoulder. "I got tired of waiting, too."

"The next time we get married, I think we ought to have the guests arrive at seven o'clock in the morning," he suggested, squeezing her still closer.

"Only if we get married to each other."

"Why, Araby Stone-Leigh, I wouldn't dream of marrying anybody else."

"Me, neither." Her head came off his shoulder. "Isn't it bad luck for a groom to see his bride before the wedding?"

Jake thought for a minute. "Only if the meeting is planned. This one was completely accidental." He kissed her cheek. "You've been listening to Mattie and Mrs. Devoe too much. Don't you know the only luck me and you are going to have from now on out is good luck?"

"You're right, of course." Araby smiled to herself. Why, already she was starting to sound like a wife! "I missed you last night."

"I missed you, too."

"Mike kept me up talking most of the night," she explained. "Deliberately, I'm sure. He wouldn't let me out of his sight for a minute. I think he knew I was going to take off for Cross Fork the first chance I had."

"I guess it'll just make tonight that much better." Strong fingers began creeping up her side with promises of what lay ahead.

"I don't know how anything could be any better." With a soft moan, she started nibbling at his ear.

"Watch it, or we may just miss our own wedding."

Araby popped the buttons on his shirt and slipped her hand inside the denim. "I have a wonderful idea. Why don't we have our honeymoon before the wedding?"

"We could." Jake grabbed her roving hand and kissed it. "But we're not. Not until tonight."

"Yes, sir, Mr. Montana, sir. Whatever you say." Araby grinned. "How's that? I've been practicing my humble little woman role."

"Sounds just fine to me." His smile faded. His mouth suddenly stopped just short of hers. "Listen."

The air caught fire with his excitement.

Her heart began to race with his. There was no mistaking the sound of horses' hooves thundering up the summit. The wild horses were close, and they were coming even closer!

Jake's words were barely more than whispers as he stared straight ahead. "Something must have scared them. Otherwise, they would have caught our scent by now and be heading the other way!"

Araby could hear them scrambling closer and closer up the rocky side of the summit turning over stones and trampling bushes and fallen logs in their way. Soon they'd come charging over the top. Soon man and wild animal could come face to face. Fear gave way to excitement. She was just as eager as Jake, but for different reasons. Maybe now she'd be able to give Darling a proper goodbye.

"I wonder if Devil's Darling is with them?" Araby wondered out loud.

From the glazed expression on Jake's face,

she knew he could not answer the question, for he hadn't even heard it. His mind was filled with thoughts of capturing that magnificent pegasus!

Crouching low in the grass, Jake eased over to the spot where Buck was grazing and took the lariat off the saddle horn. Then, he gave his horse a slap on the rump that sent him trotting back down the grassy slope towards Buddy.

Jake motioned Araby behind a boulder, then jumped behind the massive slab of granite just as the first of the mares struggled over the top of the peak.

Araby held her breath anxiously. Since the last time she had seen the wild herd, the stallion had picked up at least a dozen more mares. It seemed forever before Devil's Darling scrambled up to join the ones who had already reached the top and were grazing contently at the spot where Buck had been just a few minutes before. A devil was exactly what the chestnut mare looked like. She had a wild look about her. Her tail and mane were tangled and matted. Her coat was splattered with dried mud. All four legs had deep, nasty looking gashes cut into them. Blood still oozed from the worst of them.

Araby peered over the side of the boulder. Would Devil's Darling come charging up to her as she had done so many times before in response to her mistress's whistle? No, probably not. She was a wild horse now. Having had that taste of freedom, she wouldn't relinquish it easily.

The black stallion catapulted over the top of the peak, bucking, rearing, and pawing at the sky. After bunching his mares all together, he left them to their grazing as he pranced back and forth in front of the group with his head stiff and alert and his tail arched high. He paused for a moment, and with his great muscles rippling even at a standstill, the stallion surveyed his kingdom.

Jake eased out from behind the granite slab with his lariat raised and poised to lasso the black demon. His steps cautious and quiet, he warily approached his target.

Araby waited and watched. There was no doubt in her mind that Jake would succeed this time in roping the beautiful horse.

Much to her surprise, however, Jake lowered the lasso down to his side and stood in awe of what could so easily have been his.

A quiet breeze drifted over the summit.

The stallion whirled around quickly, nostrils flaring and breathing fire.

Jake jumped back out of the way of the powerful hind legs.

He was just as surprised as she when the stallion did not kick out against his opponent, but instead stood proud and alert, his eyes challenging.

Jake took a step towards him, then another, and another still, until finally he was at arm's length from the coal-black mass of bunched muscles and impregnable strength.

Jake then whispered something to the horse.

Araby was not quite sure what, but when he reached out and patted the rock-hard shoulder, she was certain he was courting death. She could not believe what she was seeing. Man and beast were in awe of each other.

The two stood staring at each other, for several seconds.

Finally, the stallion tossed his head and, with a loud snort that sounded more like a laugh, trotted back to his herd.

Jake stood staring at the cloud of dust long after the stallion had bunched together his mares and spirited them away down the grassy side of the slope. When Jake came back to where Araby was standing, there was a satisfied smile of contentment fixed to his face.

She didn't even have to ask him what had made him change his mind. She knew. That black stallion was born to be free. It had taken Jake a little while to figure it out, but when the time came, he realized it, too.

"I just touched the wind," he said with a sheepish grin.

Araby slipped her arm around his waist and hugged him tight. "I am so proud of you."

Jake gave her a kiss, then untangled her arms from around him. "Seems like I remember a wedding I'm supposed to go to."

Buddy was still grazing where she had left him. Buck was close by.

Araby could not resist one last look across the ridge. She wished she had had the chance to tell Darling good-bye and give her one last pat. But it was just as well, she supposed. Her little chestnut mare was wild now. She would have been too afraid to venture close to any human, even if that human was someone who loved her and missed her very much.

Still, Araby couldn't resist the temptation to whistle for her one last time.

She hadn't expected the mare to come running—not really. That only happened in story books. So why did she feel disappointed?

"Hey, beat you to the river!" Jake challenged when they had mounted their horses.

"You'll have to catch me first!" With one last look behind her, Araby charged ahead.

Buddy and Buck ran neck and neck until they were in sight of the Saint Joe. Then Buck dropped back, and Araby turned around to see why.

Buck was at a standstill, and Jake was pointing back at Indian Peak, shaking his head.

"Well, I'll be damned. Would you look at that?"

Araby looked, but she couldn't believe what she was seeing. Devil's Darling was heading right at them in a frenzied gallop.

Araby jumped off her horse and ran to greet her wild mare. She threw her arms around the chestnut neck and smoothed the tangles from her mane.

"You came back!" she whispered, laughing and crying at the same time. "You did come back to me. I knew you would."

The horse nuzzled her cheek with its wet nose.

Jake slipped the rope over her head, and Araby got back on Buddy.

They headed home. Devil's Darling trotted happily behind them.

It was a long time before Jake spoke.

"I expect you'll be getting a foal come spring."

Araby nodded. A foal out of the black stallion and her little chestnut mare would be some horse!

"And do you know what else I think?" Jake asked solemnly.

Araby shook her head.

"I think that won't be the only young'un born at Cross Fork come spring."

Araby's astonishment turned into a big smile.

"How do you figure that?"

"I got my ways," he answered, looking straight ahead.

"Well?" She sat on the edge of the saddle eager for a reaction. "You are happy, aren't you?"

He shook his head. "No."

"No?" She halted her horse. "You're not?"

His sober expression gave way to a grin. "I'm thrilled!" He leaned over and grabbed hold of her. "Thrilled! I am thrilled!"

The kiss he gave her resounded through the whole valley.

"I love you, Araby Stone-Leigh!"

"Araby Stone-Leigh Montana!" She threw her arms around his neck and pulled him to her so hard that he nearly came out of his saddle. "I love you, too, cowboy! I love you, too!"